To Kenneth,

1941. A little light
reading to pass a few
quiet hours -

Uncle Eddie
Austin Bolt

ARCHITECTS OF IDEAS

ARCHITECTS
OF IDEAS

By
ERNEST R. TRATTNER

*The Story of the Great
Theories of Mankind*

LONDON
GEORGE G. HARRAP & CO. LTD.
SYDNEY BOMBAY TORONTO

First published 1938
by GEORGE G. HARRAP & CO. LTD.
182 High Holborn, London, W.C.1

MADE IN GREAT BRITAIN. PRINTED BY
BUTLER AND TANNER LTD., FROME AND LONDON

CONTENTS

ILLUSTRATIONS

Introduction . . . . ABOUT THEORIES

A CERTAIN cynic who once compared man to a bird said that the human being starts from nowhere and arrives at nowhere—"however, his flight is superb."

Something of the grandeur of man's ascent is to be found in his speculations; when superb they constitute a vast sweep over wide ranges of fact leading humanity toward a better and more compr hensive view of its relation to the universe.

Perhaps no one will ever write a complete story of all the theories —scientific, economic, philosophical—that have been conceived in different ages by widely separated thinkers. Such a task would cover long stretches of history, taking us over territories of sadly useless investigations, into jungles of things now meaningless. Yet it would seem that theories are about the most interesting phenomena of man's mind. For a theory is a portrait of a vast idea seen and delineated. Its ability to synthesize and explain a group of facts, facts which as they stand are incomplete, leads us out of glistening bays into vast oceans of enthralling truth.

Whether he knows it or not, every person has been born into a universe and is a part of a vast cosmic system; but only a few in all the ages have understood or remotely apprehended its significance. Unfortunately, the popular idea of universal theories as vague and altogether lacking in the element of vitality has obscured the human drama in these magnificent obsessions. Obviously, this mistaken notion is due to the fact that a theory has too often been thought to be devoid of earthly concern, aloof and unconnected with practical affairs. Actually, this is far from the case, as these chapters demonstrate. Moreover, those who wish to share in the heritage of hard thinking and intense imagination will find in the lives of the great theorists a unique company of mortals—men of incredible perseverance, the makers and the shakers of our modern world.

The individual human battle in the "conquest-march" of progress is so fundamental that no attempt to understand a theory apart from the life of the theorist could possibly be considered sound. All science, said René Descartes, rests upon man, upon the one indubitable certainty that "I think and therefore I am." In this view Descartes presented a profound understanding of the essence of thought. To Francis Bacon the root of science was a natural fact. Descartes' insistence went one step beyond; he saw that before natural fact can be of use to the scientist he must observe it. And the fact of his observing it is truly the fact that matters most. For this reason it is one thing to know a theory and quite another thing to know the same theory in its historical setting and especially in terms of the theorist whose genius gave it birth. If we aspire to be honest we cannot disregard the influence of the man on his thought—and also, to be sure, the theory on the man: it is a reciprocal relationship. "Man is only half himself, the other half is his expression."

Essentially every theorist is an iconoclast; he is an iconoclast because he is an emancipator. Few men want truth—by far the vast majority prefer their bondage. Yet the history of the freedom of human thought is everywhere strewn with the vast wreckage of theories which at one time were dear to the hearts of those who believed them.

The Ptolemaic system of astronomy was based upon a theory which was accepted as long as it worked. It accorded fully with the facts which the ancients could observe and interpret. For many centuries both the theory and the system had been of service to astronomers, to navigators, and to the makers of calendars. Then, in the course of history, there came with awakening awareness a new age when the Ptolemaic system broke down hopelessly. Not even the comforts of ancient authority could save it. In its place men had to build another theory more in accord with the facts. That was indeed a painful process as we know only too well from the records which have come down to us.

With the arrival of the Copernican theory a new floor had been added to the structure of knowledge. But only a small minority were able to change their thinking to meet this newer level. Most people, then as now, cherish their convictions and are adroit in avoiding evidence contrary to what they wish to believe. They are mightily akin to the old theologian who said that he was entirely open to conviction, but would like to see anybody who could convince him. No discoveries could be made that would modify his views. He was safe in the "possession" of the truth.

In every age previous to our own there was supposed to exist a body of knowledge final and infallible. Frequently people thought of this knowledge as having been revealed directly from heaven. Embodied in rigid tradition and held sacred by all authorities, it was considered heresy to question any time-honored belief. All that men wished to know was assumed to have been already given. There was no need for anybody to inquire into the vital issues of the cosmos. The story of the theorists, however, is the story of a thin and irregular line of searchers after truth, men who battled almost alone on the vast frontiers of knowledge, for they had no "revealed Providence" to fall back on. Precisely that which was accepted by their contemporaries, that which was taught and delivered, had to be discarded. "It is the function of genius," Emerson once remarked, "to indicate to lesser minds the paths they must pursue."

In many ways mankind's intellectual progress reminds one of Edmond Rostand's chanticleer. The rooster crows, and morning appears; consequently his life is built around the idea that a causal relation exists between his crowing and the appearance of dawn. Chanticleer is very sure of this until his enemies plot to silence him. One day the dawn appears without Chanticleer's crowing summons. Thoroughly dejected, the sorrowful cock realizes his mistake. He searches immediately for a new hypothesis!

Every now and then the whole world is first shocked, then convinced and afterwards revolutionized by some majestic outcome of human thought. Take the case of Copernicus. It was indeed a horrifying suggestion that he put forth: that this round earth is not only whirling on its axis, but is actually swinging in a vast orbit about the sun. People quoted Scripture to refute such heresy. Does not the Ninety-third Psalm declare, "The world is established that it cannot be moved"? Contemptuously they asked: "Who will venture to place the authority of Copernicus above that of Holy Scripture?" Inherent in the pronouncements of Copernicus was a supreme revolution in thought. It brought about a tremendous intellectual awakening, for he wrote a new story of the heavens in lieu of the abandoned one. The discrepancy between the star-record observed by

Copernicus and the Book-record quoted by the people caused much rubbing of eyes. Out of this rubbing has come a glorious vision of the new heavens.

As a matter of fact, when the Ptolemaic system of astronomy passed away, the heavens remained just as they had always been. The stars did not swerve from their course because Ptolemy was discredited. The sun and the moon and the stars were each in their accustomed place. Nothing was disturbed except the Ptolemaic system of astronomy. And that was gone forever.

Every period of history, however "static" it may appear to be, is characterized by some change in its intellectual climate. We constantly witness not a mere shifting of the clouds but a profound transformation of thought. Of the great theories that now hold the attention of mankind there have been many foreshadowings. Not a few of the most important contemporary ideas have been held vaguely, tentatively, and in a dreamy way hinted by thinkers in other ages. The debt to the past is very great indeed. When a truth is extended or deepened by further insight or brought into a new logical connection with other truths, it becomes part of an imposing new edifice. The revolutionary conception of Copernicus had been anticipated centuries before by Aristarchus of Samos. The fact that this old Greek scientist held this opinion gave Copernicus courage to revive it. Thus, seemingly, new ideas and discoveries are often old ideas revived and rejuvenated.

Each age has its theorists who restate the knowledge accumulated in newer fields and seek to harmonize it with the old which remain undisputed. Darwin once remarked about the stimulating effect of mistaken theories as compared with the sterilizing effect of mistaken observations: mistaken observations lead men astray, mistaken theories suggest true theories.

Ultimate truth is never attained in any one generation by any one man. Truth grows by small accretions and is relative to the age in which it appears. It is undeniably true that in their day the theorists of antiquity led people to a new and better understanding of life. Theories—even the mistaken ones—are gigantic generalizations which have revolutionized human thought and conduct; they have affected the life of humanity and its fundamental relations to the universe.

It is truly to be marveled at how much of the theoretical work of the world has been done in quietness and confidence. Great results seem never to be hurried. Apparently progress comes in brief periods of insight when the theorist, gifted with a new vision, projects it out into the world where it sheds fresh light. The men in this field who have achieved most gloriously have been nobly alone. Their number has never been large. Among the billions of human beings who have inhabited the earth only a very small number has possessed the faculty of discovering the hidden relations existing between certain phenomena. In the entire history of mankind there have not been more than two dozen first-rate theorists, men endowed with the intuition of unknown things and the imagination that creates new worlds. Perhaps there is no achievement that demands such exceptional mental power, physiological endurance and immense intellectual effort as the ability to formulate a scientific theory.

An honest theory must be in all essentials a true view. It should give us a picture of something which lies behind the things not immediately accessible to experience; it must enable us to understand why things behave as they actually do. The mental process of making suppositions is as old as the race itself. Men have always entertained concepts or mental pictures in the hope that one alternative or the other will turn out to be true. Consequently we have many imposing but unreal systems of thought—vast balloons floating unattached through the thin air of pure fantasy.

Often what has passed for a theory has been nothing more than a baseless hypothesis. Much that has been paraded with a pretense at wisdom has proven to be singularly sterile, a masquerade of confused terminology and incomprehensible absurdities. It is a strange irony that men in their efforts to be logical and reasonable have so frequently spoken nonsense and written idiocies. Only an unusual mind can resist the temptation of pseudoclarity. True intellectual enterprise does not consist simply in listing mere data; the theorist does more than elucidate the obvious. The additional task required is to make the facts yield more information about themselves; for nature is more than she *obviously* is.

The genuine theorist helps us to see that the world is more than we had supposed it to be. This is because his theory possesses architechtonic qualities. A connection or coherence exists in which one part supports the other. It is not like a balloon but a tower; its top may be in the stratosphere, but it has been raised from foundations in reality.

For this reason a theory cannot be a tissue of self-contained hypotheses. Just to sit down and suppose something and then work out the consequences may be an exercise in imagination, but that is not science. A theory as such refers beyond itself and is relative to something which is real and not hypothetical. Facts must suggest the theory.

Sometimes the word theory is used as synonymous with hypothesis. Here it is taken to indicate a generalized explanation that has already passed beyond the stage of mere hypothesis. An hypothesis is a theory in the making. In dealing with an hypothesis one is aware of its partial explanation, its deficiencies—the need for further attempts to supplement it by additional concepts. Only when it has received a considerable amount of verification does it pass on to the august status of a theory.

To trace the growth of a theory is a fascinating adventure. In its embryonic stages it is made up of one or more hypotheses. The hypothesis is framed on the basis of a rather small set of facts. As additional knowledge and insight come pouring in, it is then expanded. Only as it achieves scope and adequacy does it grow into theory. Basically, a theory interprets a greater range of fact than a hypothesis. When the theory becomes so comprehensive that its scope is world-wide, then the very range and sweep of its explanation gives it that rare quality known as universality.

"Theorist" has long been a term of opprobrium. It was the withering epithet hurled at Hutton, Darwin, Freud and others. But so great has been the cumulative impact of the work of these men upon our civilization, so thoroughly have their courageous generalizations forced humanity to discard its age-old illusions and "opinions," that the prestige of the theorizing scientist in our day has reached unbelievable heights. Carlyle, it is said, sat listening once to the common talk about the ineffectiveness of ideas; then, when a pause came, remarked, "Gentlemen, there was once a man called Rousseau. He wrote a book which was nothing but ideas. People laughed at it. But the skins of those who laughed went to bind the second edition of the book."

The public acclaim of Albert Einstein—theorist par excellence—is one of the significant facts of modern times. Without understanding much about relativity the man on the street feels that Einstein is a symbol: that far beyond the phenomena which have been brought within the range of our senses, others still await to be revealed, that tomorrow there may well arise more potent or refined means of observation, or newer methods of investigation.

In this book fifteen theorists have been chosen because they have one thing in common: an impressive contemporary implication. In each case the theory is a self portrait of the man worthy to hang in any scientific gallery. Their personalities match the greatness of their achievements. They are men from widely separated ages, possessed of different dispositions, beset with the most diverse circumstances, yet they are made strangely akin by the selfless search after truth. Basically, these fifteen thoughts are differing aspects of one gigantic whole.

The arrangement of these chapters is a chronological one. "The grandest of all musics," says an old Gaelic proverb, "is the music of the thing that happens." When the heroes were asked which of all the musics of nature they preferred, the music of the waterfall, the cry of the eagle, the belling of a stag, the baying of hounds—the list is too long to repeat—they would invariably answer, "Give us the music of the thing that happens."

What is important to us is that these theories are essential to a world-view which now embraces all the cardinal concerns of man. They carry us back and forth between a vast world of inconceivable magnitude and an equally vast sub-world of inconceivable smallness. Yet the linkage between them is very intimate. Just as it takes many different rays of light to make sunshine, so it takes many different sciences to give us a view of the whole as a *whole*.

1. Copernicus . . . THEORY OF THE SOLAR SYSTEM

THE story of the great theories of mankind takes us back to a period of ancient history when Christianity was a little more than one hundred years old. In those far-off days there lived in the city of Alexandria in Egypt an astronomer by the name of Claudius Ptolemy. From the little we know about him he must have been an extremely interesting person for he not only studied the stars, but was a geographer as well. The exact dates of his life are doubtful; however, we do know that he was born in Alexandria and that his recorded observations extended to the year 151 A.D.

Among the many unique and interesting cities of antiquity Alexandria was perhaps pre-eminent. Although located in Egypt at the mouth of the Nile, it was essentially a Greek community, despite the large numbers of different peoples who swarmed within its ghettos and suburbs. At the time when Ptolemy was studying the stars and writing his books, the city of Alexandria was already the enlightened capital of the world: both its university and its library were known from one end of the Mediterranean to the other. Even in Asia, and in remote parts of Africa too, people had come to know that science and education, philosophy, music, art and literature flourished there as in no other place. For this reason Alexandria had for centuries attracted large numbers of scholars. They flocked from everywhere just to breathe the cosmopolitan atmosphere of its schools.

It is surprising how many names of illustrious Alexandrian scholars have come down to us over the centuries—Philo, Eratosthenes, Euclid, Strabo, Aristarchus, Hipparchus and a score of lesser lights. Some were original thinkers, men of wide-ranging interests and outstanding ability; some were little more than industrious collators of facts who managed to assemble the researches of their fellow men and preserve them for future generations.

Claudius Ptolemy was not so much a creative and original thinker as he was a collator. Men like Hipparchus were the real originators of new astronomical methods; Ptolemy was the perfector of their ideas and the systematizer of their knowledge. He did not hesitate to appropriate the works of his predecessors and use them as the basis of his own. To accuse him of plagiarism on this account would be, of course, quite absurd. All the great books of antiquity, whether they be astronomical, religious or medical, are compilations. In those ancient days men felt free to use the writings of the great thinkers who had gone before them. In this way many of the treasures of the antique world have been preserved.

One of the most tragic calamities in the history of human thought was the destruction of the great library at Alexandria. Thousands of rare books that once graced its shelves perished over night and have since been lost to the world. Fortunately, very fortunately, a few were preserved, among them that remarkable synthesis and compendium of ancient astronomical knowledge known to the world as *The Almagest* of Claudius Ptolemy. Translated into several languages, including the Arabic, this work found its way by the most curious channels into the schools of Europe and Asia.

Within a remarkably short space of time it became the unquestioned and authoritative textbook on astronomy. The same age that came to look upon the Bible as of divine origin came also to look upon the information contained in *The Almagest* as defending the doctrines of Scripture. Although Ptolemy had not the remotest idea of supporting the Bible, his writings were nevertheless seized upon as both evidence and confirmation. So great was the halo of sanctity thrown around Ptolemy that to question him was to question the Holy Bible itself.

But what heresy is greater than the heresy of a pointed question?

2

Ptolemy's book, as we have seen, is virtually an expansion of the views of his predecessors, notably Hipparchus. It contains a true portrait of how the ancients, to the very best of their ability, tried to picture the universe. Owing to the celebrity of the author the ideas expounded in *The Almagest* came to be known as the Ptolemaic theory. According to this theory the earth is the fixed center of the universe: the sun and the moon, the stars and the planets merely revolve about it in twenty-four hours.

Fundamentally the Ptolemaic system is the conception of the world which any child would form for himself from his own limited and superficial knowledge. He sees the sun rise each morning in the east, pass across the sky, and sink again in the west. He naturally assumes that the sun moves around the earth. He does not conceive of the earth moving, because he does not *see* it move. And this was precisely the reaction of the children of history, the Greeks, the Romans, and the early medieval Europeans. Of course, there were here and there a few isolated thinkers who speculated on the possibility that the earth and all the planets revolved around the sun, but they left no impression whatsoever on the popular and accepted notions of the day.

The child, let us say, grows older, and acquires a more than infantile interest in the heavens: each night he watches the movement of individual stars and sees how they shift their positions. He has already made his fundamental premise, that the earth is immovable and the center of the universe. He now seeks to reconcile with this premise these new movements of the stars which he has observed. Consequently he assumes that the movement of the stars in the sky is a stellar movement about the earth as a fixed center.

Next, he notices that there are some stars that move differently and faster than the others. While the great mass of stars appears to perform a regular unvarying movement about the earth, these others sometimes move faster, sometimes slower, sometimes not at all. Nor do they keep in straight paths, but wander about the sky in apparently aimless courses.

The Greeks noticed this wandering movement of certain stars. They gave to them the name of *planetoi*, or planets, which simply means wanderers, nomads, celestial vagabonds. And crude though their astronomical technique was, they were able to calculate that these planets were much nearer to the earth than the fixed stars.

But they still had their fundamental assumption on their hands, namely: that the earth does not move. All these bodies—planets, fixed stars, sun and moon—they thought revolved about the earth in circular movement. But try as they would they could not reconcile the crazy movements of the planets with a perfect circle (for it was their underlying conviction that a circle represented the perfection of the universe). So it came to pass that as further calculations of planetary distances and directions were made, and as observations detected more and more minor apparent motions of the planets, further corrections had to be added, which were incompatible with the Ptolemaic doctrine in its simplicity. The exponents embroidered the one great circle with an ever-increasing number of cycles and epicycles, till confusion became worse confounded.

3

What was the main error of the epicycle-makers? They tried to patch an ancient fiction instead of asking themselves whether, after all, its basis was laid in truth. They tinkered instead of re-creating. "Sir, had I been present at creation, I could have rendered profound advice," remarked King Alphonse X of Castile to his astronomy teacher. That happened one day in the middle of the thirteenth century.

Alphonse's remark was not the flippant statement of a monarch thumbing his nose at the heavens; it was the intelligent reaction of an untrammeled mind to the hodgepodge of complicated nonsense that medieval astronomy had grown to be. By the thirteenth century so many epicycles and "eccentrics" had been added to Ptolemy's *Almagest,* that Alphonse's blasphemy was nothing more than a sensible man's outcry against absurdity.

But Alphonse had to accept his Ptolemy in the end, for the theorizing man, who was to put astronomy's house in order, had not yet appeared. The king's zeal for astronomy, notwithstanding the fact that he was chilled by the spectacle of Ptolemy's epicycles, was sufficient to bring him to devote enormous sums of money to the preparation of the Alphonsine Tables of heavenly motions, which were grounded upon the Ptolemaic system and provided the best working basis at that time for the computation of dates, the length of the year, and the reform of the calendar.

During the two hundred years after the time of Alphonse, the medieval astronomers continued to accumulate observations; they continued also to revise and make even more involved the system of the heavens that had exasperated the king. But dissatisfaction began to grow. The coming dawn of a more scientific age had to await the investigator who would challenge the authority of Ptolemy.

That investigator appeared in the person of Nicolaus Copernicus.

4

Whether Copernicus was a German or a Pole is of little importance to us, even if there were any solid ground on which to base a decision. He was born on February 19, 1473, in the town of Thorn, which a few years before had passed into the hands of the Poles. But the region was undoubtedly German in character, and Copernicus always referred (in German) to Prussia as "our dear fatherland." His family, however, were more Polish than German—the family name was Koppernigk—and his father came from Cracow, a Polish city.

Young Nicolaus was only ten years old when his father died, and he became the ward of his uncle, Lucas Watzelrode, a Roman Catholic priest, who became Bishop of Ermeland in 1489. At about the same time it was determined that Nicolaus should study for the Church.

It was an age of dim stirrings of enlightenment. The scholastic pall of medievalism was beginning to be lifted. A new movement called Humanism, inspired by a revival of interest in the things of this world, had been sweeping through Italy. Its influence was now stretching far to the north. In fact, tinges of Humanism were evident in Nicolaus' own home, on the shores of the Baltic, near the very outskirts of civilization. These influences were largely responsible for his family's decision to give him a broad cultural foundation on which he might base his church studies. With Copernicus' matriculation at the University of Cracow, a twenty-six-year period of higher study began that eventually was to ripen into the first great theory of mankind.

Cracow at the time was the best university north of the Alps, especially in point of scientific training. Bishop Watzelrode himself had studied there, and his Humanist leanings prompted him to choose this university for his nephew. At the age of nineteen Copernicus, his mind glowing with eagerness for knowledge, new ideas, and the possibilities of thought, began his formal higher education.

Astronomy and mathematics, the twin sciences, claimed his attention almost at the outset. The fame of Regiomontanus and Purbach, the translators of Ptolemy's *Almagest*, was still resounding throughout Europe. In fact, the astronomical tables of Regiomontanus had superseded the Alphonsine as the most reliable and accurate up to that time. While at Cracow, Copernicus devoted himself principally to mathematics. He did not fail to examine with profound interest the astronomical instruments which the university possessed. Crude as these instruments were, so were the courses on orthodox astronomy. But there was nothing else available, and Copernicus had not yet come either to question or dispute the ancient authorities.

Nevertheless, the seeds of new thought were planted and took firm root in his soul. His favorite teacher, Albert Brudzewski, a leader of the Humanists, into whose confidence the young and brilliant student soon made his way, was the storm center of a hot debate between the reactionary scholastics and the progressive Humanists. Copernicus made his choice early; he threw in his lot with Brudzewski and the Humanists and never wavered from that decision for the rest of his life.

However, in this first skirmish, Humanism was conquered, and the victorious reactionaries made things so unpleasant for the champions of the new order that most of them decamped to seek out more receptive schools. Brudzewski left Cracow, and most of the other of Copernicus' Humanist friends followed him. Life at Cracow became extremely dull and unsatisfying. At the end of the year the young student returned home for a period to persuade his uncle to permit him to complete his education elsewhere—preferably in Italy.

He was now vastly more eager for knowledge; his first glimpse of the boundless vistas of science had thrilled him. The flame of investigation had been kindled. Unhesitatingly he chose his avocation—astronomy—with fierce determination to learn all that was being taught about it. And more, if possible!

Part of his desire to study astronomy was a secret feeling that he might bring order out of chaos. He had had enough of the subject to have experienced a reaction similar to that of King Alphonse; Copernicus was plainly appalled by the extraordinary chaos in which his favorite science found itself. One thing particularly impressed him (aside from the great mass of epicycles that cluttered up the sky): this was the inability of mathematicians to reckon the length of the regular year. Young Copernicus began to cast about for a way to bring law into this chaotic situation. It was this specific attempt which led him to consider the possibility that the earth revolved about the sun—a view directly opposite to the accepted teachings of the Church. At first he merely played with this idea; he had sufficient humility to wait before proposing anything so utterly revolutionary.

The two years Copernicus spent in Thorn after leaving Cracow enabled his uncle to build for him a circle of acquaintances that would be of use later on when he had finished studying and would have to enter upon the practical affairs of life. The bishop lost no time in looking about—a job for his nephew was necessary. While there was some little opposition from those who resented the playing of favorites in handing out church positions, Watzelrode was finally successful, and in 1497 Copernicus was elected a canon of the Cathedral at Frauenburg, in Ermeland, his uncle's own diocese.

5

No sooner had he been appointed to the cathedral than he was given a leave of absence to continue his education.

In Italy, he matriculated at the University of Bologna, and continued his feverish pursuit of mathematics, physics, and astronomy. Here was much greater liberty of thought than was permitted in the sterner northland. Copernicus attached himself as disciple and friend to Domenicus Maria Novara, one of the best astronomers of the age; too intelligent a man to submit to the literal and unequivocal acceptance of Ptolemaic notions. Too intelligent, that is, to submit personally. He did not dare to dissent openly—consequently his lectures before his students were full of guarded statements. For a few privileged favorites, such as Copernicus, Novara gave his arguments against Ptolemy.

Novara was a Pythagorean, and before we can discuss him, it is necessary to go back two thousand years in history to that remarkable galaxy of Greek mathematical philosophers who grouped themselves about Pythagoras of Samos, in the sixth century before Christ.

We shall view them through the eyes of the student Copernicus, who at Bologna had made great progress in the study of the Greek language and now began to read with avidity the works of Pythagoras and his followers.

First of all, Copernicus found in the Pythagoreans the source of many of the doctrines still upheld by Ptolemaic astronomy. For instance, they had developed the idea that the paths of planets and stars must be circular, because the circle was the most perfect of all figures and because it was also the most economical. Pythagoras himself had been a believer in the spherical shape of the earth, reasoning that it must be a sphere since all the other heavenly bodies were spheres, and because of the evidence sailors gave of seeing stars rise or fall in the sky as the ship moved north or south.

It must have been at this time that Copernicus read with more than antiquarian interest of the case of the old Greek thinker Anaxagoras, who, a century after Pythagoras, had been cast into an Athenian jail for maintaining that the sun was not a heavenly chariot daily driven by the gods through the skies. In those days too, Copernicus learned, there were plenty of ignorant priests fearful of new ideas, for the histories of Greece told him about Diopheites, an ecclesiastic who was sufficiently strong in Athenian politics to have a law passed which demanded "the immediate prosecution of all those who disbelieved in the established religion or held theories of their own about certain divine things." Under this law Anaxagoras, one of the greatest minds of antiquity, was made to suffer. Being a wise man, who could learn from history, Copernicus believed that scientific caution was better than ecclesiastical inquisition. Not until he lay on his death bed, comfortably beyond the powers of the Church, did he permit his manuscript to be published to the world.

There were still other things that Copernicus learned from the ancients.

In reading the old manuscripts he found some interesting ideas in the work of Philalaus, another Pythagorean. Whereas Pythagoras, with all his mathematical reasoning, had continued in the belief that the earth was the immovable center of the universe, Philalaus had been the first to suppose that this might not be so. In Philalaus' system, the earth with all the other planets actually moved; that is, they turned around a body called the central fire, which could not be seen because all the known parts of the earth were turned away from it.

The important thing to Copernicus was that this system, although obviously full of misconceptions and unnecessary assumptions, had been able to explain phenomena on the basis of a movable earth, just as he himself thought might be possible. As he read more widely in the Greeks, he encountered other examples—necessarily isolated—of investigators who had assumed that the earth might not be the center of the universe.*

There was, for example, Hicetas of Syracuse who maintained that the earth, of all the heavenly bodies, was the *only body* that moved and that this motion took place on its own axis. But Philalaus' system had been, as were many of the Pythagorean speculations, merely an hypothesis. It had received little credence and managed to survive principally because of its novelty and because of the value of the general mathematical principles it embodied. It lingered on in the modifications several other workers made of it when they discussed the possibility of the earth's rotation on its axis, placing the Central Fire at the interior of the earth, so that while the earth was no longer immovable, it still remained at the center of things.

Copernicus read also a good deal of Plato. He discovered, much to his surprise, that Plato as a young man had been at first a geocentrist—maintaining the conventional belief that the earth was the center of all things—but later on had veered to the possibility of the revolution of the earth around the sun. Plato never had spoken out boldly about these newer ideas, but had merely hinted at them now and again. (Apparently the philosopher was frightened at the daring of his own thoughts.) However, these hints

* Aristarchus of Samos in the third century B.C. was the first philosopher to suggest that the sun is the center and that the earth revolved round it in a year. Copernicus mentioned Aristarchus in his manuscript as having held heliocentric ideas, but in making his final revision struck out the passage as unimportant. As a matter of fact, although Aristarchus has been called the "Copernicus of antiquity" and credited with having worked out Copernicus' theory in its entirety, it is doubtful whether it was not with him as with many others (Nicolas Cusanus, Martius Capella, Oresme of Lisieux) a merely transient hypothesis.

were sufficient to strengthen Copernicus' own rebellion against the time-honored authorities.

Novara, as we have seen, was a Pythagorean. As such he insisted upon the idea of harmony in the heavenly system and felt that the crowd of epicycles that choked the Ptolemaic skies expressed no such harmony. He played with the thought of axial rotation and with the ideas of Philalaus and the others. As a result of all these Greek notions, Novara's study in Bologna was the scene of lively discussions between the master and the future theorist. Working together, they measured the heavens from the observatory of the university where a quadrant constituted nearly their entire supply of profitable instruments. Behind closed doors teacher whispered to pupil of certain flagrant discrepancies he had discovered between his own calculations and those of Ptolemy.

For nearly three years Copernicus stayed at Bologna perfecting his technique as an observer of the heavens under the tutelage of Novara, reading eagerly all the sources of astronomy and studying carefully every measurement and calculation he could lay hold of. In 1500 he went to Rome, where the Jubilee Year was in progress. Although he had not yet earned a degree at either of the two universities he had attended, he gave lectures on mathematics and even ventured to offer the idea of the earth's mobility as a possible explanation for some astronomical phenomena. While at Rome he had the opportunity of observing an eclipse of the moon, and in a lecture on it won much applause for his masterful summation of the mathematical implications of the event.

But now he had exhausted his leave of absence. The conclusion of the Jubilee Year gave him no further excuse for prolonging his furlough. Reluctantly he returned to Frauenburg and sought to extend his leave. The thirst for study and knowledge had not yet been quenched; there were still many things he wanted to know before he could afford to turn his attention to the routine business of being a priest. So he quite frankly told the authorities at Frauenburg that his education was not yet complete, that he wanted to study medicine at Padua and, if possible, avail himself of the opportunity for a still wider knowledge of the Church law.

This was a clever move. He knew, and argued as much, that a physician in their midst would be a valuable asset and that a more profound understanding of the law of the Church would better fit him to perform his duties.

So a new leave of absence was granted.

6

Back again in sunny Italy!

Every new idea seemed to have a representative at Padua, the picturesque university city with its arcaded streets and charming old Roman bridges. A medical school was located there with a reputation that far outranked Bologna. This was just the kind of place that a liberal would choose: a city celebrated for its Humanism, its fine arts, its botanical garden, and its anatomical theater. Away from the cold, dreary skies of the north, Copernicus again took up his academic work with that intensity of application that he sustained throughout his entire life, first as a student, then as an investigator, and finally as the greatest theorist of medieval Europe.

With several more years of study of medicine and mathematics his leave had again expired. Student days were plainly over.

He bade farewell to Italy for the last time and returned to Ermeland to fulfill his destiny in the great adventure of his life—the perfection of a theory in which he would show to an astonished humanity the earth moving through space!

7

On his return to Ermeland he was able to put off service in the cathedral for yet another period. His uncle had very wisely attached Copernicus to his castle at Heilsberg as his personal physician. (Heilsberg was only about ten miles away from the cathedral at Frauenburg.)

Now began a period of great activity for the future theorist. The man who had studied medicine in order to prolong a leave of absence turned out to be an excellent physician, and his services were in demand by many nobles and friends of his uncle. Besides this, he gave free medical treatment to the poor of the neighborhood, a practice which later stood him in good stead when powerful enemies were seeking to undermine his reputation and popularity. He interested himself in other questions too: politics, currency reform, literature. During his stay at Heilsberg, we find him translating into Latin the poetry of an ancient Greek writer, Theophylactus Dimocatta. The translation is, to be sure, of little interest to a student of the Copernican theory; but it is a sidelight on the character of its translator. He showed himself courageous by publishing it; for it declared him definitely a liberal and Humanist at a time when the reaction against these movements had become especially strong. It was this reputation which he acquired for sympathetic liberalism that was to do him harm later in life.

In spite of his wide-ranging activities, he continued to devote nearly half of each day to study and observation of the heavens. During the tedious journey home from Italy, he had had time to examine and weigh all the evidence he had amassed concerning a possible new astronomical system. Every shred of that evidence had taken him farther and farther away from Ptolemy and nearer to something quite new—quite unheard of since the days of those pagan Greeks—something thoroughly revolutionary—the movement of the earth around the sun!

8

One of the most easily observed and most interesting of the heavenly bodies is Mars, and it was upon this planet that Copernicus first concentrated his attention—on the one hand spending as much time in direct observation of it as possible, and on the other collecting all available references to it in the reliable sources he had at hand.

Of all the planets Mars was the oddest to watch in its course across the sky. Night after night he charted its movements with the crude instruments at hand and watched its speed diminish more and more until finally it was at a complete standstill. Like his predecessors, Copernicus waited for it to take up its journey again. But to his astonishment, when it began again to move, it was in the opposite direction, back whence it came.

Again he saw the speed diminish, then die away altogether. Again he observed the incredible phenomenon of a planet immovable in the sky. And again he saw it start once more to move, this time in the original direction. Now it continued, marching across the sky for a prolonged period. It seemed to have settled down to more conservative ways of life. When on the other side of the

NICOLAUS COPERNICUS

sky the same thing happened: the planet slowed down, stopped, moved backwards, stopped again, and finally moved forward.

The same phenomenon he observed in Mars he found with variations in the courses of the other planets: obviously, if such a path were the true and actual one, which, assuming the earth immovable, must be the case, either the idea of a perfectly circular orbit must be discarded and a weird meandering, lawless one substituted, or one could adopt the Ptolemaic epicycles and attempt to fit a cumbersome theory to these facts. Astronomers, Copernicus knew, had always adopted the latter alternative. But he was dissatisfied, as we have seen, with the hodgepodge of epicycles swarming in the Ptolemaic heavens. He sought another explanation.

Besides, the planets, during the time that they performed their backward maneuvers, became much greater both in light and apparent size. Either they actually took on size, or—which was of course the necessary solution—they came nearer to the earth. Here was a phenomenon his predecessors had either ignored or talked away—for the change in position was much too great to be explained by an epicycle however large or complicated.

So Copernicus turned now to his new theory which he had kept in abeyance while he tested the old one. "Heliocentrism" (the sun the center of the universe)—this was the way out! The old system of "geocentrism" (the earth the center) had collapsed under the weight of its own epicycles.

First of all, if the earth moved—a necessary deduction from that assumption of heliocentrism—what did this motion consist of? Calmly Copernicus weighed his data. All motion, he realized (Albert Einstein has restated his proposition in the present century) was the result of the motion either of the thing observed, or of the observer, or of both. Assuming the sun to be the center, he saw that the motion of the earth in respect to the sun was twofold.

The sun appeared each morning on the eastern horizon, passed during the day to the western. This was a *daily* movement. What other *daily* movements were there? Obviously, that of the rest of the stars and planets and the moon, which each night moved all together, across the sky. What was the corresponding daily movement, then, of the earth? Copernicus' mind immediately saw the solution—axial rotation—that is, one complete revolution daily of the earth upon its axis. Mathematical calculations, carefully carried through—comparison with the figures of all those thousands of predecessors whose measurements he respected equally with his own—soon established to his satisfaction that his first deduction was completely tenable. The earth actually revolved daily upon its axis, always turning one side away from the sun as it did so and causing, as a consequence, the commonplace phenomenon of day and night.

Was this all the earth's movement? Inevitably the answer was negative. That odd retrograde movement of the planets was not yet explained. Nor were other anomalies cleared up by the daily rotation—such, for instance, as the movement of the sun now nearer, now farther away from the earth. None of this could be made understandable without elaborate systematization, nor as long as one attributed the yearly revolution to the sun. Copernicus, following his theory, realized that once more the trouble lay in imputing to another body the motion which was actually the earth's. What really happened, he recognized (and established mathematically), was that the annual revolution was of the earth around the sun, sometimes closer to the sun and sometimes farther away.

He was quick to realize the altogether new revelation which this view brought to one of the most perplexing problems of the ages; he saw the implications of this theory sweeping through the cobwebs of the centuries. Clearly this alone would lead astronomy out of the blind alley of Ptolemaic geocentrism into the broad and sunlit avenue of heliocentrism.

9

Knowledge advances by steps, not by leaps, and Copernicus was in no hurry.

Like all the great theorists who followed him—Pasteur, Darwin, Freud—he took time for further observation to test his ideas. There was need for more checking-up and still further comparison of his own measurements with those of his predecessors. He believed he was on the right path; now he was willing to demonstrate it. But first to himself!

The observatory at Heilsberg consisted only of a tower from which he might watch the skies. There were no instruments in the modern sense and so it was necessary to make allowances for the probable inaccuracy of his observations. Relying more strongly upon the observations of others, regretting his own inability to attain accuracy, he devoted himself nevertheless to the gradual compilation of the most accurate table of planetary motions constructed up to that time. It is strong testimony to his greatness that for the working out of his theory he used clear-cut stark intelligence without throwing upon unreliable figures more weight than they could bear.

And the more he considered his idea the more he was struck with its utter sanity and with the corresponding sheer absurdity of those ideas which it must displace. For instance, all astronomers had for centuries agreed that the sun was tremendously larger than the earth. How absurd it was, he reasoned, dimly foreshadowing Newton's law of universal gravitation, that a body comparatively so small in mass as the earth should hold by its attraction not only the enormously larger sun, but the planets, and the whole vast sphere of fixed stars. How much more sensible it was to conceive of the earth as one of the planets revolving about the great majestic sun than of the whole universe, sun, planets, and all, as revolving each day about the pin point of the earth. It was hard to conceive that men should for so long have clung to such an absurdity.

Necessarily, however, all contradictions were not solved immediately by his theory. Objections occurred to him, which, although of minor importance, he realized could not be fully met until adequate instruments had been devised to make more accurate and detailed measurements.

There was, for instance, the problem of stellar parallax. Assuming that the earth moved, how was one to explain that each fixed star did not make a slight apparent shift in position (parallax) as the earth moved from one side of its orbit to the other? The shift, however slight, must be there, Copernicus argued; it was only that instruments to measure it were not available, and also that the distance of the fixed stars was considerably greater than had been supposed, so that the shift was infinitely smaller than would be surmised.*

As he began to submit the outlines of his theory to some of his

* Not until 1838 was stellar parallax finally measured. The German Bessel observed it from Königsberg in the case of the star 61 Cygni.

more intimate friends, another objection was brought to his attention. If Venus revolved about the sun, some argued, it should show phases like the moon, as its bulk, passing between earth and sun, obscured part of its light. The validity of this objection Copernicus quickly recognized, and asserted that here also one must wait upon the invention of more accurate instruments of observation. In God's good time, he added devoutly, the phases of Venus would be seen by human eyes. His prophecy was fulfilled in 1616 when Galileo's telescope showed them clearly.

As time went on, he added further details to his theory, though the main essentials were well worked out before he left Heilsberg.* Overlooking no reasonable possibility, he even considered the chance that an ellipse could abolish epicycles altogether. He had hoped to investigate this idea elsewhere, and wrote to that effect, but the years passed and the pressure of other affairs prevented such a necessarily exhaustive analysis. Who knows what he might not have accomplished had he been given time and sufficient facilities? But life grew increasingly demanding and harsh, and the possibilities of his youth were never completely realized. However, he wrote down all his conclusions and arranged them in logical sequence, so that in 1512, when his uncle died and he had to leave Heilsberg to assume his full duties at the cathedral, he had a completed manuscript ready for printing.

But he did not publish. Two things held him back: he had none of the impetuousness of his zealous friends, and he knew only too well how much further revision and reworking his work required. Nor was he so cocksure of his conclusions that he was willing to release them before a hostile world.

What was more important was the attitude of the Church. Not that he was prompted by piety; he was too intelligent a man to believe for an instant that any part of his theory damaged true religion. But he was acutely aware that his colleagues were not as broadminded as he; they might easily take amiss the promulgation of a doctrine that tore up a part of their teaching and tossed it to

---

* These essentials are: the sun at the center of the universe; Venus and Mercury and the earth revolving about it; the moon circling the earth in its regular 27⅓ day period; and the other planets, Mars, Jupiter and Saturn, swinging around the sun in that order of distance.

oblivion. He was a liberal, a Humanist, known as such, and the Humanists were not in high favor.

Publication could therefore wait. And it did—for Copernicus was in no mood to subject himself to an inquisition.

10

At Frauenburg facilities for observation were rather better than they had been at his uncle's castle. Copernicus chose a room on the tower from which the view in all directions save one was quite unobstructed. Only in the east was his vision barred by the great mass of the cathedral. He realized that at last he had come to a permanent situation, and he therefore proceeded to make alterations in his room that would aid him in his observations, which from now on were to be devoted to the retesting and the rechecking of his theory.

The modern observatory has what is called a meridian transit telescope which swings in a vertical plane—the meridian, which the sun passes at noon. Every star in the sky travels past this plane in the course of twenty-four hours. By marking the time at which each star makes its transit a clear record of its movements can be drawn. Copernicus, of course, had no telescope, but he arranged a vertical slit in the wall and night after night he noted the transit of the planets and compared his figures with those upon which he had originally computed. He measured the altitudes of the stars above the horizon by means of a quadrant. Thus he was able to gauge the meanderings and shifts in direction that counted for so much in his theory.

Unfortunately, the pressure of affairs at Frauenburg became more urgent than ever. His services as a physician were constantly in demand, now by the new bishop, now by his friends and acquaintances all over Ermeland. At one time he was called to far-away Königsberg, in Ducal Prussia, for his medical skill had become widely known.

His fame as an astronomer also was spreading. In 1514 he was invited by the Lateran Council to join other astronomers in the long-needed revision of the calendar. Here was an opportunity, if he wanted, to gain considerable publicity for his theory: he had only to go to the Council and show how the calendar must be revised, if at all, in the light of the new theory. But he did not consider the time ripe—he was still a young and healthy man—to thrust his head into the lion's mouth. He rejected the Council's invitation, explaining that he considered all efforts at calendar revision useless, since the course of the sun and the moon were so imperfectly known.

11

The years passed and his theory withstood relentless testing in the light of his own renewed measurements. As he gained more courage, he began to communicate his results to a wider circle of friends. In 1522 he wrote a brief commentary in which he gave a general outline of his theory in non-technical terms. This little manuscript had a wide circulation. Men of science were quick to recognize what it implied. Its fame soon spread to Italy, where the Pope heard of it. And now an amusing thing happened. Pope Leo X, the first to be confronted with the heliocentric idea, failed to be worried by it in the slightest! On the contrary, he requested one of his cardinals to write to Copernicus and ask for some mathematical demonstrations of his thesis.

Leo X looked on the theory as a mere hypothesis. It even assumed for a while the aspect of a "pet" idea at the Papal court; in fact, Copernicus became quite the fashion. No one apparently dreamed of taking the young astronomer seriously; and besides, the mathematical demonstrations of his views were not known, so that their danger as potential truths was apparently minimized.

But if the Catholic Church was slow in realizing the menace to its dogma that lay in the new doctrine, the Protestants were not! Luther, Copernicus' contemporary, was highly indignant and contemptuous of the astronomer. Did not the Bible definitely state that Joshua bade the *sun* and not the earth stand still? What sort of fool was this Copernicus that he turned his back on Holy Scripture and common sense? Probably just a vain fellow seeking a dubious notoriety through sensational pronouncements. And in this opinion Luther's colleague Melanchthon wholeheartedly concurred.

But Copernicus, having decided to withhold final publication indefinitely and to continue to disseminate his teachings orally to a limited group of friends, did not waste time in refuting his enemies. He had his hands full, what with his church duties and private affairs, without taking time to squabble with quibblers and theologians.

He had grown to be quite a prominent figure in the chapter at Frauenburg; he represented it diplomatically on many missions, and brought fame to it through his medical and astronomical skill. In 1522 he wrote, at the request of King Sigismund, an essay on the reform of the currency of Prussia which had long been depreciated by a series of disastrous wars. For a period of some five or six years he was chosen to be administrator of the city of Allenstein where he had all he could do to check the depredations of marauding bands of robber knights. And when the bishop died in 1537 Copernicus was among those mentioned as his successor.

12

But this bishop's death marked the beginning of a gloomy period for Copernicus, for the new bishop bore him no love. No one knows exactly whence arose the enmity that Johannes Dantiscus bore him; but it certainly existed and showed itself in many annoying and irritating ways. It may have been that Dantiscus resented the efforts of Copernicus on behalf of Tiedemann Giese, his dearest friend, in the latter's competition with Dantiscus for the bishop's miter. Or it may have been that Dantiscus, after a licentious youth, had turned fanatically devout and resented the well-known fact of Copernicus' liberalism and Humanist leanings. At any rate, the last few years of the astronomer's life were embittered by incessant quarrels.

The affair of Anna Schillings was typical. This woman, a distant relative of Copernicus, had been engaged by the astronomer as his housekeeper. The new bishop cast a stern eye upon the two, and finally deciding that the sixty-five-year-old Copernicus was carrying on a liaison with the fair Anna, straightway demanded Copernicus to dismiss her and never to see her again. Seeking to avoid trouble Copernicus complied. But the bishop's suspicions continued; he kept pestering Copernicus with reports that he had been seen with the Schillings woman here and there. It was, to be sure, bitter gall for Copernicus to have to throw his household out of gear in order to please a young zealot who, having a wife and daughter

in Spain, relics of his more natural days, thought himself qualified
to cast the first stone.

With Dantiscus constantly harassing him, Copernicus continued
to put off publication of his work. It was now virtually completed
and ready for the printer; nevertheless he had calmly resigned himself to the prospect of dying without seeing his theory published.
He thought it best to leave to others the task of issuing his work
posthumously. And he would have done so had not something
unusual happened. There came to visit him one spring day in 1539
a young man, Joachim Rheticus, from the Protestant University of
Wittenberg.

13

Rheticus had been teaching mathematics in Germany when rumors of Copernicus' new theory reached him. Like so many of the
astronomers and mathematicians of the age, he too was dissatisfied
with the Ptolemaic system which the clear light of heliocentrism
had only made more absurd. He obtained leave of absence to visit
Copernicus in order that he might learn from the astronomer the
details of his theory. Originally intending to stay but three months,
Rheticus remained instead nearly three years. This in itself was a
daring bit of action considering that he was a Lutheran in a Catholic country where the bishop of that particular diocese was hostile
toward all Protestants. But Rheticus stayed on, and it was he who
finally persuaded Copernicus to publish his work. When the final
revision was finished, Rheticus took the completed manuscript to
Nürnberg for publication.

Copernicus, still anxious to avert papal displeasure, dedicated his
work to the Pope, hoping thereby to gain for his views the protection of the Church. Aware that the new theory was destined to
smash a large part of Catholic dogma, he hoped to make the inevitable reconciliation easier by issuing the work under the auspices
of the Church.

However careful he was to smooth the path of acceptance for
his theory, he was unwilling and adamant against any attempt at
compromise. What he had discovered and patiently worked out he
knew to be unassailable, and he would allow no evasions of meaning in order to soften a clause here or blunt the point of an argument there.

He asserted his unwillingness for any compromise when he received a letter from Andreas Osiander, a Lutheran preacher interested in astronomy and mathematics, whom Rheticus had left in charge at Nürnberg. Osiander suggested that the work be offered as a hypothesis, pure and simple, bearing no relation to the actual facts other than to serve as a good working basis for calculations. In this way, Osiander suggested, there would be no conflict at all with Ptolemaic astronomy and religious dogma.

Copernicus sternly rejected the proposal.

The year 1542 passed by, and the astronomer, now in his seventieth year, went about his ecclesiastical duties, waiting for his book to come from the press. But in the beginning of the winter he was taken seriously ill. A series of paralytic strokes and severe hemorrhages laid him low. When the year 1543 opened, the friends who gathered about his bedside knew that they were waiting the end.

But life dragged on over the winter. Copernicus grew weaker and weaker, sinking into long periods of unconsciousness. He was ready to die, but he had one last wish—he wanted to see his book. Springtime came, and with it a particularly prolonged period of unconsciousness in the month of May. On the 24th he awakened for the last time, very weak. A messenger was standing by with a copy of his book. He thrust it into the hands of the dying theorist who had just enough strength to scan its title page. He smiled faintly, attempted to turn a page—his eyes closed.

Nicolaus Copernicus was dead.

14

The name of the book was called *De Revolutionibus Orbium Coelestium* (Concerning the Revolutions of the Heavenly Bodies).

Copernicus saw only the title page and he died with a smile on his lips. Had he turned that page he would have discovered perfidy—the treachery of Osiander. For that coward, disregarding Copernicus' explicit injunction, had inserted a preface to the work in which he incorporated the suggestion that the theory be presented merely as an "interesting hypothesis." Worse still, no name was signed to the interpolation, so that all readers assumed it was Copernicus himself who had sought to save his hide at the expense of truth.

Copernicus' friends were indignant at the fraud and sought to have it exposed, but their efforts were fruitless. That is how it came about that the first of the great theories of mankind entered the world under false pretenses.

Undoubtedly, Osiander's preface served its purpose well; for nearly half a century after the death of Copernicus only vague mutterings here and there gave token that the Church was aware of the new doctrine. But before the century was over, there appeared the man who, quite alone, presented the Copernican theory with all its implications to the opposition of the Church.

This man was Giordano Bruno, born in 1548 near Naples.

15

When Giordano Bruno was fifteen years old he entered the Dominican Order; at twenty-four he fled from his monastery because suspicions of heresy had accumulated against him. He was said to have entertained doubts as to the nature of the Trinity, and to have made various statements which his conservative hearers felt it their duty to report to the ecclesiastical authorities. When Bruno learnt of the agitation against him he left Naples and began to travel.

It was about this time that he became acquainted with the work of Copernicus. In possession of a free and untrammeled spirit, he had no doubt of the validity of the new astronomy. The only question to be raised was: How far could humanity pursue this new revelation?—that is, how far could one push the Copernican theory to its ultimate philosophical and scientific conclusion? Bruno's answer to that question was to be the signal for the start of the first great battle of theology against the advances of modern science.

Bruno went to Rome first, and there offered an example of the recklessness that he displayed throughout his life. A fugitive from the Inquisition at Naples, he sought refuge in Rome at the very convent where the Roman Inquisition had its headquarters! But luck was with him, and he was able to move to Venice, Padua, and then on to Geneva in Switzerland which was the home of Protestantism. Here also he came into conflict with the authorities, for he did not hesitate to express his contempt for the new Protestantism which he regarded equal to orthodoxy in its shallowness. With magnificent unconcern he lectured in Geneva against the old astronomy, championing Copernicus; and to make things worse for himself he printed railing denunciations against de la Faye, one of the leading professors. Geneva soon became unhealthy for him, and he moved on to France, first to Toulouse, and then to Paris, where he enjoyed considerable vogue as a brilliant conversationalist, an engaging lecturer, a fierce and unrelenting debater and a striking personality. With his penchant for satirizing all manner of assininity, it is no wonder that the liberals in the French capital took him warmly to heart. But despite his great popularity he did not remain there very long and we next find him on his way to the British Isles.

In England he came into conflict with the Oxford dons, a group of men who were the very essence of everything hidebound. And here again, in true Bruno fashion, he did not spare his opponents. He dug a sharp-pointed pen into their sensitive flesh, pouring into each wound the vitriol of a biting invective. Not content with this he hurled the mass of his tremendous erudition against their cardboard intelligence. It was simply too much for them. After six years of treading on the conservative toes of London, he returned to Paris for a brief visit. When we pick up the thread of his wanderings again we find him at various universities in Europe. He studied and lectured, always hewing to the line of his argument which pushed the Copernican doctrine farther and farther to its ultimate application.

At the University of Marburg he asked the authorities for the right to speak in public. Evidently his reputation as an iconoclast had preceded him, for the privilege was denied by the rector who wrote the following account in his register for that day: "When the right of publicly teaching philosophy was denied him by me for weighty reasons, he blazed out, grossly insulting me in my own house, protesting I was acting against the law of nations, the custom of all the universities of Germany and all the schools of humanity. He refused then to become a member of the university— accordingly his fee was readily returned, and his name erased from the album."

A month later Bruno lectured at Wittenberg before going to Helmstadt where the rector of the evangelical church issued a sentence of excommunication against him. It caused Bruno no annoyance—he merely shrugged his shoulders—("It is more blessed to be wise in truth in the face of opinion than to be wise in opinion in the face of truth.")—and moved on once more, this time to Frankfurt-am-Main where he remained for nearly two years.

All during his travels he had been thinking and developing his philosophy and at the same time leaving behind him a trail of brilliant books, pamphlets, and essays in which the fruit of Copernicus' great work was reaped.

16

What was there in Bruno's philosophy that so bitterly aroused the antagonism of the universities of Europe just as they were beginning to awaken from the dreariness of medievalism?

That which was implicit in the Copernican theory Bruno stated bluntly, namely: that the earth had been displaced as the center of the universe; that with the earth no longer central man also lost his post of center; that the earth was not the hub of a great universe created for its inhabitants, but a tiny planet among an infinitude of stars throughout the great infinity of space. In other words, the earth was nothing more than a minute speck in a measureless universe.

While Copernicus had expanded the universe enormously, he did not venture to maintain the infinity of the universe. For him, as for the older astronomers, there remained the thought of a universe bounded. Bruno broke these bounds and boldly asserted the existence of numberless worlds in space illimitable. He formed a more comprehensive notion of the new theory than Copernicus himself.

Bruno was satisfied that Copernicus' work had shown that the world was demonstrably capable of infinity. And why should it not be? Was not God omnipotent? Why should He, being omnipotent, will to create a world with limitations? Bruno could accept nothing less than an infinite world without bounds. "This world," he declared, "is merely one of an infinite number of particular worlds similar to this, and all the planets and other stars are infinite worlds without number comprising an infinite universe, so that there is a double infinitude: that of the greatness of the universe and that of the multitude of the worlds."

With words like these Bruno tore from the Copernican theory

the casuistic veil Osiander's preface had placed over it. He translated into popular thought the implications of the Copernican theory which had been realized heretofore by only a few. No longer was it advanced as "an interesting hypothesis." On the contrary, he hurled it at the Church in all its hard and overwhelming truth. His arguments for and his deductions from Copernicus were now placed in direct opposition to the great body of Catholic tradition, for Bruno was loud and determined in his insistence that the facts of astronomy be taken at their full face value and that truth must be known despite dogma or any vague "necessity for faith." Pushed to its ultimate significance this meant that the Church would have to revise not only its *physical* conception of the world, but also its *spiritual* conception as well. The all-importance of man as the most perfect and significant of God's creatures had long been a fundamental doctrine of Catholic dogma. But Bruno argued that, inasmuch as the earth is not the entire universe nor even the center of the universe, the word "Catholic" had lost its meaning. What Church could claim to be universal and catholic, and offer salvation to all life, which dominated only an insignificant speck of a planet among an infinity of stars?

Nor was this blow solely aimed at the Church. The idea of man's central importance had been treasured through countless ages—by the Greeks, the Arabs, the Hindus, the Romans, the Chinese. Bruno showed that the Copernican theory justified an altogether different emphasis upon man's place in the universe: he became an incident in the history of a small planet. Apparently a terrific blow had been struck at man's vanity by the comparatively simple process of substituting the sun for the earth as the center of the planetary motions!

By thus stripping the Copernican theory of all evasions and subterfuges Bruno brought home to the Church the alarming nature of the new astronomy. At the same time he prepared the way that was soon to lead to his own destruction.

17

In view of all these things it would appear to have been sheer foolhardiness on his part to leave Frankfurt and go to Venice (within easy grasp of the Church) at the invitation of a Venetian nobleman,

Giovanni Mocenigo. It may have been his eternal restlessness—
or perhaps the expectation that in Venice he could enjoy the society
of his countrymen from whom he had been so long parted. It is
known for certain that he received assurances of protection from
Mocenigo; and banking on those promises he went to Venice.

Now Mocenigo was probably a paid spy of the Inquisition which
was seeking to capture Bruno. He had told Bruno that he wanted
to be instructed in the so-called magic arts. Bruno was, of course,
fully aware of his inability to teach any such nonsense, and when
he arrived in Venice he reminded Mocenigo of it. The Venetian
nobleman was sure Bruno wâs withholding his knowledge, hoard-
ing it, miser-like, to render it the more valuable. He thereupon
planned to trap him. First he would try to get all he could out of the
philosopher and then to turn him over to the Inquisition for
heresy.

Growing bored with his dull pupil, who kept pestering him with
silly questions, Bruno announced his intention of leaving Venice.
But before he had a chance to pack his things his apartment was
invaded by six gondoliers who made him a prisoner in Mocenigo's
house. On the next day Mocenigo lodged a formal denunciation of
his guest with the office of the Inquisition which immediately transferred him to the local dungeons.

Several weeks later he was taken from the prison of the Inquisition to appear before the court. With a clear realization of his
danger he became more moderate in speech, maintaining that his
teachings were not heresy but philosophically valid and distinct
from religion which was a matter of faith. He declared also that
Aristotle's work was much more directly contrary to the Church
than his own. In order to clear himself he finally made a formal
abjuration of any errors he may have committed and asked for
absolution.

His case looked fairly promising. He might have escaped with
only a penance and an injunction to resume the cowl of the Do-
minicans, if Rome, now grown fully aware of the danger to the
Church contained in Bruno's championing of Copernicus, had not
insisted that he be extradited and given over to the central Inquisition for questioning. This was done, and he was incarcerated in
the dungeon at Rome in February, 1593.

18

For six years he languished in the Roman dungeons.

Delegation after delegation of theologians and monks went to his cell seeking to induce him to abjure his teachings. Rome was fully prepared to battle to the end; but how much greater a conquest it would be for the Church if this brilliant mind could be won over to the doctrines of the Faith instead of fighting against them. For six long years they argued with him, threatened him, berated him, in an effort to coax him back to orthodoxy and the service of the Pope. But it was all to no avail for Bruno stuck to his colors and would not retreat. "It is a poor mind," he declared, "that will think with the multitude because it is multitude: truth is not altered by the opinions of the vulgar or the confirmation of the many."

Finally, in February, 1599, he was brought before the Holy Office of the Inquisition at the same convent where he had once sought refuge when fleeing from Naples. His heresies were recited, and then he was excommunicated and stripped of his priestly and monastic offices. Still he refused the opportunity to recant.

Lastly, he was handed over by the Church to secular authorities "to be punished with all clemency and without effusion of blood" —the conventional formula for burning at the stake. Bruno, aware to what he had come, stood proudly before his judges and spoke piercing words: "You who sentence me are in greater fear than I who am condemned."

Eight days more he waited in a dungeon while fresh efforts were made to force him to recant. Obdurate to the last, he refused every invitation of his exhorters to yield.

On February 17, they led him to the stake in the Campo di Fiore. While the flames mounted a crucifix was offered him to kiss, as was the custom. Sternly he turned his face away from the symbol. Those who witnessed his death—and they were his enemies—testify that no cry or groan escaped him.

The fear of death was no part of Bruno's philosophy. "I have fought," he asserted in language strongly reminiscent of Socrates; "that is much—victory is in the hands of fate. Be that as it may with me, this at least future ages will not deny of me, be the victor who may—that I did not fear to die, yielded to none of my fellows in constancy, and preferred a spirited death to a cowardly life."

19

On his journey to Venice Bruno had spent a few weeks in Padua. Shortly after he had left that city to visit Mocenigo, the University of Padua extended a teaching invitation to a young man who was the next in line to carry forward the theory of Copernicus. That teacher was Galileo Galilei—the "creator of modern science following in the steps of its prophet."

With the advent of Galileo true experimental science was born; and with it was sounded the death knell of many old beliefs founded upon tradition, hearsay, dogma, and misinterpretation of the evidence of nature. From the moment that Galileo abandoned the study of medicine for mathematics and physics, he insisted upon putting the ancient beliefs to test. And how the old unquestioned assumptions began to fall to the ground! For example, he attacked the so-called law that a heavier body falls faster than a light one. In the presence of his adversaries at the University of Pisa he climbed to the top of the famous Leaning Tower and let fall simultaneously two weights, one a hundred times heavier than the other. Those who came to scorn sat mute as the two bodies struck the ground at precisely the same time—exactly as Galileo had predicted.

But the evidence of their own eyes was too painful and shocking. "This meddlesome man must be suppressed," murmured the university fathers as they quit the square in utter embarrassment. So Galileo was forced by their denunciations to leave Pisa and accept an invitation to teach at the University of Padua. He had long been acquainted with Copernicus' ideas which struck him as inescapably logical, but still he held off a little before venturing to proclaim publicly his adherence to the new astronomy. Soon he gathered courage. First he made private confession of his belief to another astronomer, Johann Kepler, and then to a few intimate friends. In 1598 he was re-elected to his professorship with an increase in salary which made him surer of himself but not too sure.

In all probability Galileo would have been more outspoken had not the shocking news of Bruno's burning at the stake (1600) frightened him into silence. However, an event of the year 1604 finally gave him an opportunity to speak. In this year astronomers were astonished to see appear a *stella nova*—a new star—which flashed brightly in the heavens, faded, and then disappeared. Galileo was gleeful. Of all the crude ideas of Ptolemy that had been accepted by people and Church that of the unchangeableness of the heavens was among the most cherished. Yet here, right before one's very eyes, a change in the makeup of the sky had come about. Galileo immediately went to work. In three lectures he explained the phenomenon in the light of the newer astronomy that was now taking shape. (The significance of Copernicus lies in the fact that he prepared the way for Galileo.) The attendance at his lectures was tremendous.

Encouraged by his success, he went further in demolishing the ideas of the older astronomy and soon gained the bitter enmity of his colleagues. But his popularity was yet large enough to protect him; he went unmolested for the time being.

Five years after the appearance of the *stella nova*, a mighty instrument for the advancement of astronomy was thrust into Galileo's hands. Rumors had come to him of the invention by a Dutchman of a glass contrivance with which distant objects might be seen much nearer and larger. Galileo realized at once the importance of this discovery. In a moment of inspiration, without waiting to see the invention, he went about constructing a telescope for himself. By placing lenses at either end of a lead tube he began to reveal the mysteries of the stars.

Discovery after discovery now rained in his lap. To his amazement he could count ten times as many stars as were visible to the unaided eye! First he found that the planet Jupiter, which the older astronomers had assigned to its solitary orbit far remote from the central earth, was not solitary at all: four moons were attending it. Certainly now the whole structure of the old planetary system of Ptolemy was gone.

More was to follow.

He now turned his glass upon the sun and quickly discovered that this majestic orb (held by the Church to demonstrate the perfection of creation) had spots upon it. Furthermore, the spots moved from one side of the great body to the other—proving, therefore, that the sun revolved on its own axis. And the moons of Jupiter turned about it, each in its own orbit. In other words, here were four planets which definitely did not revolve about the earth. Next, the moon showed itself under the telescope to be no smooth, even body, but rough and pocked with craters and mountains and valleys. Where was the old perfectibility and immutability of the planets taught by ecclesiastical revelation?

To the orthodox astronomers who had just awakened to the danger of Copernicanism and had marshaled their arguments against it, the most crushing blow of all was the fulfillment of Copernicus' prophecy regarding the phases of Venus. Through the telescope these phases were plainly discernible.

It will be remembered that in the plan of the solar system conceived by Copernicus, the planets Mercury and Venus are nearer the sun than is the earth. In the course of their revolution around the sun (to which they owe their light) Copernicus claimed that these two planets must exhibit phases like those through which the moon passes. Although Copernicus could not prove this to be true, he claimed, in consequence of his theory, that some day the proof would be forthcoming.

And so it happened.

In the year 1610 when Galileo turned his telescope on Venus he saw changes in the planet exactly like the changes of the moon. "We are absolutely compelled to say," declared Galileo, "that Venus and Mercury also revolve around the sun, as do also all the rest of the planets—a truth believed indeed by the Pythagorean school, by Copernicus, and by Kepler, but never proved by the evidence of our senses as it is now proved in the case of Venus and Mercury."

In these words Galileo summed up the final unanswerable argument for the Copernican theory.

20

One might suppose that in view of these revelations the opposition to Copernicus would have gradually subsided, however grudgingly. Nothing of the sort happened. The telescope was denounced as an instrument of the devil who sought to delude mankind. Orthodox astronomers refused to look through the glass, arguing in characteristic style that in order to see any moons near Jupiter man had to make an instrument which would create them.

The most amusing of the arguments launched against Galileo were those of Francesco Sizzi in regard to the satellites of Jupiter. He argued that there had to be seven planets, no more, no less; for were there not seven windows in the head (two eyes, two nostrils, two ears and a mouth)? Was not the week made up of seven days? Furthermore, the days of the week had been named for the planets. "If we increase the number of the planets," continued Sizzi, "this whole system falls to the ground." And to top it all off, Sizzi added: "Moreover, the satellites were invisible to the naked eye, and therefore can have no influence on the earth, and therefore would be useless, and therefore do not exist."

Galileo was permitted to go along for a short while without molestation. In 1611 he paid a visit to Rome and was graciously received by the Pope. But this triumph was short-lived. Four years later he was summoned again to Rome and succeeded in convincing the Pope of the logic of his arguments. But the storm was brewing. It finally broke when Galileo was denounced to the Holy Office of the Inquisitor which excused his errors upon his promise not to repeat them. Stirred by the heresy of the new astronomy, the College of Cardinals met in 1616 and formally condemned the Copernican doctrine. This time they exacted from Galileo a promise never to teach or maintain it again.

The theologians were assured now that this damnable heresy was done with. Galileo was permitted to return home and resume teaching upon the strict understanding that he was to ignore the Copernican theory altogether. As an additional safeguard against Copernican ideas the works of the new astronomy were placed upon the Index of Prohibited Books; the Cardinals had proscribed unequivocally "all books which affirm the motion of the earth." And there the matter rested for nearly fifteen years.

21

In 1630 Galileo once more dared to present the Copernican theory. Encouraged by the accession to the Papal throne of an old friend, Cardinal Barberini, he wrote a brilliant work in which he sought to evade the promise he had made by presenting both the

Ptolemaic and Copernican theories together, in the form of a dialogue, so that he could not be accused of either affirming or denying Copernicus. He wrote also, at the instance of the Papal censor, a pious preface in which he threw ridicule on the Copernican theory as wild and fantastic and contrary to Holy Scripture. In this form the censor permitted it to pass, whereupon the censor lost his own job and brought Galileo face to face with an angry Inquisition.

The dialogues were published in Italian and were an instantaneous success. The pious preface brought laughter down upon the Church that had allowed herself to be fooled by such an obvious pretense. How could it have been otherwise when the clear truth of Copernicus was placed in juxtaposition to the stark nonsense of Ptolemy? All over Europe people were reading Galileo while the Pope and his Cardinals in Rome grew furious at the trick that had been played upon them.

Galileo was once more denounced and summoned to appear immediately before the Central Inquisition. Sick in body, the old man—he was now sixty-six—was forced to leave home and make the long journey from Florence to the Vatican. Arriving there he faced the Inquisition once again. But this time no leniency awaited him.

Altogether he appeared four times for examination. First he claimed that his new work confuted Copernicus rather than upheld him. Then he promised to write further dialogues making this clearer. Then under pressure he admitted that he may have been "misleading" and vain of his own skill in debate, which may have led him to set up stronger arguments for the Copernican system than he was able to refute. Next he asserted that he had not broken his promise, which had been not to hold or defend the doctrine, for he had merely discussed it. In his last examination, held behind closed doors, his spirit was thoroughly broken. At the order of the Pope, whose friend he had been, he was subjected to the Inquisition's tortures until he finally signed a complete and final abjuration of all his errors: "I Galileo Galilei, being in my seventieth year," he recited on his knees before the tribunal, "having before my eyes the Holy Gospel, which I touch with my hands, abjure, curse and detest the error and heresy of the movement of the earth." * At the same time he promised he would denounce to the Inquisition any other scientist found to be upholding Copernican ideas.

Now that the Inquisition had him in hand he was sentenced to imprisonment for the rest of his life and exiled from his friends and family. Strictly carried out, this order remained in force for nearly nine years. At the end of that time, 1642, blind, broken, seventy-eight years old, Galileo died.

Apparently the churchmen had been successful. They had hounded the leading scientist of the age, humiliated him and finally brought him to an ignominious death. They had published his abjuration throughout Europe and demonstrated their power to make men recant.

But all their efforts were in vain. For the career of the Copernican theory continued unchecked.

22

To other men descended the task of completing the Copernican conquest. Bruno had advanced it fearlessly, and Galileo had accelerated it with experimentation and indisputable observation. Now Johann Kepler (1571-1630) went about the business of perfecting it.

But before Kepler there was the tragic figure of Tycho Brahe the great Danish astronomer who, in his student days, fought a duel at Rostock, had his nose sliced off, and replaced it with a gold and silver dummy. Brahe (1546-1601) did many noteworthy things: he devised a simple means of determining latitude and was the first astronomer to give serious study to the comets. But unquestionably his most important achievement was the training of his assistant Johann Kepler whom he urged "to lay a solid foundation for his views by actual observation, and then by ascending from these to strive to reach the cause of things."

The scion of a noble house, Tycho Brahe surrendered the good will of his family in order to pursue the study of mathematics; but his ability earned him the admiration of the Danish king who

* There is an old and persistent legend to the effect that Galileo on making this confession muttered to himself the words, *E pur si muove* ("Nevertheless it does move.").

now became his royal protector and gave him an island near Elsinore and enough money to build an elaborate observatory. Here for many years Brahe worked and watched his beloved stars, completing the finest astronomical tables ever worked out. Here also he achieved that pathetic compromise known as the Tychonic system by which he sought to get rid of the difficulties of the Ptolemaic astronomy while staving off the revolutionary theory of Copernicus. The Tychonic system endeavored to put the old astronomy in order by keeping the earth motionless at the center of the universe and having the sun and moon revolve about it (yielding to Copernicus only to the extent of having the other planets go round the sun).

Upon the death of his patron and protector, King Frederick II, Brahe was forced to leave his Danish island. He withdrew to the city of Prague where he obtained the patronage of the local monarch. It was here in Prague that Johann Kepler came to join him.

Brahe's attempts at compromise prevented him from becoming a true Copernican. But this much must be said in his honor: that he extended to the improverished and destitute Kepler a very great friendship and put at the disposal of his guest a vast amount of careful work which enabled Kepler to clear away the ambiguities and inaccuracies that prevented a full acknowledgment of the Copernican theory.

23

Kepler was a Copernican from the first day that his brillaint mind encountered the *De Revolutionibus*. And throughout his life, filled with financial troubles, mishaps and sickness, he held steadily to that theory. He was invited by Brahe to join him in his investigations. Out of this union of astronomical minds the world was given three fundamental formulations of planetary motion known as Kepler's laws.

Nothing angered Kepler quite so much as the stupidity of those who opposed Copernican ideas without having an elementary knowledge of mathematics. When he came to write his book which he called *Introduction upon Mars* he excoriated the vicious meddlers. "He who is so stupid as not to comprehend the science of astronomy," wrote Kepler, "or so weak and scrupulous as to think it an offense of piety to adhere to Copernicus, him I advise, that leaving the study of astronomy, and censuring the opinions of philosophers at pleasure, he betake himself to his own concerns, and that desisting from further pursuit of these intricate studies, he keep at home and manure his own ground."

Kepler was admirably successful in carrying the Copernican theory still farther away from the old order: he abandoned the circle and epicycle completely in plotting the orbits of the planets, substituting for all the devious arrangements of Plato, Aristotle, and even Copernicus the simple, yet at that time little understood, ellipse. An ellipse is a flattened circle, and Kepler found that by assuming the path of each planet to be an ellipse, with the sun in one focus, all the phenomena were finally satisfied. We have seen how close Copernicus came to making this discovery for himself. Unfortunately he never had the opportunity to undertake a full exploration of its possibilities. But even if he had it is not likely that he could have even remotely reached the definiteness of Kepler's conclusions. All previous astronomers had assumed the existence of uniform circular movement; and it was only when Kepler abandoned this view that he was led to the truths embodied in his three famous laws of planetary motion.

After Kepler's laws had become common property the Copernican theory progressed more rapidly. Not that it received universal acceptance. By no means. As soon as it was seen that some ground must be yielded by the older astronomy a number of compromises were tried. Among these the Tychonic system was perhaps the most popular. The learned Jesuit Riccioli, vainly endeavoring to put life into a mummy, published in 1651 what was called *The New Almagest*, in which he proposed still another conciliation in a pious attempt to avoid admitting the painful fact of the earth's motion.

But it was all a waste of energy. The old astronomy was now hopelessly shattered; it could no longer be denied that the stars of the firmament nodded their approval of the Copernican doctrine. To serious men of science Ptolemy and all that he stood for were irretrievably gone. The old astronomical structure which the medieval scholars and theologians had built upon his teachings and supported by that most highly prized of all oriental anthologies, the Bible, had been cast into the limbo of outworn ideas. After having endured for fifteen hundred years it was to be no more.

2. Hutton . . . . . THEORY OF THE STRUCTURE OF THE EARTH

OUR knowledge of the structure of the earth is so very recent that writers and commentators on the subject never fail to express astonishment over the antiquity of astronomy as compared to the modernity of geology. Why did man so long neglect the study of his own planet in order to gaze at objects millions of miles away from him?

The purpose of this chapter is to trace the early beginnings of man's awareness of the earth and its physical features and to show how this original curiosity led up to a profound understanding of the history of our planet. From time immemorial man has been in possession of all kinds of theories relating to the origin of his earth. These theories on origins (called cosmogonies) are discussed in another chapter. Here we confine ourselves to those thoughts touching the nature of the structure of this midget globe—our earth. "This subject," declared James Hutton in the opening paragraphs of his *Theory of the Earth,* "is important to the human race, to the possessor of this world, to the intelligent being, man, who foresees events to come, and who, in contemplating his future interest, is led to enquire concerning causes, in order that he may judge of events which otherwise he could not know."

2

Men have always lived on the soil and they have always been in the presence of rivers, hills, valleys, lakes, canyons, mountains, and oceans. Primitive people, no less than ourselves, felt the necessity of explaining the earth and its features. They wanted to know what caused earthquakes, floods, volcanic eruptions, especially the things that awed them and excited fear. Consequently, long before geology was placed upon a scientific basis there floated about the ancient world various explanations of earth phenomena. Most of these ac-

46

counts were fragmentary, fanciful and legendary, while others, surprisingly enough, contained a few facts.

One of the most pernicious types of errors in dealing with theories is to read into ancient texts modern conceptions. As a matter of historical analysis the ancients knew very little about the structure of the earth. The Babylonians and the Jews contributed nothing. Babylonia, a vast country of sand, showed very little rock to interest its thinkers. The ancient Hebrews, on the other hand, could make no progress in this direction because they ascribed all natural phenomena to Yahweh, their god. Those manifestations of nature that were unfavorable to their happiness were believed to be signs of the deity's wrath. Of an earthquake they declared that "Yahweh looketh on the earth and it trembleth," and they described a volcanic disaster by saying that "Yahweh rained upon Sodom and Gomorrah brimstone and fire out of heaven."

Leaving the oriental world and coming to the Greeks and Romans we find a somewhat different story. As early as the fourth century B.C. that old Greek traveler Herodotus (484-425 B.C.) noted the occurrence of petrified shells in the Egyptian hills and concluded from them that the ocean had once spread over that country. He could clearly see that the yearly deposit of silt laid down by the Nile upon its wide flood plain made that country "the gift of the river." On one occasion he cautiously suggested that the famous gorge of Tempe, which was attributed to the work of the god Hercules, was not formed by that divine hero at all but rather that "the mountain had been torn asunder by an earthquake."

It took a long time for men to abandon the idea that earth processes were governed by capricious and temperamental gods. Here and there over the centuries we find a few daring thinkers who challenged traditional views. That was the case of Aristotle (384-322 B.C.) who advanced an intelligent appreciation of geological phenomena. Aristotle is the first individual of whom it is recorded that he took notes and collected books with a view to an encyclopaedic organization of existing knowledge. His insistence was upon facts (not hearsay evidence) and he strongly urged his followers "first to classify them, having particular facts under general heads and co-ordinate them into theories." It is no wonder that Dante designated him "the master of them that know."

But more than this, Aristotle possessed the mind of scientific genius. He represents the high watermark of scientific achievement of antiquity both in actual observations and in theoretical speculation. Aristotle gave much thought to the work done by surface agencies of erosion in modifying the land. The changes which the face of the earth undergoes were understood better by him than any of his predecessors and contemporaries. Some of the things he said seem strangely modern. For example, "The sea now covers tracts that were formerly dry land, and dry land will one day reappear where we now find sea. We must look on these mutations as following each other in a certain order and with a certain periodicity." After observing the rivers entering the Mediterranean on the north, he gently ridiculed Plato for holding the belief that rivers originate in a great subterranean reservoir within the earth. Aristotle pointed out the fact that the large rivers flowing into the Mediterranean rise in high, mountainous country; that mountains condense the moisture in the atmosphere, absorb it, and subsequently discharge it into channels which grow into rivers. From studying the Nile he observed that rivers deposit material on flood plains and build up the land. (Each year the Nile deposits upon its delta over fifty million tons of rock debris.)

3

Neither the ancient Greeks or Romans went very far in explaining natural processes. Most of their contributions were fragmentary, disconnected and interlarded with myth. The information they had on rocks and minerals, earthquakes, floods, and volcanoes was entangled in a texture of beliefs that matured in a prescientific age. Take for example the subject of volcanoes. Because of the location of Greece and Rome in a belt of frequent volcanic activity the ancients turned their thoughts to the contemplation of underground forces. Unfortunately, their information was limited; they knew but four or five volcanoes located in the Mediterranean area. (Only in modern times has man come to know the existence of scores of volcanoes scattered over almost every part of the earth.) Not only were the ancients limited in their knowledge about volcanoes but most endeavors to investigate them closely were regarded as acts of impiety. North of the northernmost tip of Sicily lies the belching island of Vulcano which the ancients believed to be the portal of the netherworld dominated by the furious god Vulcan (from which we get the word *volcano*). Yet such is the spirit of progress that at the first recorded eruption of Vesuvius the elder Pliny lost his life in an attempt to approach the mountain and examine the action which was taking place there.

Despite much superstition and fear it must be admitted that the ancients knew a few things based upon their common-sense observation. Consider for example the writings of that fine old Greek scholar Strabo who gave the world an intensely interesting series of books on *Geography* (in seventeen volumes!) written somewhere around the year 7 B.C.

Strabo was a man of independent financial means with equally independent philosophical convictions. Like Hutton, who was to follow him many centuries later, Strabo was a patient and painstaking examiner of theories—particularly those attempting to explain the origin of stratified rocks and fossil shells of sea creatures embedded in them. After long and careful study he came to the conclusion accepted by modern science that many regions, now dry land, were once covered by ocean waters and that these same areas may alternately rise and sink with reference to the sea level. "Everyone will admit that at many periods a great portion of the mainland has been covered and again left bare by the sea."

Imagine what it meant in Strabo's day to speak of the earth in action—some portions of it moving up and others going down. From time immemorial men have thought of the earth as solid, assuring themselves that their feet were set firmly upon immovable ground. Of course this was the simplest way of understanding the structure of earth. With Strabo we contemplate the beginnings of another idea whose magnificent panorama will unfold itself before us, demonstrating that not only does the earth spin on its axis and turn about the sun, but that the earth itself and every feature of it is constantly changing. The "everlasting hills" that the ancient Hebrews spoke about are not everlasting, the vast waters in the sea are pulled by the sun and moon into tides; and the earth is constantly changing its shape because there is action in it similar to that in water. Indeed, the modern story of geological evolution is, in brief, the story of a succession of stages each of which may be conceived as heaving up accumulated deposits as land areas, their gradual denudation, and the laying down of the formations for the next geological stage.

On the side of theory Strabo is regarded as the father of modern views of mountain-making. He also originated the hypothesis that volcanic outbursts act as safety valves for the earth, releasing pent-up subterranean vapors.

4

Following the destruction of ancient Greece and Rome those long centuries known as the Dark Ages were productive of no increased knowledge about the earth. In the books of the medievalists such knowledge was relegated to a mere footnote. Yet throughout these centuries we find here and there, scattered through theological treatises, discussions about fire and water which were accepted as the active and formative forces of earth. Their relative importance was the one great subject of debate; hence it was unavoidable that the conceptions of the ancient philosophers should reappear time and again in the theories of medieval thinkers. Unfortunately, medieval Christendom did not use either its eyes or its common sense. Its supreme interest was theology, certainly not geology.

It is hard to get rid of old ways of thinking. It took Europe several centuries to pass through the medieval cloud of intellectual darkness. Slowly, very slowly, men began to investigate nature at first hand. Soon there arose in almost every land of Europe a growing group of scientists who were patiently contributing new data to the knowledge of chemistry, physics and the constitution of the earth's crust. These were the men who were beginning to see the earth as a record of the operation of law; they were preparing the only possible foundation for a science of geology.

That medieval prodigy of nature, Leonardo da Vinci (1452-1519), deserves an honored place among these early pioneers as one of the first who investigated the structure of the earth in an endeavor to know it in terms of scientific principles. By profession an engineer, Da Vinci was also an artist, a musician, a sculptor and a geologist. "Study science first," said he, "then follow the practice which is born of science." Placing the earth on a scientific basis has been a long-drawn-out job beginning with such men as Leonardo and carried on in a piecemeal fashion up to our day. Every advance has been of inestimable value.

Da Vinci understood the true origin of fossils. While constructing canals in northern Italy, he cut through stratified rock (rocks which lie in layers) and unearthed numerous shells, fossils of clams, snails, crabs and other marine creatures. These he correctly interpreted as due to the submergence of the land beneath sea level, thereby reviving the ancient Greek idea that stratified rocks were old ocean floors. This scientific view was not in accord with medieval ecclesiastic thought which regarded fossils as evidence of Noah's Flood. It is incredible how long and with what tenacious force so many unfounded geological beliefs persisted. When they began to crumble all manner of strategy was invented to reconcile ancient teachings with the scientific facts. The discovery of shells on the Alps, for example, was hailed as confirming the reality of the Deluge which was supposed to have covered all the high hills. Curious that the difficulty of washing shells up the mountainsides did not seem any too serious a problem to the faithful.

By close observation in the north Italian valleys Leonardo came to understand the agency of running water in sculptoring the earth's surface. No one up to his time had investigated so competently or so thoroughly the laws relating to the movement of water and hydraulics generally. He showed how rivers erode their valleys, how they deposit pebbles on valley terraces; how a fine detritus accumulates at river mouths, how plants and animals are buried in it, how the organic remains then pass through physical changes and become petrified while the river mud hardens into solid rock, and finally how the rock containing the embedded fossils rises above sea-level and becomes dry land.

The heritage left by Leonardo was not lost. Such is his magic that once you know him you treasure ineffaceable memories of his work. Great scientist that he was, he was also a great theorist anticipating much that was discovered by those who followed him. But advanced ideas, which he and his successors championed, did not go unchallenged. In 1661 Thomas Burnet wrote his *Sacred Theory of the Earth;* and in 1696 William Whiston published his *New Theory of the Earth.* These fanciful books were typical of a pious effort to discredit scientific thinking. Both authors concern themselves with the Deluge, the wickedness of mankind and how the biblical catastrophe affected the crust of the earth. According to Whiston, Noah's flood was caused on November 18, 2349 B.C., when the tail of a comet passed over the equator and caused a downpour of rain!

5

It took an enormous amount of energy to roll aside the mass of philosophical and doctrinal tradition that blocked the path of progress. Slowly, and by imperceptible degrees, the misinformation that had deceived, perplexed and misled mankind began to crumble.

The close of the eighteenth and the beginning of the nineteenth century was a period made memorable in geology by the pioneer labors of a brilliant phalanx of scientific investigators. Basically, these men felt there was a demand for new experience not simply to achieve an extension of previously held concepts, but to create a thorough-going fundamental revision. As a result of this attitude their investigations and teachings stirred new activity throughout Europe. Round them gathered a spirited group of young men attracted both by the freshness of the new knowledge and above all by enthusiasm for a science which had largely to be pursued out-of-doors, offering wide scope for the physical as well as the mental energies of youth.

The characteristic feature of this period, that which gives it significance in the development of geology, was the determined spirit to sift the facts, to seek untiringly new observations and new truths both in the field and in the laboratories. The fascinating subject of earth sculpture thus began in earnest. It was a form of intoxication for these young men; out of this intoxication discoveries were to bubble.

Interest was directed toward the investigation and description of the accessible parts of the earth's crust. The composition and arrangement of the strata were now studied with enthusiasm. The bolder and more venturesome inquirers beat their way into wild recesses of mountain chains and climbed snowy peaks whose difficulties had long been thought insurmountable. From many countries travelers explored the uninhabited plains of Siberia, the remote mountain ranges of distant Asia and the new Americas, bringing home with them fresh scientific material of the highest importance. Much of their work is of a richness and variety that baffle description.

By their unwearied efforts in collecting and identifying fossils and rock specimens, no less than by their unabated zeal in the laboratory, they established the young science of geology upon a platform of equality with other spheres of scientific knowledge. The time was now ripe for theory.

6

Abraham Gottlob Werner (1749-1817) was professor of mineralogy at Freiberg, Saxony. His unrivaled leadership in geology was gained both from his eloquent skill as a teacher who possessed great charm of manner and from the inspiration which he successfully poured into his students. Werner came from an old established family which had engaged in mining and metal working for three hundred years. As a child he played with mineral specimens which his father, an overseer of iron works, had given him. Small in stature, he had a pug nose and a shy disposition, but he was a brilliant and gifted speaker. For a man who bulks so large in the development of science, Werner wrote surprisingly little. His reputation was built almost entirely upon the spoken word which he used with surpassing effect.

When he became professor at the Freiberg mining school, it was a small job in an unimportant academy founded for the training of the local Saxon miners. Within a few years he raised his post to world significance. Students flocked to Freiberg from every quarter of the globe. Werner was unquestionably the most sought after and popular teacher of the science of minerals and rocks. By the power of his personality he came to be regarded as a kind of scientific pope whose pronouncements were upheld as infallible. His disciples were everywhere, and they were loud and blatant in their Wernerian faith. As long as he lived, Freiberg remained the acknowledged center for the study of the earth sciences.

What made Werner so interesting was his astonishing intercourse with ideas. Other teachers of mineralogy were dry as dust, but Werner knew how to make the subject attractive; he had a way of interrelating knowledge, keeping his classes spellbound with this kind of magic. He was forever bringing together an endless variety of apparently detached information and then unveiling secrets which might well have seemed undiscoverable. The story of minerals fed the flame of his soul because it was not only the story of nature but also because it was interwoven with history, adventure, agriculture, mining, building, jewelry, love, intrigue, man and woman. In each lecture he forged links between minerals and almost everything under the sun. Out of such blendings of information students acquired new insights. No wonder Werner's contemporary fame was tremendous.

But if ever there was a dogmatic theorist intolerant of views differing from his own, Werner was that man. For this reason his influence in the field of geological theory proved disastrous. Yet his services to mineralogy were exceedingly great and are not to be minimized because he erred so grievously elsewhere. When his pupils left Freiberg, they went out into the world as fine mineralogists, but also (and this is the unfortunate part) with the ardor of missionaries to win proselytes to the Wernerian faith, "not patiently to investigate nature but to apply everywhere the uncouth terminology and hypothetical principles which he had taught them." And great was the confusion thereof.

Werner, whom his admirers loudly hailed as the father of modern geology, exhibited a curious admixture of characteristics. On the one hand he was an enthusiastic collector of facts, but he saw only those facts which seemed to confirm his speculations. In illustration of his dogmatic method take, for example, his system of rock formations. Before he had ever set foot out of Saxony he taught that rock formations (as found in his own little corner of Europe) were universal and that these strata could be recognized by the same characteristics anywhere in the world. Accordingly, he arranged the crust of the earth in a series of formations, describing the variety of rocks, the details of their position and structure, their succession, as well as their economic value.

Like most other attempts to simplify complex problems, Werner's chronological scheme succeeded in becoming ridiculous. Werner was an untraveled man and what he did not see did not bother him. His system of rock succession was simple because his observations were restricted to the kingdom of Saxony, and if (as in this case) there are no volcanoes in Saxony this merely meant

JAMES HUTTON

After the portrait by Raeburn

that volcanic action is utterly unimportant! He and his followers constantly boasted that they accepted only facts and discarded all theory. "Never in the history of science," remarked Geikie the geologist, "did a stranger hallucination arise than that of Werner and his school, when they supposed themselves to discard theory and build on a foundation of accurately ascertained fact. Never was a system devised in which theory was more rampant; theory, too, unsupported by observation, and, as we now know, utterly erroneous. From the beginning to the end of Werner's method and its application, assumptions were made for which there was no ground and these assumptions were treated as demonstrable facts."

7

The Wernerian theory was a catastrophic view: it postulated sudden changes in nature. Later on in this chapter we shall see with what great skill James Hutton demolished this conception. There are so many phenomena upon our globe which seem at first sight to bear testimony to the action of sudden and catastrophic forces that the tendency to account for all past changes by these violent actions is easily understandable. However, what so often *seems* to be true is not true at all. The sun, for example, *seems* to rise in the east and set in the west: actually it does not and only those whose views were founded upon imprecise data could believe that it did.

The advocates of the Wernerian doctrines were sometimes called Neptunists (after Neptune, the mythological god of the ocean). All existing rocks were believed to have been deposited from primeval water—a chaotic fluid. One form of the theory had it that "the whole earth was taken to pieces at one time and dissolved in an all-embracing ocean," after which layers of inorganic material were deposited from this chaotic fluid as the water evaporated or receded. This theory gave us what has been called an onion-coat earth, since rock layers would be deposited all around the earth at once, the layers eventually resembling the coats or skins of an onion.

Perhaps the greatest absurdity of the Wernerian doctrine was this belief in a universal shoreless ocean out of whose hot and fecund waters the substance of all the rock formations of the earth had been precipitated. The French scientist Buffon (1707-1788) had originally propounded the universal ocean theory to explain the origin of fossils. Werner believed that the whole globe had once been surrounded with an ocean of water at least as deep as the mountains are high. How this primeval ocean could have held all the rocks in solution, and how the successive deposits were caused to be precipitated, were never explained.

The earth, to Werner, showed universal strata like the layers of an onion, the mountains being formed by erosion, subsidence, cavings-in. He entirely ignored the evidence for crustal disturbance and held the sorry belief that all sedimentary rocks had been laid down in the positions they now occupy, whether horizontal or inclined at an angle of sixty degrees. And because he was strongly opposed to the acceptance of volcanic action as one of the chief causes of geologic formation, he summarily dismissed the long and careful researches of other men on the nature of vulcanism and the origin of basalt. The interior of the earth, according to Werner's Neptunist doctrines, was cold; and as he had no conception of movement within the earth's crust, he explained volcanoes naively as burning beds of coal spontaneously ignited.

Men who utilize science are not necessarily those who are able to advance it. Werner's pupils went out into the world as able mineralogists but as poor theorists, and what was more harmful still, unbelievably stubborn men and reactionary when confronted with new facts. They denied the igneous origin of such rocks as basalt even though other scientists proved that rocks of precisely similar character had often been seen flowing in a melted state down the sides of volcanoes. As enthusiastic Wernerians they spread far and wide the ideas of their great but misguided master.

8

Take the case of Leopold von Buch (1774-1853). Here was a distinguished Wernerian student and one of the most illustrious geologists Germany ever produced. He was one of a large group who went forth to proselytize for the cult of Wernerianism. As a loyal Neptunist, Von Buch proclaimed the orthodox beliefs of his master regarding the aqueous origin of all rocks. However, his faith received a rude jolt when he visited the old volcanic region of central France and became convinced of the volcanic origin of the basalt rock in that region. As a strict adherent of the cold-earth theory he was loath to admit that what he had learned from Werner was wrong; so while admitting the obvious volcanic nature of the basalts in France, he stoutly remained loyal to the Wernerian belief in the aqueous origin of the basalts in Saxony.

Not for long could he be lulled into fatal apathy by the narcotic of Wernerianism; and not for long could he continue to be in opposition to those who saw in vulcanism the important factor in earth history. Von Buch's emancipation from the fading dogmas of Wernerian misinformation was slow; gradually however he came over to the ranks of the Vulcanists. Logical ideas are keys which are shaped in reference to opening a lock, and in Von Buch's case it was just a question of time until he held in his own hands the right tool. This was impressively accomplished when he became convinced that the higher mountains of Europe had never been covered by the sea, as postulated by Werner, but had been elevated by successive uplifts.

Frederick the Great once said that "the greatest and noblest pleasure which we can have in this world is to discover new truths; and the next is to shake off old prejudices." Many Wernerian students might be mentioned who were much slower than Von Buch in altering their position on the absurd Neptunist doctrines (the cold-earth theory) of Werner. In the history of science it is amazing how much valuable attention has been directed from the observation of nature into barren controversy. The unforgivable stubbornness of the Wernerians, an exhibition of an unfathomable shallowness, prolonged the battle. But the time came when others, like Von Buch, realized the importance of the internal heat of the globe (the hot-earth theory) as the most powerful agency in shaping the structure of our planet.

9

While the followers of Werner were blatantly and piously preaching their Neptunist doctrines, already stiff with dogma, a modest and unassuming Scotsman, gifted with practical inquisitiveness, was sifting out new facts not understood by the crusaders from Freiberg. This man was James Hutton whose *Theory of the Earth* has become a part of the unshakable basis of modern knowledge.

The original treatise, which made its appearance under that title in a learned journal, is one of the finest classics in all geological literature. It completely demolished the dogmas of Wernerianism.

Hutton, who was born in Edinburgh on June 3, 1726, was trained in the schools of his native city. His strong bent for chemical science induced him to select medicine as a profession. After studying at Edinburgh, he went to Paris and then to Leyden where he took his medical degree in September 1749. On his return to Scotland he did not follow his profession: medicine was abandoned and he took to agriculture, having inherited land in Berwickshire. He began to study scientific husbandry, taking a practical interest in his soils and water-courses. During years of highly successful farming Hutton introduced new methods while developing his knowledge of geology. As soon as he had amassed a sizable fortune in a chemical adventure (manufacture of sal ammoniac from coal-soot), he felt free to devote all his time and energies to the pursuit of science. In 1768 he leased his farm and with ample means moved to Edinburgh.

From his earliest days Hutton had exposed his mind to nature's exhibitions, taking delight in studying the surface forms of the earth and the rocks. He wanted to know how those Scottish rocks, so gnarled and broken, had come into being. Scotland abounds in many beautiful glens and valleys, mountains and seacoasts: How were they created? Such a mind is magnetized—it finds everywhere what it is seeking. During frequent journeys in England, Flanders, in Holland and Wales, Hutton widened his geology.

With the passing of the years he became a skillful mineralogist, for minerals suggested to him constant questions as to the earlier geological condition of our planet. He brought together an amazing collection of rocks. Every fact in nature, no matter how insignificant, became full of meaning; for even the insignificant is an historical record, the revelation of a cause, the lurking place of a principle. No amount of effort or detailed observation did Hutton consider too much in order to establish his own careful examination. In the course of his wide studies he read whole libraries of travel books in an effort to amass the most detailed information concerning the earth and its features. By 1764 he was ready to undertake an excursion through North Scotland; ten years later he made a complete tour of Wales. Always pursuing an idea, Hutton was at the same time always tracking a living active principle. Great theorist that he was, he based every conclusion on observed fact— as the subtitle of one of his books expresses it, to progress "from sense to science."

Essentially Hutton saw the earth not as a curiosity shop of detached wonders, but as a cosmos. Behind the endless confusion of detail he beheld a few great simple processes that have been going on age after age. For the best part of his life he had pondered these facts, tossed them about in his mind, tested them, and sought repeated confirmation before he began to fix them in written words.

On various rambles into the beautiful country around Edinburgh he was often accompanied by interested friends. His observations, many of them made during these little trips, on the effects of erosion in producing the diversity of Scottish scenery have had a profound influence on modern geology. Realizing the originality of his views and his ability to epitomize them, his close friends begged him to put them into written form. After long years of coaxing Hutton at last set himself to the job, and in 1785 he read his preliminary paper on the *Theory of the Earth* before the Royal Society of Edinburgh. Ten years later he finished it.

10

The publication of his work in two volumes (the third was still in manuscript when he died) attracted little favorable notice. This has happened time and again in the history of science where a great work, such as Kant's *Theory of the Heavens* or Gregor Mendel's account of his discovery, fell flat. In Hutton's case this was due to several causes, partly to his unattractive style of writing, partly to the title he used which was the same as that of so many valueless publications, and also in a measure due to the originality of his ideas; for they were so obviously contrary to those taught in the schools and universities. In a word, Hutton's theory was too unorthodox. It is the usual reaction of stereotyped minds when confronted with a new and upsetting thought to grow weary, so that the tired intelligence, like a tired huntsman, yields to the ruses of the quarry turns round, goes home content to think that the best way to solve problems is not to solve them.

E

Then again, to most people science means little more than an increased command over the forces of nature. They pick up the newspapers and read about this clever invention or that new marvel and conclude that all science is represented by sensational triumphs. They do not fully realize or comprehend the prime importance of the scientific attitude of mind and often when they meet it they frankly do not like it. Why? The reason the average man does not wish other persons to think scientifically is that he does not wish to think scientifically himself, the effort and the responsibility of doing so being too great for him. In Hutton we find fully developed the most precious possession of the human race: the scientific attitude of mind, the primacy of those processes of thought that lead to scientific achievement. Here are Hutton's own words, a veteran in the art of scientific thinking: "I do not seek to support an insufficient theory with a precarious argument but would wish to have every means employed by which truth might be made to appear. It is in no way necessary that I should be right in this conjecture. . . . Here are facts which are indisputable."

How utterly different was this Huttonian point of view from the theorizing mind of Werner! In many respects the thought-processes of the German geologist remind one of Francis Bacon, author of the *Novum Organum* and sometimes called the father of experimental philosophy. It may be doubted whether Bacon ever merited that title. (Certainly Werner did not merit being called the founder of modern geology.) Bacon disregarded in his own works the very principles of scientific investigation he so carefully expounded. When he had collected so-called facts by the hundreds, he then proceeded to speculate upon them as if they were unalterable truths, whereas in many cases they were merely old wives' tales or hearsay evidence. The best principles in the world will not help a theory founded upon static data. So far did Bacon's personal views mislead him that he persistently rejected the Copernican theory, though it formed the best possible example of his own scientific method of procedure, of collecting data and observations and arriving at conclusions from them. Mentally, Werner was of the Baconian stamp.

So many theorists in all ages have projected their thinking on a plane beyond the knowledge of their day. That was the fate of Hutton whose views were half a century in advance of the recognized geology of his contemporaries. So distinguished a thinker in Edinburgh as Professor Robert Jameson (1774-1854), who held the chair of Natural Philosophy, was a staunch advocate of Werner. In 1808 he formed The Wernerian Natural History Society which held its meetings in the museum of the University of Edinburgh. With pointed reference to Hutton he once wrote: "We should form a very false conception of the Wernerian doctrine were we to believe it to have any resemblance to those monstrosities known under the name of theories of earth. . . ." Jameson ultimately became convinced of the truth of Hutton's views, thus proving that only slowly do professors learn a proper modesty and a proper uncertainty.

The example of Doctor Jameson is cited to illustrate how Hutton's audience of geologists had to grow up. They were so completely trammeled by Wernerian beliefs that it took fully a generation for them to get their heads out of the sand. They had to learn for themselves how to tap the fountain of science at its living source. Was not this also proved by the case of Louis Agassiz? Agassiz was the first to conceive and formulate the theory of a series of great ice-caps spreading over a large part of the earth, remaining thousands of years and bringing about an ice age. Fully thirty years were required to enable other scientists to see the pictures in the great geological past that he saw, but at last all saw them. No geologist now doubts that Agassiz was right.

The story of the great theorists of the world is often the story of men at whom derision was hurled. Those who fought them did not have their wisdom and subtlety of mind, or their charity of heart. In 1793 Richard Kirwan, a Dublin mineralogist and president of the Royal Irish Academy, attacked Hutton's work in sharp and ignoble terms. (Kirwan was also a member of Doctor Jameson's Wernerian Natural History Society.) Advanced in years and convalescing from a severe illness, Hutton pulled himself together and resolutely went to work, determined to answer Kirwan by revising his treatise. Shortly after Kirwan's paper had appeared in the *Memoirs of the Irish Academy*, Hutton began his new job. Within less than two years of intense effort he brought the whole of his subject matter under more skillful treatment. In 1795 the revised work appeared in two octavo volumes.

11

Hutton's original treatise is a memoir divided into four parts and presented in ninety-six pages. The first two parts discuss the origin of rocks. The facts of geology are so numerous that one is apt to be overwhelmed by what seems to be an endless confusion of unrelated detail. Gradually one becomes aware of a few great but relatively simple processes. The same processes which are taking place today are just those processes which took place in eons gone by. Hutton's primary insistence is, "What is happening now, happened in the past." In other words, the events of past geologic ages can be most satisfactorily explained from a careful examination of present conditions.

What is happening now?

Simply put: two forces are at work, the same forces that always have been and always will be at work, (a) decay and (b) repair—both operating over immeasurable periods of time.

Decay. The surface of the earth is constantly suffering disintegration and removal. The rate of decay may vary from place to place, but essentially all mountains, rock, and soil are disintegrating and being removed into the seas by the slow effects of atmospheric weathering, chemical decomposition and the mechanical action of water. Rivulets and rivers have constructed and are now constructing their own valley systems. These flowing waters transport the worn material of the land to the ocean upon whose bottom the deposits slowly accumulate to form rock-strata. In the removal of this debris mountains are carved out and valleys formed.

Repair. The accumulated debris of the land carried to the sea is there spread out on the floor of the ocean to form new strata. The accessible parts of the earth's crust composed of sandstones, conglomerates, shales, and limestones are disposed in layers very similar to the layers now accumulating in all lakes, seas, and oceans. Thus the great rocks which constitute the visible part of the earth were formed under sea just as sand, gravel and mud are laid down there now. The renovation of the earth springs Phoenix-like out of its decay—indeed, this decay would prove fatal were not the earth a renewable organism in which repair is correlative with waste.

Hutton studied the globe as a machine adapted to a certain end, namely, to provide a habitable world for plants, for animals, and, above all, for intellectual beings capable of the contemplation and the appreciation of order and harmony. While the earth is a machine it is more than a mechanism; it is an organism that repairs and restores itself in perpetuity. This view destroys the static conception of the earth: the idea that its existing condition is the finished product of forces no longer in action. To Hutton the earth is not something done but something endlessly doing. Under his guidance we see the long and stately panorama unfold—mountains rise and disappear, sea and land repeatedly change places. In this manner he explained the vast work of decay and repair (dissolution and restoration) and brought them together as a general principle, even as Newton brought together a mass of details under the single law of gravitation.

Hutton's theory can be made very plain and simple by drawing a parallel between the cyclical forces that play upon rain and the cyclical forces that play upon soil. Let us first look at rain. The rain descends on the earth, streams and rivers bear it to the sea; the aqueous vapors, drawn from the sea, supply the clouds, and the circuit is complete. Similarly, the soil is formed from the mountains; it is then washed as sediment into the sea by the action of running water; geologic forces elevate it after consolidation, into mountains. What is this powerful agency that converts the loose deposits into solid rock, and elevates the consolidated sediments above the level of the sea to form new islands and continents?

According to Hutton, this agency could only have been heat; certainly not water, as Werner and his school believed, since the cement material, such as quartz, feldspar, fluorspar, is not readily soluble in water and could scarcely have been provided by water. Because most solid rocks are intermingled with other material, which may be melted under the influence of heat, Hutton suggested that at a certain depth the sedimentary deposits are actually melted by the tremendous weight of the superincumbent water. This weight causes the mineral elements to consolidate once more into coherent rock-masses.

Hutton believed that sedimentary rocks found high above the

present ocean level had been lifted by upheaval, and not, as the Wernerians insisted, deposited from a universal ocean.

In the third part of his treatise he shows that the present land-areas are composed of rock-strata which were laid down and con-solidated during the past ages in the bottom of the ocean. These, he said, have been pushed upward by the expansive force of heat, while other rocks have been bent and tilted during the upheaval. All strata are sedimentary, consolidated in the bed of the sea by the pressure of the water and by subterranean heat. How are strata raised from the depths of the ocean? By the same subterranean force that helped consolidate them. The power of heat for the expansion of bodies is, says Hutton (possibly having in mind the steam en-gine), so far as we know, unlimited.

Werner believed volcanoes were only transitory and very recent affairs caused by the spontaneous combustion of coal beds. Hutton denied this. To him volcanoes were due to the interior heat of the earth and inseparably connected with movements of liquid rock. Because of the "cold-earth" theory Werner was misled into believ-ing that granite owed its origin to water. Hutton showed that the very opposite was true: granite was formed by the agency of ter-rific heat. Essentially, Hutton said, "Volcanoes are safety valves" affording exit for the molten rock and superheated vapors, thereby preventing the expansive forces from raising the continents too far.

The evidences of volcanic eruption in the older geological epochs are next discussed. Hutton expresses the opinion that during the earlier eruptions the molten rock material spread out between the accumulated sediments or filled crust-fissures, but did not actually escape at the surface; consequently, that the older *magmas* had solidified at great depths in the crust and under enormous pressure of superincumbent rocks.

In the fourth part, Hutton concentrates attention on the pre-existence of older continents and islands from which the materials composing land areas of today must have been derived. Present continents are composed from the waste of more ancient lands. This means that the continents and islands of future eons will be made up of materials obtained from land areas now existing. All present rocks are without exception going to decay and their materials de-scending into the ocean. Once in the ocean these loose materials are converted into stone and later elevated into land. Heat is the agency that consolidates these loose sands into rock.

In this fourth part Hutton also discusses the evidences of pre-existing animals from which existing animals must have sprung. Very logically he argues that the existence of ancient animal life assumes an abundant vegetation. Of course, direct evidence of extinct floras is presented in the coal and bituminous deposits of the Carboniferous and other epochs. Other evidence is afforded in the trunks of trees that are found in marine deposits and have clearly been swept into the sea from adjacent lands.

The treatise concludes with a strong emphasis upon the time factor, the vastness of the geological eons necessary to accomplish this "system of decay and renovation." From a geological standpoint time is "a thing of indefinite duration."

12

No one before Hutton had demonstrated so effectively and conclusively that geology had to reckon with immeasurably long epochs, and that natural forces which may appear small can, if they act during vast periods of time, produce effects just as great as those that result from sudden catastrophes of short duration. In fact, the conception of sudden and great catastrophes advocated by Werner and his followers was abandoned in favor of inexorable nature working little by little, by the raindrop, by the stream, by insidious decay, by slow waste, and eventually accomplishing surface transformations on a scale more gigantic than was ever imagined by the older geologists. Even so-called catastrophic changes, such as are associated with the sudden action of earthquakes, volcanoes and landslides, represent the end of a long and gradual process.

As Newton had widened man's conception of space, so Hutton enlarged his conception of time. Countless ages were required to form mountains, rocks and the soil of our continents and islands; but "time, which measures everything in our idea, and is often deficient to our schemes, is to nature endless and as nothing."

This subject of time is one of the most important factors in the history of science and scientific theory. When the astronomer Cassini in 1672 gave proof that the sun was nearly a hundred million miles away from earth people at first regarded the figures as too shocking. Similarly it required courage to claim that the geological record proved the earth to be older than the seven thousand years which theologians deduced from the Bible. Because time is harder to measure than space our indebtedness to the insight and originality of Hutton is great. It is not too much to say that his insistence on vast eons as the true geological time-scale had a far-reaching influence on all branches of science; for time plays a tremendous role in the architecture of modern thought. Given immeasurable periods in which to work, nature not only changes all things inorganic but also (as Darwin was to show) all things organic. Since Hutton's day evidences for the geological time-scale have been greatly developed. The following ages for the various strata of earth are now given as the best estimates:

Million B.M.

Eocene (Oregon coal seams, Alabama limestone, etc.).......60
Carboniferous (Pennsylvania coal).................260-300
Upper Pre-Cambrian (Lavas along Lake Superior)........560
Oldest known rock.........................more than 1500
(B.M. Means Before Man)

Hutton did not undertake to explain the origin of things. He conjured up no hypothetical causes, no catastrophes, or sudden convulsions of nature; neither did he (as Werner did) believe that phenomena now present were once absent. He undertook to explain all geological change by processes in action now as heretofore. "In interpreting nature," so he presents his argument, "no powers are to be employed that are not natural to the globe, no action to be admitted of except those of which we know the principle, and no extraordinary events to be alleged in order to explain a common appearance."

The guiding rule of Hutton's theory is that the present condition of the earth is due to processes which we can see in operation and that these same processes have been in operation as far back as the earth's history is legible. Past events in the history of the earth must be interpreted in the light of what is happening today. He believed that the present alone would unlock the secrets of the eons long ago, and for that reason he looked directly to the earth for a solution of the problems of its history. Throughout his life he maintained the true scientific attitude—an open mind for all unsolved problems. Unlike Werner he did not attempt to harmonize facts of nature with preconceived beliefs. Facts known to everyone often have to wait hundreds of years before their true significance is understood. Although many facts expressed in Hutton's famous treatise were known, he was unquestionably the first man to paint the picture of the earth's history as a logical connected whole.

The gospel of a theory is true as long as it is "according to fact." In all of Hutton's thinking the inductive method of reasoning is used. He made the earth tell its own story wherein the facts hang together and the parts interlock. He saw correctly that the earth had not always worn its present aspect; that it had passed through a long history of varied changes; that earth movements came at different times; that from a study of the rocks themselves a consecutive story of the globe could be told. He saw the balance which exists between erosion and deposition: that just as an old land surface is worn away the materials for a new continent are being provided; that deposits rise anew from the bed of the ocean, and another land replaces the old in the eternal economy of nature. The summary of Hutton's argument is expressed in the closing words of his treatise that "we find no vestige of a beginning—no prospect of an end."

13

When we compare Hutton's theory of the earth's structure with that of Werner and other contemporary or older writers, the great feature which distinguishes it and marks its superiority is the strict inductive method applied throughout. Every conclusion is based upon observed data that are carefully enumerated, no supernatural or unknown forces are resorted to, and the events and changes of past epochs are explained from analogy with the phenomena of the present age.

Hutton was more than a geologist; he was a philosopher who believed that all activities that make humanity what it is and suggest, with blended hope and despair, what it might become, are inexorably geared to the earth. To this unassuming citizen of Edinburgh knowledge of man's relationship to earth is the first requisite of a philosophy of man. There was in him the passion to induce others who had acquired scientific knowledge to use their talents in promoting a general understanding of the constitution of the universe. These thoughts he elaborates in *An Investigation of the Principles of Knowledge and the Progress of Reason from Sense to Science in Philosophy* (3 volumes quarto).

Like other theorists in the line of thinkers who dominate these pages, Hutton was the author of more than one important generalization. Besides projecting his theory of the earth, he was author of the *Theory of Rain*, a paper he read before the Edinburgh Society on February 2, 1784, and subsequently published as Part I of a rather large book entitled *Dissertations on Different Subjects in Natural Philosophy* which appeared in 1792. Not only did he give to the scientific world two original theories of his own, but he devoted his insight, imagination, philosophical spaciousness, and scientific acumen towards the understanding of the theories of other men. Half an hour spent in thumbing the pages of the *Dissertations* reveals a mind that was a veritable intellectual mountain range. In this unique book Hutton passes in review the important theories of his day on fire, heat, light, gravitation, electricity. He subjects each theory to a probing analysis in a driving endeavor to see the unseen; each fluid hypothesis invites his investigation. "Man," he once wrote, "is not satisfied like the brute in seeing things which are; he seeks to know how things have been, and what they are to be." The pages of the *Dissertations* usher us into the presence of an alert theoretical mind possessed of an appetized intelligence, the inquisitive spirit which notices whatever is unusual and sees a problem in every commonplace occurrence.

A happy personality won for Hutton a long life of usefulness in the pursuit of the higher reaches of the human spirit. Besides the philosopher and scientist there was something of the poet in him. Not that he ever wrote any verses, but to his unsleeping mind nature everywhere walked clothed in grandeur and glory. Charles Kingsley, in that delightful book, *Wonders of the Shore,* spoke about the naturalist in words most applicable to Hutton. "Happy truly is the naturalist. He has no time for melancholy dreams. The earth becomes to him transparent; everywhere he sees significances, harmonies, laws, chains of cause and effect endlessly interlinked."

His early delight in studying the rocks and the surface features

of the earth brought Hutton into the open where he saw in the
ways of the simplest things the great processes of the universe. During his memorable visit to Glen Tilt we are told that when he found
a number of granite-veins in a river bed "the sight of objects which
verified at once so many important conclusions in his system, filled
him with delight; and as his feelings on such occasions were always
strongly expressed, the guides who accompanied him were convinced that it must be nothing less than the display of a vein of
silver or gold that could call forth such strong marks of joy and
exaltation." As one comes to know Hutton one cannot escape accepting the broad philosophical quest that is in evidence in every
sentence Hutton wrote and is etched in invisible words underneath
every printed line in his books. Simply put: through man's searching of the earth, into the depths of the seas and the farthest reaches
of the heavens, he has been given a better understanding of his own
stature.

Hutton's vast learning brought him into close relationship with
the leading scientists and thinkers of his day. There was Doctor
Joseph Black, author of the *Theory of Latent Heat,* to whom
Hutton dedicated his fine volume of *Dissertations;* there were Sir
James Hall, Lord Kames, Watt, Adam Smith of *laissez faire* fame
and others. Of particular importance to us and to the world at
large was John Playfair who did for Hutton what Huxley did for
Charles Darwin: he popularized the master.

Shortly after Hutton's death Professor Playfair assumed the task
of explaining to the world the compelling originality and greatness
of the Edinburgh geologist. After five years of consummate effort
Playfair gave to science a book that discussed, explained and illustrated Hutton's beliefs better than Hutton himself could have done.
Published in 1802 under the title *Illustrations of the Huttonian
Theory,* it at once opened the eyes of scientific men, for it was written in clear and elegant manner and brought into prominence many
subjects which had received too brief or too subordinate a treatment in Hutton's own writings. So clear and understandable was
Playfair's *Illustrations* that it came to be recognized as a model, for
the author "possessed the art of facilitating to others the attainment
of that knowledge which he had himself acquired by profound
study."

14

Although Hutton dealt with no cosmogony, it became increasingly more evident, from the day he published his *Theory of the Earth*, that our planet is bound by ties of the closest resemblance to other members of that family of worlds to which it belongs, and that the materials entering into their constitution and the forces operating in all are the same. Other theorists of later date, combining the knowledge of geology and astronomy, have given us plausible explanations of the origin of the earth as a member of a planetary system. We will see this in the chapter on Thomas C. Chamberlin. For himself Hutton avoided this vaster cosmic speculation, and rightly so. For he felt that the time was not ripe to formulate a seasoned theory on the origin of the planetary system. For this reason Hutton wisely felt it to be his duty to ascertain what evidence there is in the earth itself that will throw light upon the history of the planet.

Some of Hutton's views have been changed in detail by the progress of science, many have been greatly elaborated and some few ideas completely discarded; but in the main the essential features of his theory have stood foursquare to all the winds that blow. It must be remembered that in Hutton's time physics and chemistry, as we now know these two sciences, were in an undeveloped state. Consequently several errors arose in connection with the origin of minerals and rocks which had to be corrected.

No geologist would now agree with the principle that heat has hardened and partially melted all sedimentary rocks, and just as little would he ascribe to heat the origin of flint, agate or silicified wood. On the other hand, the hypothesis known as regional metamorphism is an extension of Hutton's conception of the action of heat and pressure upon rocks. Metamorphic rock is rock that has undergone an intense alteration of its original structure. Such changes are produced by heat, pressure and earth movements, so that it is often difficult to decide the precise origin of the rock. Consequently it is convenient to class all such doubtful cases as metamorphic. Limestone, for example, subjected to heat under great pressure, crystallizes and forms marble.

Hutton had never been attracted by the possibilities of experiment: he believed that the processes of nature are too complicated and on too large a scale to be successfully imitated in the laboratory. It took no little ingenuity and daring to attempt experiments on heating under pressure in order to produce alteration of rock. This bold adventure was undertaken by Sir James Hall (1761-1831), who succeeded in producing crystalline rocks from an igneous melt in his laboratory. With one titan blow he rudely shattered Werner's ideas that crystalline rocks in all cases had been precipitated from sea water. The experiments on rocks initiated by Hall and carried out over a period of thirty-five years were subsequently confirmed by others who followed him. These results completely overthrew Wernerian ideas and incontestably substantiated Huttonian principles.

In the winter of 1796 the illness that had plagued Hutton in 1793 returned. He was now in his seventieth year and physically feeble. The devotion of his sister Isabella (Hutton never married) carried him through that Christmas and on into the next year. Always active in mind, he now began to prepare a book entitled *Elements of Agriculture*. He did not live to finish it for he died in March.

An incredible quantity of manuscript and notes was left behind. Hutton was an indefatigable writer quite in contrast to Werner who disliked anything connected with pen and paper, going so far, as Cuvier relates, to leave unopened and unanswered a letter inviting him to become a member of a learned society.

A portrait of Hutton by Raeburn shows a slender figure with a high forehead, a thin face and a somewhat aquiline nose. The friends of Hutton throughout the world are thankful for this remembrance of the man. But even if this Raeburn portrait were lacking, there is another picture, far more important, that has come down to us in a short but very beautiful memoir on his life written by Professor Playfair. In it he eulogized his friend's great theoretical talents in these words: "The experienced eye, the power of perceiving the minute differences and fine analogies which discriminate or unite the objects of science, and the readiness of comparing new phenomena with others already treasured up in the mind; these are accomplishments which no rules can teach."

Summing up the work of the theorist from Edinburgh, we may justly say that, as Copernicus opened the new heavens, so James Hutton revealed the new earth.

3. Dalton . . . THE THEORY OF THE STRUCTURE OF MATTER

ALL early explanations of nature are the work of the imagination. They are guesses, for man is a creature constantly given to premature decisions on inadequate grounds. To get rid of all guesses, which belong to the infancy of mankind, and to arrive at the facts is the work of science. In each case some time-honored gigantic conception, like another traditional Goliath, had to be felled by small bits of knowledge.

2

In dealing with theories it is often difficult to trace the varying phases of their early development from indistinct glimmerings of long ago to the heights of some great effulgence in the mind of a genius-theorist. Yet we have before us just such a task in our attempt to understand the atomic theory, for we must properly begin with nothing more than primitive man's simple sense of wonder: he wanted to know what things are made of. Out of this elementary desire has come our vast modern knowledge of the structure of matter.

Early man had already shown himself upon the earth as a questioning animal, never satisfied and constantly outstripping himself. In all ages he has been a creature *en route* to a theory. "He does not form a closed system of needs and gratifications for his needs," once wrote Paul Valéry. "Hardly are his body and his appetites appeased when something stirs within him; it torments him, informs him, commands him, goads him on; it directs him secretly. And that something is the mind; the mind armed with all its inexhaustible questions."

3

So often in tracing the origins of early pre-scientific ideas we are forced to gaze back through indefinite vistas of time to the dim outlines of forgotten civilizations. Like the countless generations of men who preceded them, the ancient Greeks saw at first hand the earth, the air, water and fire. Everything seemed to grow out of these four basic things, and in the fullness of time return again unto them. This simple observation, which may be referred back to an almost universal primitive mode of thinking, led to the thought that all matter, the visible universe, is made up of four elements.

In its simplest terms the theory of the four elements stated that in this changing world of ours there were four substances that never changed—earth, air, water and fire. These four units make up all the varieties of matter; from their elemental nature all the complex forms that fill the earth have been spun. Everything which man sees with his eyes, touches with his hands or weighs in his scales must share the qualities of these four changeless things.

Oftentimes the origin of a word gives remarkable insight into old thought-processes. Element comes from *elementum* of obscure origin, which in all probability means "to nourish." Apparently the substances that the ancients called elements were believed to be those basic but mysterious things from which the universe was composed and from which all other things derived.

A typical proof that the four elements consist of fire, air, earth and water lay in pointing out the fact that when a piece of wood is burnt (a) fire appears, (b) water boils and hisses from the ends of the burning wood, (c) smoke ascends into the air, where it vanishes, thus proving that it is of the same nature as the air, and (d) an earthly ash is left.

4

All theories have a life-history; they are born, they live and very fortunately the vast majority die young. The mortality rate among them is high, and that is as it should be. It is only too sad that some live on for centuries only to block the path to progress. The theory of the four elements enjoyed an enormously long span of acceptance largely because it was backed by the prestige of Aristotle. "To go beyond Aristotle by the light of Aristotle is to think that a borrowed light can increase the original light from which it is taken."

Almost coincidently with the collapse of the classical world of Greece and Rome the theory of the four elements entered medieval thinking where it held undisputed sway over the minds of suc-

ceeding generations; it became the main theoretical idea of the
age of alchemy which arose out of the ruins of the antique world
of thought. As the master-concept, the four elements ruled proudly
for fifteen hundred years until decay set in and it gradually disappeared.

From a theoretical standpoint the long centuries of alchemy
were extraordinarily static; they contributed nothing toward a
better understanding of the intricate structure of matter. For the
most part the learned scholars, doctors and philosophers just talked
into their beards. The person who is brave enough to read their
discussions is bound to appreciate the caustic words of Omar
Khayyam—

> Myself when young did eagerly frequent
> Doctor and saint, and heard great argument
> About it and about: but evermore
> Came out by the same door as in I went.

But one need not belittle or ridicule an age simply because its
ideas are now regarded as erroneous and archaic. To understand
them even in part leads to an appreciation of the continuity of
man's intellectual effort. Once the distinguished French scholar
Bouché-Leclercq, after he had made an exhaustive study of astrology in relation to the thought of antiquity, declared that it was
not a waste of time to find out how other people have wasted theirs.

The alchemists from the third to the fifteenth century were men
who spun out a vast amount of belief; their books abound in references to the four elements, the sulphur-mercury doctrine, the
theory of transmutation of metals, the mystical notions of the Philosopher's Stone (often called the elixir of life) and scores of other
ideas full of theology, mythology, magic, astrology and the like. But
such thinking was not only unproductive of results in the realm of
theory, it was equally unproductive in the field of experimental
knowledge. If anything, alchemical theory deteriorated rather
than advanced, for it was heavily encrusted with mysticism and
obscurantism.

What finally brought the long reign of alchemy to an end was
science and the growing spirit of science which refused to be
swayed by false methods of reasoning. The alchemists, having a

preconceived idea of how things should be, made all their experiments to prove their theories. When in 1661 the English scientist Robert Boyle introduced the modern idea of the elements, he reversed this attitude of mind, and with this transition from one point of view to an exactly opposite one the great citadel of alchemy began to crumble.

In brief, this is how it happened:

In his *General History of the Air* Robert Boyle (1627-1691) gave his views on how he thought the atmosphere might be composed. Although his explanation was somewhat crude, it had the effect of demolishing the old notion. For Boyle showed that air was not an element but a mixture of gases and not a simple one at that.

What Boyle did for air, Henry Cavendish (1731-1810) did for water. In 1784 Cavendish announced his discovery of the composition of water. Far from being a simple element as advocated by the Egyptians, the Chinese, the Hebrews and the Greeks, Cavendish showed that water is made up of hydrogen and oxygen.

For a long time, of course, it was known that the earth too was not a simple element because metals such as silver, iron, copper, gold and the like could be extracted from it. As greater knowledge poured in from a diverse group of investigators the earth came to be understood as the most complex of the so-called four elements, inasmuch as the earth can be separated into many chemical compounds whose natures vary according to the locality from which the soil or rock has been taken.

When it came to fire however a long and bitter controversy had to be waged before it yielded its medieval ghost. Although fire is a most important, if not the foremost, chemical process, still no one in ancient or medieval times understood it or was able to explain it. It continued a deep and impenetrable mystery. Not until the eighteenth century was the crude semi-alchemical theory about fire (called the theory of phlogiston) completely overthrown. It remained for Antoine Lavoisier (1743-1794), that prince of chemists, whose needless execution remains a deep blot on the French Revolution, to accomplish this feat when he showed that fire in and of itself is not a material substance. Combustion, Lavoisier showed, involves an interaction of the combustible material with oxygen; and the rate of combustion is influenced by the rate at which oxygen is supplied.

F

To Lavoisier we owe the word oxygen; and his alone is the honor of explaining the known facts of combustion.

With the total destruction of the main theory of alchemy, earth, air, water and fire came to be known as the defunct elements. With their demise there also went into the discard the idea that each of the four substances had a guardian spirit. Gone now were the sylphs that were supposed to live up in the air, the undines that lived in the water, the gnomes down under the earth and the salamanders that inhabited fire.*

It was unquestionably impious on the part of science to rob people of these semi-religious fancies. Science of course is unyielding, and for this reason alchemy today, with all its vast theology, is nothing more than a dim and spectral region. However, if one needs to seek comfort at the wholesale destruction of old ideas perhaps the words of Ernest Renan are the most satisfying: "The truths which science reveals always surpass the dreams which it destroys."

5

Besides their speculations on the elements the Greeks also wondered whether matter could be divided indefinitely. That is, if you took a quantity of some substance and then took half of it, and half of that again and again half of that, would you ever arrive at anything that could not be divided? On this question they gave two answers, Yes and No. Those thinkers who said "No" believed that matter is continuous, filling all space with different degrees of density. If matter be continuous, so they argued, then all matter is infinitely divisible.

Those thinkers who said "Yes" believed matter to be porous, made up of separate particles, entities in themselves and in some fashion merged together in sufficient number to make up all physical bodies. What we see about us as an apparently solid and nonporous object is in reality composed of discrete particles. These particles they considered to be ultimate units—the building stones

---

* "Spirits of wine," "spirits of ammonia," "spirits of salt" remind us of these old medieval conceptions. The properties of all substances were supposed to be due to the "spirits" residing in them. Cobalt, for example, is derived from a word meaning *goblin* which was believed to haunt underground places such as mines and caves. Nickel comes from a word meaning *demon*.

of matter and as such they were regarded as indivisible, indestructible and eternal.

Modern science has followed along the lines of those who made the assumption that matter is the sum of its many indivisible particles. But it was not until after centuries of argument, experiment and intellectual growth that the scientific mind formulated the correct picture of the atomic structure of matter. John Dalton was the first man to penetrate scientifically into the inmost recesses of matter and to emerge with a broad and magnificent conception of its interior state.

When the Greek philosophers conjured up the concept of the atom as an imaginary entity, they did not even remotely realize that these particles of matter belonged to a world of bewildering complexity. The idea of atomic structure remained an interesting curiosity until Dalton. But no more than that. Not only is Dalton's basic theory and viewpoint different, but the underlying factual content is too. Even where it is said that the atomic idea is as old as the Greeks, it must be remembered that Dalton introduced accuracy where there had been vagueness; from an interesting intellectual speculation Dalton's genius produced an exact scientific theory capable of experimental verification. The Greeks were long on speculation but short on experimentation. That is why Aristotle had such a strong hold on medieval scholars; they could argue endlessly on the subjects he provided! In those days it was not necessary to prove anything by an appeal to experiment; one had only to use "logic" and such canons of doctrinal teaching as had been "revealed" to the saints. It was nothing less than a revolution in the processes of thought when Roger Bacon (1214-1294) adopted the motto: SINE EXPERIENTA NIHIL SUFFICIENTER SCIRI POTEST ("There is no certain way of arriving at any competent knowledge except by experiment.").

6

This newly found experimental way of thinking became the most significant part of the intellectual equipment of an illustrious scientist, Robert Boyle, born in Lismore Castle, Ireland, the fourteenth child of the Earl of Cork. Because his thinking is a vital link in the story of the atomic theory, a brief survey of his contribution must be interpolated here.

Boyle is worth remembering: the long age of alchemy virtually ended with his introduction of the modern chemical idea of an element. Unlike the alchemists, he did not use long Latin phrases, nor was he limited by their fears, superstitions, taboos, or cumbersome words. Alchemists wrote with an intentionally obscure terminology. Boyle presented his ideas in simple English. In the interests of secrecy these older savants recorded their results in a mass of mystic symbols. But with Boyle clarity, not befuddlement, was the chief aim.

With sufficient means always at hand Boyle pursued science without financial obstacles. Even as a lad he had had splendid advantages and encouragement, among them a grand tour of the European Continent in the company of a tutor. At the time he visited Florence, Boyle was only fourteen years old, yet the wide-awake youngster was sufficiently advanced to have been influenced by the work of the great Galileo.

Upon his return to England we find him, many years later, living at Oxford where he carried on extensive experiments. His activities touched almost all branches of chemistry, anticipatory of great achievements a century later. Out of his numerous experiments on air came the beginnings of new knowledge on that subject as well as his famous improved air pump which is still exhibited in London in the rooms of the Royal Society for the Improvement of Natural Knowledge of which he was one of the most active originators.

An extraordinarily gifted and painstaking observer, Boyle did not advance any definite chemical theory; indeed, there were in his time not sufficient well-established data to warrant him in projecting one. Yet we owe to Boyle the use of the term "analysis" in the modern chemical sense. He was the first to use it, and the word has since carried with it Boyle's profound approach to problems. Though he lacked a theory, the demands of analysis led him to ask the following question:

What is the world made of?

Boyle answered this question very simply and right to the point. For in the questions he asked and the answers he gave, he showed an intuition so well described by one who said, "He smells the truth." Boyle's answer was that if you pulled anything to pieces and dissected it down to the last limits you would find that it was made of one or more elements, and that when you got down to these elements they always stayed the same and never changed into anything else. To illustrate this point, take for example common salt. Salt is a compound which can be broken up into two constituent elements. If you were to heat it very highly it would split into sodium and chlorine.

Let us take another example, one from Boyle's own writings; we shall then realize how great a strain he laid upon simple and direct thinking when he stated that two substances (mercury and sulphur) are present in red mineral cinnabar. Cinnabar consists of them just as a house consists of bricks and wood, or a piece of cloth of different threads. This seemed extremely paradoxical because one does not actually *see* mercury and sulphur when one looks at red mineral cinnabar any more than one sees oxygen and hydrogen when one looks at water.

Not content with stating these facts, Boyle endeavored to understand them. Man, in order to be the observer, must see not only what happens but why it happens. This Boyle did. He saw with marvelous clarity that there is a difference between elemental substances and compound ones. Why is red mineral cinnabar a compound and not an element? Because it can be broken up. You can see Boyle did not have in mind the so-called elements of the Greek thinkers, earth, air, water and fire. He had in mind the more numerous distinct substances of modern chemistry, such as sulphur, copper, mercury, lead and gold, which we call elements today. Boyle's definition of an element was practical; instead of postulating any definite number of elements he was content to investigate the subject experimentally and so to find out how many there actually are. Twentieth century chemistry lists more than ninety of these elements. In Boyle's day the embryo science of chemistry knew less than two dozen. Yet Boyle's definition of an element as a "substance incapable of decomposition" has come down to our day unchanged. By the precision of this luminous idea he made chemistry a new science. Consequently there was inaugurated an exact era enlightened by truth and free from fundamental errors.

7

In that massive chain that forges the cable of knowledge from one age to another, it is important not to forget that Boyle was an atomist. Steeped in the granular views of various philosophers, Boyle championed the thought that all elements are made up of little particles of matter far too small for the eye to see. This doctrine influenced Newton, who had had correspondence with Boyle on chemical subjects. With the prestige of the Cambridge scientist behind it the atom came to be accepted as the fundamental basis of all matter by the natural philosophers of the eighteenth century.

Newton in turn influenced Dalton.

But the Newtonian theory was a physical atomic theory. In Newton's opinion atoms were regarded as infinitely hard (a judgment which we know today is not true). Chemical combination, by which one element combines with another to produce a compound utterly unlike either, was far too intricate and profound a process for Newton to explain. Not until John Dalton gave to the world the results of his experimental work did the true understanding of these chemical relations emerge into sunlight. It was one of the most marvelous feats of human intelligence. With Dalton a new science arose from the shaken ashes of an old mystery.

8

In a thatched cottage in the little English village of Eaglesfield, Cumberland County, John Dalton was born on the sixth day of September, 1766, the second son of a poor hand-loom weaver. The lad grew up learning mathematics, a little physics, some English grammar and other subjects in the local Quaker school. Always of a very serious disposition, young Dalton at the age of twelve attempted to become a teacher. At fifteen he went to Kendal, a neighboring village, to assist his cousin who kept a school. Here he spent twelve years, finally becoming joint master with his elder brother Jonathan when the cousin retired.

But the two awkward Daltons had little success in attracting pupils. One of the students years later wrote in reminiscence: "The school was not generally popular, owing to the uncouth manners of the young masters, who did not seem to have mixed much in society." From what we know of him we might say what Wellington once said of Napoleon, "He was emphatically *not* a gentleman."

While at Kendal young Dalton was greatly encouraged by the philosopher John Gough (1757-1825), who, although blind from infancy, was master of several languages and knew every plant within twenty miles by touch, taste and smell. Gough was also an expert meteorologist. To Dalton he communicated this passion to know nature at first hand, to observe carefully and to keep minute and systematic records. As Dalton rarely mixed in society or went out for amusement, it was comparatively easy for him to act on Gough's encouragement. In 1787 he began a meteorological diary, which he maintained thereafter for fifty-seven consecutive years, making more than two hundred thousand observations.

Through the efforts of John Gough, the young Quaker from Kendal was appointed teacher of mathematics and natural philosophy in the Academy in Manchester. Dalton was now in his twenty-eighth year, and he had behind him his first publication, *Meteorological Observations and Essays* (1793), which contained the germs of his great future theory. In the following year the Manchester Literary and Philosophical Society elected him to membership. And this began a long period of mutual helpfulness. Dalton needed just such a society; it elicited his Gargantuan energies. For in a full half-century of membership, during which he held successively the offices of secretary, vice-president and finally president, he read before this Society one hundred and sixteen papers on scientific subjects. "If I have succeeded better than many who surround me," he once said in later life, "it has been chiefly—nay, I may say almost solely—from unwearied assiduity."

Dalton spent his entire life (he died in his seventy-eighth year) teaching, experimenting, theorizing, and relating his observations to the Manchester Literary and Philosophical Society. His social manners always remained imperfect; but we are not concerned about that, for we are dealing here with a man who by his thinking rather than his social graces has left a persistent influence on the lives of mankind. Apparently Dalton did not care about people—his life was one of immense disinterestedness in them, and his manner was correspondingly both awkward and gruff. Those deep-set eyes, square chin and massive jaws were set on the problems of science and a desire to achieve in all things precision. And he who increases precision increases control over life.

There are some men who work best alone. They are frequently called lonely spirits. But who shall say that Spinoza or Henry Cavendish were lonely? Or that Kant, because he chose the deep resources of his own mind, missed much by keeping aloof from the pernicious emptiness of small chatter? There is, to be sure, a difference between being lonely and being alone. Most people are lonely because they cannot stand being alone—that is, they can stand everything in the wide world except themselves. Like Spinoza, Dalton was a man of modest tastes with a simplicity enriched by the vivid colors of a fine imagination.

And Dalton was color-blind. Not until his twenty-sixth year did he become aware of his handicap—and then only because his deficiency had caused him several embarrassing incidents. When the full meaning of abnormal vision dawned upon him, he was sufficiently the scientist to make a detailed report of it to the Manchester Society and to offer his own explanation. The explanation he gave was unfounded, modern scientific research has established, but Dalton's own analysis attained sufficiently wide reputation to attach his name to the condition, so that color-blindness until very recently was commonly called Daltonism.

There is an old saying in biography that great men taken up in any way are profitable company. The multiple and varied interests of genius are to be seen in Dalton's life. He was very much at home in meteorology, botany, mathematics, hydraulics, insect life, navigation, geography, grammar—and above all in chemistry.

It was by no means an accident that the atomic theory was worked out by John Dalton. He brought to the analysis of matter the same scientific attitude of mind that characterized everything he did. He was a votary of the relentless logic of facts. And even though he was often in error, owing to the crudity of his instruments and inaccuracies in experiment, he never deviated from the objective and honest approach of science.

In all his many interests he showed the influence of John Gough under whose tutelage he had learned the scientific attitude, the need for the laboratory, and a deep respect for masses of observations. To this early Gough tradition Dalton himself added an original and independent mind possessed of an exceedingly vivid imagination. This led him not only to collect facts but to theorize about them.

For many years Dalton's main interest was a subject usually regarded in those days as very dull. He studied the weather with tenacity and thoroughness. Gough's example, as we have already seen, had started Dalton keeping systematic records. Among other things, Gough had often discussed with his disciple the subject of the weather; and Dalton chose this field for his nearest and dearest hobby. It proved to be a happy choice, for it was through the study of the atmosphere that Dalton began that train of thinking that led him to the atomic theory.

9

Since the days of Robert Boyle it had been known that the air is not a simple element but a compound made up of gases. Dalton's monumental work consisted in his experiments with different groups of gases. Leonardo da Vinci once said that experiments never deceive—"Experiment is the interpreter of nature." From what Dalton saw with his own eyes in those experiments, and from the conclusions which his genius prompted him to draw from them, came the modern theory of the atomic structure of all matter.

The mind of the theorist is so constituted that it can never rest content with an outward view of things. He lives with symbols and speaks in words so that the abstract and the concrete are touched in the same flight of thought. Dalton took pencil and paper in hand; he sought to draw in black and white the vision that was taking shape in his mind, for it occurred to him that the atoms of each element are different. Oxygen is made up of atoms, nitrogen is made of atoms, hydrogen, too—yes, all gases and all solids, indeed all elements are basically atomic. But the atoms of each element are absolutely different from all others. Thus, any one atom of sulphur exactly resembles any other atom of sulphur, but is different from the atoms of every other element. You can take atoms of oxygen and combine them with atoms of hydrogen and get water. While you now have a fluid, this fluid is nevertheless still made up of atoms of oxygen and atoms of hydrogen.

The Greek theorists had only said that water was built up of atoms—water atoms. They stopped right there, for theirs was indeed a very simple picture. But with Dalton it was different. In reality the so-called water atoms of the Greeks were not atoms at all, for a particle of water is made up of hydrogen and oxygen. Furthermore, the Greeks did not possess even the remotest idea of how different elements combine to produce a compound. Even had they known that water was made up of two gases, they had no means of knowing how. But Dalton did.

He now began to use his pencil and draw pictures. He knew exactly what he was drawing. He had had a long apprenticeship in the ways of observation and precision. And now his vision was clear. First he drew circles to represent the atoms. Then separately he drew marks within these small circles to represent the atoms of each element. The oxygen atom he represented by a simple circle; the hydrogen particle by a circle with a dot in the center; nitrogen by a vertical line bisecting a circle. And so on, like this:

○ Oxygen	⊕ Sulphur	Ⓩ Zinc
⊙ Hydrogen	Ⓢ Silver	Ⓛ Lead
⊕ Nitrogen	● Carbon	Ⓟ Phosphorus

Chemical compounds he represented by placing these symbols in juxtaposition:

⊙○ Water	⊕○ Nitrous gas
⊙● Olefiant gas	●○ Carbonic oxide

In picturing more complex structures he simply carried out his basic principles so that:

Carbonic acid looked like this

Ammonia

Alcohol

Ether

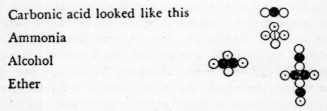

Those persons who were privileged to listen to his explanatory lectures may have taken these pictures as nothing more than graphic illustrations. But they were infinitely more than that to Dalton. For him they were real, as actual as if he had seen them with his own eyes and handled them with his own hands. All these pictures he worked out for himself slowly, painfully, blunderingly.

It was admittedly crude, but it proved to be a highly important representation. Fellow scientists ridiculed it as pictorial jugglery. Nonetheless it took its place as the first system of atomic notation—remarkably clear. How different was this Daltonian conception from the views of the old Greek philosophers? They had claimed that atoms were infinite in number and infinitely various in forms. Dalton saw that this was not true; there are only as many different kinds of atoms as there are different elements.

Not only did Dalton stress the view that the atoms of the various chemical elements differ from each other, but he boldly asserted that they possess different weights. Each atom has a fixed and unvarying weight of its own. But how can one arrive at the weight of an unseen particle? Dalton theorized that he could achieve for every atom only its relative weight. It became only necessary to choose some substance as a standard. He started with the lightest atom he knew anything about: hydrogen. Taking its weight as a basis for his calculations he assigned to it the number 1. Hence the weight of the atoms of all other elements must be relative to hydrogen and must be greater than 1. Thus if one pound of hydrogen unites with five and one-half pounds of oxygen (as Dalton's experiments led him to calculate), then obviously the weight of the oxygen atom must be five and one-half times that of hydrogen.

In a paper that he read before the Manchester Society on October 21, 1803, Dalton said that his investigations into the relative weights of the atoms "is a subject, as far as I know, entirely new; I have lately been prosecuting the inquiry with remarkable success." We do not know the exact nature of the experiments that led him to the results that are found on page 287 of the first volume of the new series of the *Memoirs of the Literary and Philosophical Society of Manchester*. But there they stand!

Many of the original atomic weights assigned by Dalton to the various elements are now known to be inaccurate. But these were errors made in the early morning of chemistry when he had only his own crude instruments to work with. Even so his results were remarkable. They represent the first table of atomic weights.

10

From time to time Dalton made considerable changes in these tables in his eager search for accuracy.* As we follow his thinking we are always conscious that we are in the presence of a "research" mind. Detecting and identifying facts and discovering their varied relationships is research. Without research there can be no theory. Facts are the body of science; theory which combines these facts is its spirit.

While Dalton was developing the many interesting facts of his doctrine, a stormy controversy broke out between two chemists, Joseph Proust and Claude Berthollet. It was a serious fight over a subject of impressive significance in the history of atomic theory.

Proust (1755-1826) maintained that chemical elements always unite in definite proportions by weight to form compounds. By the quantitative analyses he made he was thoroughly convinced that all compounds obeyed this law with extreme accuracy. "According to my view," said Proust, "a compound is a privileged product to which nature has assigned a fixed proportion."

Berthollet (1748-1822), in a book entitled *Essai de Statique Chimique,* strongly opposed this doctrine, holding to the opposite view: namely, that proportions could vary indefinitely, that in fact variability is the rule and definite proportions the exception. Proust and his followers maintained that the composition by weight of pure nitric oxide is always 14 of nitrogen to 16 of oxygen. Berthollet and his followers maintained that this was not necessarily so, that the composition of nitric oxide is not constant and that to 14 of nitrogen there could be different amounts of oxygen around 16, depending on the method of preparation of the compound.

Dalton examined the arguments of the two exponents and soon became convinced that Proust was right despite the fact that Berthollet was at that time the most authoritative living chemist, besides enjoying the prestige of having been a companion of Napoleon on the Emperor's expedition to Egypt in 1799. By bringing his atoms into play Dalton confirmed the overwhelming truth established by

* Each year the International Commission on Atomic Weights produces a revised table which today usually undergoes little change. Notwithstanding the errors in Dalton's weights the principle was clear.

JOHN DALTON

After an engraving by J. Stephenson

Courtesy of The Robert Fridenberg Galleries

Proust that every compound is made up of two or more elements combined together in definite numerical proportions by weight. To explain why the same amount of oxygen always unites with the same amount of hydrogen to form water it is clearly necessary to know that there are atoms of each element which unite on a basis of definite numerical proportions by weight. Salt, for example, is made up of two elements: the atoms of sodium and the atoms of chlorine. How do they unite to form salt? For every 23 parts by weight of sodium there are found to be 35½ parts by weight of chlorine. That is, the sodium atoms combine with precision with the atoms of chlorine to produce salt. It is plain that if the atoms which make up the elements never vary in weight, then the composition of every true chemical compound never varies. This is the law of definite proportions. It needed an explanation and Dalton provided it.

11

A good theory not only guides experiment, it anticipates it.

Dalton was forever going back to his subject to make new discoveries by suggesting new connections between old ideas or new applications of old methods. His desire was to complete the mastery of atomic structure and to provide himself with new opportunities for a deeper and more accurate grasp of it.

So far he had used his theoretical knowledge to explain and clarify the chemical laws formulated by other men. It was one vast ungrudging effort toward accuracy. Now he began some experiments of his own to elucidate a new law of chemistry which was to give additional and more conclusive evidence that his vision of the atoms was no idle dream or absurd hallucination. The facts he had in hand conspicuously matched the expectation deduced.

This law is known as the law of multiple proportions.

Simply put, the law states that many pairs of elements combine to form more than one compound. If you combine the same elements in different proportions by weight you get different results. Dalton had been working with olefiant gas (acetylene) which is made up of 12 parts by weight of carbon and 1 part by weight of hydrogen. By varying the proportions—that is, by combining 12 of carbon with 4 of hydrogen—he got carbureted hydrogen (methane). Or, take water. Oxygen and hydrogen can unite to form water (on the basis of 2 parts by weight of hydrogen with 16 parts of oxygen). However, if you change the proportions say, 32 parts by weight of oxygen with 2 of hydrogen, you get not water but something different called *hydrogen peroxide*. Thus if one element forms several compounds with a second element, the weights of the latter which unite with a constant weight of the former stand in the proportion of simple whole numbers such as 2:3, 1:3, etc. (But always the numbers must be simple whole numbers, never fractions, for Dalton's system did not allow numbers to be split.) Proust too had observed that some elements combine in more than one proportion by weight. But he failed to observe that these varying proportions bear a simple multiple relation to one another. In other words, Dalton added the knowledge that the increase is made by simple ratio. "You are right in this," wrote the great Swedish chemist Jöns Jakob Berzelius (1779-1848) in a personal letter to Dalton. "You are right in this that the theory of multiple proportions is a mystery without the atomic hypothesis; and as far as I have been able to see, all the results gained hitherto contribute to justify this hypothesis."

12

A theory does one of two things: either it proves its capacity to elucidate the facts or it breaks down under the strain. The law of multiple proportions confirmed Dalton's theoretical position. He found that his generalization was a simple way of co-ordinating tangled phenomena; it not only elucidated the facts, but it disclosed previously unobserved relationships. By means of this theory the scientist was now able to penetrate into the details of the world not directly accessible to his senses. Moreover, it showed the vast world of matter to be a system subtly interconnected. That which was vague and faulty could now be clarified, and even relationships that were previously announced but still partly obscure were presently open for illumination.

The Daltonian doctrine may be summed up as follows: the simple atoms of an element (1) are all alike in size and weight, and (2) cannot be created or destroyed; but (3) may unite with other atoms in simple ratios to form compound atoms or molecules.

In this simple broad generalization John Dalton bound together out of his clear organizing head the law of multiple proportions,

Proust's law of definite proportions, Lavoisier's law of the conservation of matter and the law of reciprocal proportions. Actually the law of the conservation of matter became a corollary of the atomic theory, for if atoms are uncreatable and indestructible, then all matter composed of them must possess these same characteristics. "No new creation or destruction of matter is within the reach of chemical agency," Dalton wrote in his *New System of Chemical Philosophy*. "We might as well attempt to introduce a new planet into the solar system, or to annihilate one already in existence, as to create or destroy a particle of hydrogen. All the changes we can produce consist in separating particles that are in a state of cohesion or combustion, and joining those that were previously at a distance."

Dalton was deeply impressed with the universality of his theory and its practical application. Had he been a man given to pride he could have been justifiably vain. But Dalton, despite his gruff ways, was a simple, kindly soul. Just as the invention of printing gave wings to the interchange of thought, so Dalton felt that the atomic theory would lift chemistry to the high plane of an exact science and spread far and wide the beneficence of its extraordinary effects.

Above all his theory gave him a strong sense of the interrelatedness of all things chemical; without it the masses of observations and experiments coming down from ancient days to the modern age were "without law and order by which the whole becomes intelligible."

In the long course of man's existence on earth he has been the victim of a thousand illusions, fallacies, wrong assumptions, half-grasped notions and grotesque speculations. What a host of distorted ideas! Occasionally there arises out of this awful jungle a genius with strength enough to make his own clearing in the forest and sufficient skill to erect a palatial theory possessing architectonic qualities. Such a genius was Dalton—a classical architect of ideas.

13

A recluse in his habits, Dalton had but few friends. He preferred to explain his views before the Literary and Philosophical Society of Manchester. In several papers that he read before that body he hinted at his atomic theory, but it was not until 1803 that he made known his table of atomic weights. As we have already seen, it was in October of that year that he read a paper before the Society, setting forth the various stages in the long course of careful reasoning which led him inevitably to think in atomic terms.

In addition to his papers Dalton gave an account of his views to one of his very few friends, Thomas Thomson (1773-1852), the influential professor of chemistry at Glasgow. Thomson was so completely won over that he lost no time in incorporating the theory in the third edition of his *System of Chemistry* (1807).

A year later Dalton published the first volume of his own book entitled *A New System of Chemical Philosophy*. With the appearance of these two books the atomic theory of matter belonged to the world.

14

In the history of science so many theories have been full of postulated entities (to make the system intelligible) and fictions needed for their explanatory value, that it is not at all surprising that the Daltonian doctrine of atoms met with opposition. Many were the jeers leveled at the Quaker theorist of Manchester. His atoms were regarded as "false," "unnecessary," "an attempt to give an unnatural precision to ideas which are and must be vague." Even when critics were more charitable they regarded his atoms as a fiction needed only for their explanatory value—demonstrably nonexistent, employed temporarily to further investigation but ultimately to be abandoned.

For more than half a century after his death many eminent men of science looked upon the Daltonian brain child as an illegitimate speculative error. Gradually of course they were won over. Even as late as 1904 Professor Wilhelm Ostwald, one of the leading chemists of the world, was making an attempt to persuade scientists to abandon the idea of an atomic structure of matter. He too finally withdrew his objections.

Why?

Because the increase of scientific knowledge demonstrated that atoms are not imaginary things. It was discovered that they possess a structure of dimensions lying far beyond the limits of microscopical visibility, and that they are just as real as any other object in the universe. Far from being mere "aids" or "pictures" or "models" or "helps," they were found to be in truth real.

15

Oftentimes a theory will outstrip the genius who gave it birth. The atomic doctrine came to rest its reception on the amazing number and significant kind of things it rendered coherent and intelligible. Some of these newer significant things Dalton could not see at all, for he did not fully grasp the rounded circle of atomic meaning which automatically opened up a new world of experiment, conjecture and inference.

There was the case for example of the distinguished French scientist Louis Joseph Gay-Lussac (1778-1850) who, shortly after Dalton published his theory in 1808, gave to the world his results on the volume relations of reacting gases, in which he showed that the volumes entering into combination bore to each other and to the products (if gaseous) a simple numerical ratio. In other words, Gay-Lussac discovered that gases, under the same conditions of temperature and pressure, always combine in definite numerical proportions as to volume. Exactly two volumes of hydrogen, for example, combine with one volume of oxygen to form water. ("Volume" means any volume-unit for measurement such as a quart, a liter, or a gallon.)

One would suppose that Dalton would have grasped at the opportunity of applauding the discovery of Gay-Lussac, that he would have found tremendous satisfaction in witnessing further confirmation of his atomic theory which the work of the French scientist certainly afforded. Strange to say Dalton did not react that way at all. He chided Gay-Lussac for inaccuracy and disputed his contribution. Doctor Thomas Thomson wrote him a letter in which he spoke glowingly of the Frenchman's work: "The most important paper respecting your atomic theory is by Gay-Lussac. It is entirely favorable to it, and it is easy to see that Gay-Lussac admits it."

Thomson's words fell on deaf ears. Dalton was obstinate and refused assent. Fortunately for science, so impersonal is its forward march, Dalton was left almost alone in his singular opposition to Gay-Lussac. Other men saw and moved on.

There have been instances in the history of thought when a

great idea overwhelms and obsesses the man who gave it birth. He becomes its slave and death alone parts them. Usually such men are intolerant. It is hard for them to realize that anyone is able to improve upon or advance their original ideas.

Dalton's attitude towards the work of Gay-Lussac was repeated in his antagonism to the work of Baron J. J. Berzelius, the Swedish chemist, who, next to Dalton himself, was then perhaps the most influential scientist in the world. Berzelius (who championed and advanced the atomic theory) devised a system of chemical notation that was acknowledged on all sides as a vast improvement over Dalton's.

Dalton, as we have seen, had originated the first system of atomic notation (chemical shorthand), consisting of circles with various configurations and markings within them. To indicate a compound, he joined one circle to another. In the really complex compounds, such as were being discovered by many men, the analysis showed them to be made up of so many different kinds of atoms that Dalton's circles were speedily seen to be cumbersome and awkward. Since each circle had to be large enough to show the markings within it, and each atom had to be represented, it was apparent that any compound particle containing more than three or four atoms (and of course most of them do contain more) would be an extremely inconvenient thing to write down in this kind of atomic notation.

So Berzelius, conceiving the Daltonian system to be an awkward and outworn vehicle, devised another method of notation. Each element (that is, the atom of each element) was designated by a letter of the alphabet (or in some cases two, never more). Thus oxygen was designated as O, hydrogen as H, silver Ag (from the Latin name *argentum*), copper Cu (Latin *cuprum*), chlorine Cl, and so on. Sulphuric acid, for example, contains two atoms of hydrogen, one of sulphur and four of oxygen. Under Dalton's system it looked like this

whereas Berzelius wrote it simply as H_2SO_4.

Great as was Berzelius' advance over Dalton, the Manchester

philosopher nevertheless fulminated against the Swedish system,
denouncing it as a chaos of atoms calculated "to cloud the beauty
and simplicity of the atomic theory."

But Dalton was wrong, very wrong—apparently unable to see
that others could promote the growth and refinement of his ideas.

16

All men are perplexing creatures; they are rarely consistently
consistent or consistently inconsistent. Despite Dalton's opposition
to the work of Gay-Lussac and Berzelius, the atomic theory spread
rapidly for the whole world of chemistry was ripe. One chemist
after another took up his theory, studied it, applied it to his own
problems and was amazed at its power to clarify age-old puzzles.
So great was its world reception that learned societies in many
countries began to take cognizance of the lone scientist who had
explored those hidden and all but trackless recesses of nature.
Everywhere men were now eager to hear Dalton and pay tribute
to his genius.

London called him, Glasgow and Edinburgh, too. With each
lecture his popularity grew. The French elected him to their Academy, and in 1826 the Royal Society of England conferred upon him
its first Royal Medal. Sir Humphry Davy made the presentation
address in which he embodied these exciting words: "Mr. Dalton's
permanent reputation will rest upon his having discovered a simple
principle universally applicable to the facts of chemistry, in fixing
proportion in which bodies combine, and thus laying the foundation for future labors respecting the sublime and transcendental
parts of the science of corpuscular motion. His merits in this respect resemble those of Kepler in astronomy."

John Dalton now became John Dalton, F.R.S. (Fellow of the
Royal Society). Later on he added six more honorary letters after
his name: Oxford conferred upon him a D.C.L. and the University
of Edinburgh its LL.D.

In the summer of 1822 Dalton visited Paris. The graciousness
of French hospitality combined with warm evidences of high esteem
for his accomplishments made a profound impression on the man
who first saw the light of day in a lowly thatched cottage in rural
England. Laplace invited him to his estate at Arcueil, where Dalton

was introduced to Berthollet, Biot and others—"a most agreeable and interesting visit and a beautiful place." The next afternoon he saw Gay-Lussac, who was now president of the French Academy where Dalton was to be seated as a corresponding (English) member.

Within the short span of a few days he strolled the gardens of Arcueil with Laplace on one arm and Berthollet on the other, conferred with Gay-Lussac and Humboldt on meteorology, visited the laboratory of Ampère where he looked at powerful apparatus for showing new electromagnetic phenomena and walked to the Jardin du Roi for dinner with Monsieur and Madame Cuvier and their beautiful daughter Clémentine.

He visited London again. "It is a surprising place and well worth one's while to see once, but the most disagreeable place on earth for one of a contemplative turn of mind to reside in constantly." He preferred Manchester, his laboratory, his experiments and his evenings at the Literary and Philosophical Society.

But he always remained the same, a humble Quaker dressed in the habit of a Quaker—knee breeches, gray stockings and buckled shoes. The simplicity of his clothing matched his sturdy uncompromising mind—plain, outspoken (sometimes rude), with no desire for display or self-laudation of any kind. To the end of his days society was foreign to him; he preferred his recluse habits and to the very last he kept his provincial accent and bucolic manner.

By 1840 Dalton was conscious, vaguely, as his years passed, that he was deteriorating. He was beginning to complain of his failing powers—"I succeed in doing chemical experiments, taking about three or four times the usual time." His heavy frame, always robust and muscular, was now slowly giving way. The atomic theory, his microcosmic vision, remained in his mind clear and unstained; but beyond this there was little. The theory that was being expanded and developed in clarity and detail by other scientists in Dalton's mind remained virtually stagnant.

Among investigators the rarest are those with a presentment of new truth. In recognition of this gift the citizens of Manchester erected a life-sized marble statue in honor of their fellow citizen who had brought such distinction to their city. Dalton himself was pleased with this token of affectionate veneration; "he acquiesced with the modesty, simplicity and excellent feeling that grace his character."

When the news of Dalton's death was heard throughout the world on the morning of July 27, 1844, not only was the scientific community saddened, but men and women in all walks of life knew that they had lost a unique member from within the commonwealth. Forty thousand persons, in reverent testimonial to his lofty intellect and humble spirit, filed past his coffin as it rested on a simple catafalque in the darkened Town Hall of Manchester.

On August 12 he was buried in Ardwick Cemetery.

17

It was already evident to a large group of advanced thinkers, even before the death of Dalton, that the atomic theory would bring together the science of chemistry and the science of physics, and by fusing these two branches of knowledge open up unknown worlds which no previous generation of men had even vaguely imagined. The study of the atom soon became a borderland enterprise between chemists and physicists, two companies of indefatigable searchers for extreme precision. This overlapping inquiry within the short span of half a century yielded an enormous amount of accurate information.

Science is specialization. But it is also collaboration, for the essence of science is to arrive at identity through the complexities of difference. A series of investigations, started in many fields, converged upon a single focus proving (a) that atoms are real, that they are entities even though the average diameter of the atom is not more than one-three-hundred-millionth of an inch, and (b) that all matter is electrical. The old idea that electricity was something distinct from matter, something superadded to the atom, was discredited. Nothing in all science is now more assured than the knowledge that the structure of the atom is electrical.

In the middle nineties of the last century an astonishing set of discoveries, which centered in the atom, came in quick succession. In 1895 Röntgen discovered the x-rays; in 1896 Becquerel announced the phenomenon of radioactivity; and in 1897 the British physicist J. J. Thomson told the world about the electron. John Dalton knew a great deal about the laws governing atoms, but nothing about what goes on *within* the atom. The electron was the first of the primordial particles within the atom to be isolated and studied. From these early investigations a wholly new and unanticipated world sprang into being—the world of subatomic reality.

The discovery of the electron was the first proof that the atom had any parts. Dalton assumed that atoms were ultimate bits of matter not further divisible. But the work of those younger men who followed him has given ample evidence that, far from being the hard impenetrable unit as originally conceived, the atom is the most porous entity in the universe.

As seen today the atom is a highly complex structure built up of three sorts of units: the electrons, which are units of negative electricity, the protons, which are positive, and the neutrons, which have no electrical charge. These are held apart within the atom by forces which are not yet fully understood. All the protons in any atom are gathered close together at the center, along with some of the electrons, forming a compact dense portion which is called the nucleus.

Taken as a whole, the modern atom was believed to be (up until a decade ago) a kind of miniature solar system with the center (nucleus) corresponding to the sun because it contains practically the entire mass of the atom. The outlying planetary electrons were pictured as revolving at relatively remote distances in their orbits.

Aside from the majestic thought that the subatomic worlds within the atom seem to afford the key to the ultimate unfolding of the age-old secrets of the universe, it is a marvelous feat to be able to possess some comprehension of this invisible structure. And even if the older planetary view is now undergoing necessary modification we will eventually have another picture more in harmony with the demands of the theory of relativity on the one hand and the quantum theory on the other.

In 1924 Louis Victor, Prince de Broglie, advanced the hypothesis that the electron was not a single particle of electricity, but that it was composed of, or possessed of, a group of waves similar to those of light. So far have the wave properties of the electron been confirmed that an atom is now regarded as a region permeated by waves. Whether we are to continue to picture the atom as a miniature solar system, or as an electrical machine, or in terms of wavelike ripples in a bowl of water, the important thing is that the atom is here to stay and the fabulous success of recent atomic physics has only just begun.

In less than a century after the labors of Dalton, the atoms he loved so well are given a new pictorial dress. No longer are they spoken of as the hard "brickbats" or the "billiard balls," or even the "foundation stones" of matter. Impenetrability is gone! In its place we have the modern atom with its electron, proton, neutron, positron, conceived by the cumulative work of J. J. Thomson, Planck, Rutherford, Bohr, de Broglie, Millikan, Heisenberg, Schroedinger, Dirac, Compton, Chadwick, Anderson, and a whole army of youthful investigators who are determined to penetrate completely this wonderworld of the invisible and bring back elemental forces wherewith to revolutionize man's existence on earth.

The outermost frontier is not the atom but the world buried deep within the atom.

"I am of the opinion," said Sir William Bragg, "that atom energy will supply our future needs. A thousand years may pass before we can harness the atom, or tomorrow might see us with the reins in our hands."

4. Lavoisier . . . . THEORY OF FIRE

AGAIN we go back to the Greeks, to those ancient thinkers who thought so much and guessed so much more. As science grows by accumulation it is always helpful to see how each of its triumphs was slowly achieved. Out of very simple beginnings have come magnificent results.

The theory of fire illustrates the gains of cumulative effort.

2

As early as the fifth century B.C. we find that certain Pythagorean philosophers—especially Heraclitus—believed that fire was the ultimate matter or principle of the universe. According to this antique view, combustion meant the reduction of a body into its elementary form. The Pythagoreans taught that during combustion a complex structure is turned, by the agency of fire, into one of more simple constitution. The idea that a body diminishes on being burnt implies that it has lost something. Consider a candle. A taper burns and is reduced in size: apparently some part of what was imprisoned in the candle has now departed. This belief in *something lost* persisted up until the eighteenth century and was embodied in a powerful theory that misled science for three generations.

Plato, Aristotle, Empedocles and other less-known thinkers had something to say on fire, but their explanations of combustion were based on no experiments. True, they pondered the nature of such phenomena as light, heat, motion and electricity. Here and there in their writings one comes across a sentence that shows a flash of shrewd and penetrative insight. However, too little was known about these agencies for the thinkers of antiquity to arrive at any adequate knowledge about them. For one thing, the philosophers could not discuss the interrelations between these phenomena simply because no one ever suspected that such interrelations existed.

3

In the chapter on John Dalton we saw that fire was considered one of the four elements. Under the name of fire the ancient and medieval thinkers included everything either really or apparently of the nature of flame. The fact that flames issue from burning bodies led to the view that fire and its manifestations were elemental things, not quite as tangible as water or earth but nonetheless material.

But the real nature of fire was not understood. When people thought at all about the subject they either attributed to it some semireligious or mystical significance, or they adopted the so-called common-sense view: that fire is a very fine material substance, an excessively light species of matter universally distributed throughout nature. In varying and mysterious degrees this "fire-matter" entered into intimate association in the composition of all things. This material view, which regarded fire as a substance, is the conception that held sway during the long dark ages of alchemy, when the theory of the four elements was playing the dominant role.

It is truly an amazing thing when one comes to think of it that fire, which man discovered in the early stages of his culture, should have remained a complete mystery up until the eighteenth century. This, of course, does not mean that man did not understand how to use fire. On the contrary, the mastery of fire for use is one of the very early turning points in the development of humankind— an achievement justly celebrated in innumerable myths and legends, the possession of all primitive folklore. Prometheus, snatching the element of fire from the region of fire (empyrean), is the symbol of this mastery.

There is, to be sure, a wide difference between mastery and mystery. A man may master the driving of an automobile and at the same time be utterly mystified by the mechanical principles involved in its construction and operation. For countless centuries men had used fire for cooking, for warmth, for illumination, for signaling, for ritual purposes. Fire became so intertwined with daily life that it was taken for granted, so familiar that it needed no explanation.

The phenomenon of burning or combustion is perhaps the most

familiar, the most spectacular and the most impressive of all chemical processes. When, in the course of intellectual progress, the demand finally came for a scientific explanation of fire and its associated phenomena, the best that could be done to explain it was phlogiston *—the answer of Professor Georg Ernst Stahl (1660-1734). Although it proved to be wrong, it takes its place in the history of chemistry as the first theory evolved by that science in its triumphant march towards truth.

4

If you want to know what the phlogiston theory is ask yourself: What happens when something burns? Professor Stahl essayed an explanation and failed miserably. Yet his abortive answer is one of the most interesting attempts at theory in the annals of science.

Stahl was born at Anspach in Bavaria, a small town about ninety miles north of Munich. His chief interests were medicine, chemistry and anatomy, broad fields of knowledge that were just beginning to awake from their medieval slumber. An omnivorous reader, Stahl had amassed a huge store of knowledge by the time he received his medical degree from the University of Jena. He was only twenty-three years old, but no one was more eager than he to push onward the frontiers of knowledge. By the time he was twenty-seven this prolific and versatile theorist became Court Physician at Weimar. Already he was a veteran in the art of thinking, having battled through many foggy days in his early gropings. Scores of theorists have exalted to the domain of natural law what turned out to be a baseless hypothesis, yet their efforts involved an enormous amount of labor and sacrifice. This certainly was true of Stahl and his phlogiston doctrine.

What led Stahl early in his career to the study of fire was a genuine interest gained in his youth from that eccentric but keen spirited teacher of chemistry, Johann Joachim Beccher (1635-1682), author of a curious book which he dedicated to God—whom he called the Almighty Compounder—written "in a strange, familiar, yet striking style, leaving the sympathetic reader in doubt as to whether it is *im*pious, or merely im*pious,* or actually though fan-

---

* The word phlogiston comes from a Greek word meaning *burnt.*

tastically pious." Himself a fiery personality, Beccher made the
whole subject of combustion extraordinarily fascinating, for it occupied a central position in his fantastic pagoda of chemical speculations. More of an alchemist than a chemist, this odd and extravagant enthusiast of fire propounded a theory of his own which later
proved to be a starting point of Stahl's phlogiston doctrine.

But Stahl was an original thinker and his debt to Beccher is
much less than has been granted. To trace his predecessors is not
sufficient to account for the rise of an idea in the mind of a theorist.
The historical sequence may at times prove grossly inadequate.
Take the case of Dalton. To say that Gassendi, Boyle, and Newton
believed in the granular structure of matter may give one a misleading version of what happened in Dalton's mind. Only after Dalton
had been at work for many years did he gain some help from other
thinkers. Even then it was on the physical and not on the chemical
side of the problem. The same is true of Darwin. Actually he knew
very little about his numerous predecessors; many years after the
evolutionary theory had assumed shape in his mind he came to
realize that others had anticipated him along related lines of
thought. Stahl originated the phlogiston theory, not Beccher. He
was its author, but not the author of many strange ideas which
were later incorporated into it.

5

Stahl claimed that phlogiston is an inflammable principle which
escapes when a substance is burned. The more inflammable the
substance, the more phlogiston was supposed to be present. Apparently Stahl did not think of phlogiston as having any weight. (His
followers, however, did.) It seemed to him that it was a phenomenon somewhat like light, an agency which could cause various
effects and still be devoid of weight. Many different things can be
burnt, such as wood, metal, coal, paper, cloth—substances differing
widely from each other yet alike in being combustible. To Stahl
this meant only one thing: that these differing substances have a
principle in common which he chose to call *phlogiston*.

This hypothetical "fire-stuff" of Stahl's was supposed to be embedded in every combustible substance. If you burn, let us say, a
metal or a piece of wood, the ash which remains is the original

substance now denuded of its phlogiston. Stahl proved to his own satisfaction that sulphur was a compound of phlogiston and sulphuric acid. He did it in this way: he took coal (supposedly rich in phlogiston) and with it he heated sulphuric acid. Sulphur was again regenerated. This experiment offered to Stahl a satisfactory explanation of his theory. Fire or flame was therefore regarded as free phlogiston—something deeply imprisoned and now set free only because the substance which contained it underwent a process of reduction.

Some theories go through a long period of travail and agony before they are accepted. Usually these are the true theories. By a curious irony a false doctrine seems to gain an amazingly quick popularity. No sooner had Stahl announced the principle of phlogiston than the leading chemists throughout Europe widely shouted their assent. The explanation of burning that Stahl offered (as equivalent to a loss of phlogiston) seemed to solve a host of difficulties besides having the merit of co-ordinating many observations which had hitherto been viewed in isolation. Stahl was now the great hero. He was called to the chair of medicine, chemistry and anatomy of the University of Halle, and with the increase of his fame came his final appointment, Physician to the King of Prussia at Berlin.

Actually Stahl's theory was nothing more than the swan song of alchemy. Upon investigation its pseudo clarity was made increasingly painful. This, of course, was not immediately evident for the simple reason that old ideas give way slowly because they carry with them deeply ingrained attitudes of aversion and preference. When confronted by facts which had been overlooked in the unwarranted enthusiasm for the theory, the followers of Stahl (now called phlogistonists) invented all manner of absurdity. Wasn't that exactly what happened in the case of the Ptolemaic theory? As observation detected more and more which was incompatible with that ancient doctrine, did not its exponents embroider it with pious confusion? They first tried to pin the thoughts of the new to the fabric of the old, and the result was a bizarre and shapeless thing. Then they worked even harder to patch the Ptolemaic error instead of asking themselves straightway whether, after all, its basis were

ANTOINE LAURENT LAVOISIER AND HIS WIFE

After the painting by David

Courtesy of The Rockefeller Institute for Medical Research

laid in truth? The phlogistonists likewise wasted their time in tinkering with Stahl's theory.

Take such a case in point as this. To the phlogistonists all metals were regarded as compounds made up of the calx (ash) of the metal plus its phlogiston. If you burnt a metal you were supposed to have released the imprisoned phlogiston so that all that was left was its calx. It was noted however that when a metal is calcined (burnt) its calx actually weighs more than the original product. How does one explain that? On the basis of Stahl's theory the loss of phlogiston should have caused the calx of the burnt metal to weigh less. If the balances showed (as they certainly did!) that the calx weighed more, then obviously the most natural inference would be that the calx must have taken on something rather than having emitted it.

The phlogistic schoolmen answered this argument by subterfuge 'n two ways. At first they said that the variation in weight was an unimportant matter unworthy of one's attention; then they concocted the idea of negative weight, an explanation based on the principle of levity. This meant that phlogiston makes bodies lighter just as bladders attached to a swimmer lighten him), so that driving it out of a metal actually leaves the residue heavier.

It is now known, of course, that the picture presented by Stahl and his followers is almost the exact inverse of the real facts: instead of giving off a substance a metal in burning takes on oxygen which increases weight, so that the calx actually weighs more than the metal. In the light of what was later proved to be the true story of burning, the conclusions of Stahl and his disciples were the merest moonshine. Science is a gradual secession from unwarranted assumptions. The kind of a theory that Stahl offered was little more than pastry. "My child," once wrote Anatole France, "beware of pastry. Pastry is factitious, adventitious. It is whipped cream which fails to hide the poverty of the cake."

6

In appraising the work of a theorist one must always take into account the knowledge of his time and the use he made of that knowledge. This, to be sure, is the only fair and charitable way in which to judge any man of science. Considering the age in which he lived

Stahl was an unquestionably penetrating and ingenious thinker. Like others before him he did the very best he could with the limited knowledge available. Yet an enormous amount of damage must be laid at Stahl's door. He was a leader as well as a misleader of the science of his day. His theory befogged investigators for more than a hundred years. Only after its destruction was it properly viewed as a monument of misplaced ingenuity. While it breathed it was a powerful obstacle that sidetracked the ablest minds into a cul-de-sac. Fortunately, here and there a few chemists were strong enough not to allow the phlogistic dogmas to bother them, but on the whole the entire world of science was held back and its spirit retarded.

Why were the leading chemists gullible? It is hard to say. Perhaps this explanation may be ventured: characteristic of any age is a body of beliefs and a group of feelings associated with them. This involves an inability to examine and discard a way of thinking which seems at the time to be rooted in the very structure of the mind itself. It seemed so true, so obvious, so much a matter of simple common-sense observation that when a candle burns a flame is emitted out of the candle itself. Thus when Stahl associated combustibility with the presence in the combustible body of a constituent he called phlogiston, the world was ready to accept his explanation. The principle of phlogiston seemed to be something axiomatic like the venerable principle of the perfect circle in Ptolemaic astronomy. The fundamental postulate that the world, having been created by God, must therefore be perfect, combined with the idea that the circle was the perfection of symmetry, led to the dogmatic belief that the planets must necessarily move in circles. To think otherwise was outright heresy. It took Kepler almost a lifetime to emancipate himself from the circle idea as the only possible orbit for a planet. It took science nearly a hundred years to free itself from phlogiston. Once the emancipation was effected there was inaugurated a line of discovery endless in variety and extension.

7

Out of the smoke of argument and counter-argument lasting a century there emerged that demigod of French science, Antoine Laurent Lavoisier, whose achievements have already been briefly mentioned in the chapter on John Dalton. It was he who completely demolished the phlogiston theory and showed Stahl's ideas to be nothing more than a mirage above the shimmering sands of arid speculation.

With Lavoisier science was action not words; from those who emphasized talk he demanded verification. "Chemists have made phlogiston a vague principle," he remarked with cutting sarcasm, "which is not strictly defined and which consequently fits all the explanations required of it; sometimes the principle has weight, sometimes it has not. . . . It is a veritable Proteus that changes its form every instant. It is time to lead chemistry back to a stricter way of thinking." And he did. By the irresistible force of facts he drove phlogiston from its fastness, first by the reach and fathom of his demonstrations, and secondly by overhauling the old assumptions. Long before he announced to the world his oxygen theory of fire he had proved to himself that Stahl's doctrine was just another hypothesis in a jumble of claims and counterclaims that was choking science.

Knowing the world for what it is, the wonder grows that there can appear any man so eccentric as to regard the pursuit of truth as the paramount issue of life. Like a fresh strong wind Lavoisier swept through the world of chemistry exhibiting a shocking insensibility to the cherished notions of his fellowmen. So cleansing was the storm he generated that the age-old webs of medievalism were torn down. Yet his work was no sudden and unheralded revelation. The time was ripe for the formulation of a correct theory of fire; it needed but the genius possessed of a venatic instinct for first principles, a sort of pointing at them as a dog does at game, that grasp "which the healthy imagination takes of possible truth."

Like Boyle, Lavoisier was born of an opulent family, and like Boyle he came early in life under the influence of able teachers. The world of science was laid before him and invited his devotion. A young man of many talents, his precocious mind quickly absorbed the mathematics, chemistry, astronomy and practical business affairs of France. At the age of twenty-three he was an authority on illumination, in proud possession of a gold medal especially awarded to him by the king in recognition of his brilliant essay on the artificial lighting of the streets of Paris. At twenty-five he was admitted to membership in the French Academy. "I am sure that your eyes are dancing with delight now that your nephew has been elected to the Academy," wrote a friend to his Aunt Constance. "How splendid that at so early an age, when other young men are occupied in amusing themselves, he should have made great contributions to the progress of science, and have obtained a position which is usually won, with great difficulty, by men past their fiftieth year!"

Upon his entrance into the Academy, Lavoisier combined a public life and a scientific career of ceaseless and untiring energy. He was assigned at once to several committees which had under consideration a variety of subjects. First, there was the question of the drinking water of the city of Paris. Water, from whatever aspect, had always been an absorbing study with him. His vast and accurate knowledge of it is one subject, among many, which renders his name so illustrious. Water—and foods, too. For Lavoisier is justly regarded as the father of the science of nutrition. But there were other public matters equally clamorous for his attention. Paris needed hydrants for protection against fire, and Lavoisier was farsighted enough to advocate them. He submitted a report to the Academy covering the approximate cost of their manufacture and installation, together with very careful drawings showing the efficiency of different types of pumps. The pursuit of all things in a scientific spirit took a veritable demoniacal hold of his mind. It led him into a bewildering variety of subjects: the cultivation of cabbage, the working of coal-mines, the decomposition of niter, the manufacture of starch, a study of ink, fossils, tapestry making, engraving, dyeing, tobacco, oils, grease, marble, cess pools, manufacture of plate glass, fuels, nutrition of vegetables. The list is too long.

He wanted money, more and more of it, to be able to devote his time to science, to equip laboratories, to finance experiments, to purchase expensive equipment and make his own apparatus, however costly. Since he was an independently rich young man, these visions were not idle pipe dreams; yet he felt his income was not enough.

8

A few days after his nomination to the Academy, Lavoisier entered the business world with the thought of increasing his wealth. He bought an interest in the *Ferme,* a company of financiers who for a certain sum, fixed every six years and paid annually to the Government in advance, purchased the privilege of collecting the national taxes of France. The company had an ancient history, going back to the fourteenth century; it was organized at first to meet a temporary emergency in the Government, and subsequently continued to supply a valuable and permanent need. It was characteristic of Lavoisier that before entering the *Ferme* he had made a detailed study of its history, its operations, and its place in the general economic structure of the country. He also knew, alas, only too well, that the *Ferme* was universally hated, not only because people dislike tax collectors in general, but also for those corruptions, real and imaginary, which from time to time had brought the company into public disfavor. Lavoisier's colleagues in the French Academy on the whole objected to his alliance with this corporation. And they were right, notwithstanding the fact that Lavoisier's motives were free from taint.

Actually, the young scientist had visions of being helpful to his country. He would exert his influence to stop abuses; by serving on the *Ferme's* committees he could suggest ways and means which would lead to positive reforms redounding to the credit of all. Then too the *Ferme* would certainly give him wide scope for his administrative ability and scientific interests—problems of agriculture, soils, foods, animals, housing, manufacturing of all kinds, chemicals, transportation. What an array of practical interests to whet his appetite! Could a young man wish for anything better? Lavoisier took his appointment seriously.

The actual work of the *Ferme* was heavy. Lavoisier met it with energy and enthusiasm. He did not mind the long journeys into various parts of France, for on these occasions he combined with his business mission scientific observations of various sorts. Each time he returned to Paris to make his reports his associates at the *Ferme* recognized his growth, his grasp, and his increasing administrative skill.

In the course of his work in the *Ferme*, Lavoisier struck up a close friendship with a much older official, the wealthy and influential Jacques-Alexis Paulze, whose beautiful daughter Marie was in her early teens. The house of Paulze was well known in Paris as the meeting place for men interested in the related fields of

H

banking, government and economics. Leaders like Turgot, Minister of the Treasury, Condorcet, and Pierre Samuel Dupont de Nemours were to be seen here in frequent and important discussions where plans for the Bureau of Statistics on taxes and commerce were known to have been drawn up.

Into the Paulze home came Antoine Lavoisier—a welcome prospect for Marie. Both were good-looking, she short in stature and only fourteen years old, he tall, handsome, and twenty-eight. They fell in love with each other to the delight of Monsieur Paulze, who prayed for this escape for his talented young daughter from the hands of another suitor, the penniless Comte d'Amerval, fifty years old. After a brief courtship, Marie Paulze became Madame Lavoisier on December 16, 1771, in the presence of a brilliant gathering of notables.

9

The bride and groom went to live in a house of their own, given to them by Lavoisier's father in the Rue Neuve-des-Bons-Enfants. Their income was liberal; not only did the husband have his resources, but Marie in her own right could nearly match his. Here in this residence the young couple passed three gloriously happy years; here Marie Lavoisier early in her married life began to train herself to be her husband's lifelong assistant, illustrator, translator, and amanuensis; and here too she began to entertain in the spirit of old aristocratic France, achieving a grace which made her salons famous and unique in the world of science.

In 1775 Lavoisier's father died, and in that same year he was appointed head of the French Government's Powder Works. The appointment came through Turgot, who acted upon a suggestion made by Lavoisier himself that the Government undertake its own production of gunpowder in order to reduce costs and insure adequate production. Up till now the manufacture of gunpowder had been in private hands, men who charged the Government enormous prices and were putting out an inferior product. Turgot canceled their contracts and proceeded to establish a *Régie des Poudres*—a strong administrative committee of four able men. Lavoisier was appointed chief *régisseur*. The choice of this young man to so important a post met with wide approval, particularly from Dupont de Nemours who said of Lavoisier, "He is a man as well known for his distinguished work in chemistry, essentially necessary for this kind of administration, as for the energy, the ability and honesty which he shows in the business of administration of the taxes."

What a joyous day it was in the life of the Lavoisiers when they packed their household effects and moved to the Arsenal. Turgot had assigned them a private residence there, which was to be their home for the next seventeen years, until the French Revolution drove them from it. These were intensely busy, crowded years, full of administrative tasks in connection with the Arsenal, the *Ferme,* the Academy. Then there was scientific work of a varied nature to be reported upon, data to be collected, experiments to be undertaken, and theories to be carefully thought out. All this Lavoisier had to do while giving technical advice to the Government, serving on the Committees for Agriculture and for Weights and Measures, maintaining a huge correspondence with widely scattered men, and writing a book which was to revolutionize the science of chemistry. Multiple tasks of a superman.

One of the very first things that Lavoisier did, upon taking up his residence in the Arsenal, was to establish a private laboratory with his wife as assistant. Out of his own pocket he fitted up work-rooms with all manner of costly apparatus; then he threw the doors of his home wide open to admit any scientist who wished to communicate with him and learn of his experiments. As his fame grew his laboratory became the meeting place for the leaders of the scientific world. Men came from far distant places to see him, Priestley from England, Benjamin Franklin from America, Ingenhousz from Austria, Fontana from Italy.

10

Himself a young man, Lavoisier encouraged other young men to visit his laboratory, to witness its demonstrations and occasionally to assist him. Pierre Dupont, realizing how much of an opportunity this presented, was able to have Lavoisier accept his son, Eluthère Irénée Dupont, as a paid assistant in the Arsenal. This marks the beginning of the Dupont fortune; for Eluthère, having escaped from Paris during the Revolution, came to the United States with an advanced knowledge of gunpowder obtained from

Lavoisier's laboratory. He was quick to realize that Americans were manufacturing a product of a very poor grade, and therefore decided to set himself up in that business. On a tract of land in Delaware, near where Wilmington now stands, he established in 1802 the firm of E. I. Dupont de Nemours.

Because Lavoisier's laboratory contained the very latest and best apparatus procurable, many young French scientists came there to do some work of their own and experiment under his direction. Lavoisier was their inspiration. Not only was he generous with his time and money (his aunt, Mlle. Punctis, died in 1781 and left him her entire fortune), but he showed an understanding at once penetrating and vigilant, the more remarkable for the caution and sureness of its march. In recalling those early years in the Arsenal laboratory Madame Lavoisier long afterwards wrote: "Some scientific friends, and a number of young men proud to be allowed to assist in his experiments, would meet in his laboratory early in the morning. They would have their meals there . . . and discuss scientific subjects, and it was in this atmosphere that the theory which has immortalized its author was born." Here in this laboratory, until he was condemned to death by the terrorists of the French Revolution, Lavoisier embodied the philosopher's thirst for truth, the artist's struggle for self-expression, the pioneer's wrestle with nature, the prospector's zest for discovery and the idealist's pursuit of supreme excellence.

11

How did Lavoisier demolish the grandiose edifice erected by Stahl and the phologistonists? The first blow was administered by his experiments on the calcination of metals. Stahl claimed that a metal was a compound made up of its calx plus phlogiston, and his followers added the absurdity that phlogiston possessed weight— a negative weight—which made the metal weigh more after burning than before! Basically, Stahl's theory maintained that when a metal was calcined it was converted into an ash, *giving up* its phlogiston in the process.

An experiment is the language of the scientist addressed to nature. Lavoisier wanted a reply. He began by examining every phase of the process of calcination whereby the phlogiston in the metal was supposed to be driven off. In all previous attempts to explain the phenomenon of combustion an effort was made to show that something was removed. The phlogistonists said that burning is a process of decomposition. Far from finding that phlogiston, or any other substance, was thrown off, Lavoisier discovered the very opposite: that "something" was taken on and it was this something that caused the ash of the metal to weigh more. Ten ounces of lead weighed more than ten ounces after having been burned to a calx. Actually, they ought to have weighed less, if phologiston were really a material substance.

By repeated experiments, by accurately weighing his reagents and products over a period of eleven years, Lavoisier concluded that oxygen was this "something" taken on—oxygen taken right out of the air. At every step of the way he *measured* the quantities of the substances with which he was working. He found that when metals, sulphur, phosphorus, carbon and similar substances are burned in air they increase in weight to an extent exactly equal to the volume of oxygen which they derive from the atmosphere.

These experiments called a halt on the unbridled fancy of the phlogistonists. No longer would they be able to ask serious-minded men to believe in the existence of a hypothetical substance that could not be separated or isolated or weighed. Lavoisier showed that phlogiston and its purely imaginary properties could not stand the test of the laboratory. The long chemical war against phlogiston was therefore on its way to victory, notwithstanding the fact that Stahl's theory was sufficiently dramatic, sufficiently widespread to cause feeling to run high. When in 1789 Lavoisier published his *Elementary Treatise on Chemistry*, the world learned that the conception of phlogiston and all that went with it was unnecessary; together with negative weight it slowly vanished from science.

By introducing the balance into chemistry as an instrument of precision, Lavoisier placed the new science upon the definite quantitative basis of an exact discipline. It provided the *coup de grâce* to the whole system of outworn methods. As soon as the balance was applied to chemical processes, Stahl's theory was doomed. By the keen temper of his logic Lavoisier realized from the outset that there could be no progress without the ability to weigh and measure all things chemical. "I often say," once declared Lord Kelvin, "that if you can measure that of which you are speaking and express it by a number you know something of your subject; but if you cannot measure it nor express it by a number, your knowledge is of a sorry kind and hardly satisfactory. It may be the beginning of the acquaintance, but you are hardly, in your thoughts, advanced towards science, whatever the subject may be."

Weight and proportions, numerically expressed, formed the basis and test of each experiment undertaken in the Lavoisierian laboratory. Nothing was left to chance or vague hypothesis. Exact cognizance was taken of every quantity gained or lost. That is why the results were so accurate—and so revolutionary. Through Lavoisier's efforts the balance is today perhaps the most characteristic single tool of scientific chemistry. The increased exactness of all chemical knowledge, down to the amazing precision possible with our modern balances, the so-called microbalances, by which a difference in weight of one two hundred and fifty thousandth part of a miligram can be detected, is mainly due in its origin to this citizen of the old *régime*.

12

The theorist is a man possessed of a rare combination of talents. He must reach a high standard in several different directions and must combine intellectual gifts not often found together. He must take the knowledge available in his day, rediscover it, reinterpret it and synthesize it. He must refuse to live in the past, although he must gladly seek light from the past to illuminate and make clear the path toward the future. Above all he must be an experimenter—"to substitute the description of facts for a sham explanation of nature." In Lavoisier the French people produced just such a genius-theorist.

Having explained burning he now undertook to explain respiration (breathing). For countless thousands of years men have known that in common with other animals they have lungs and that breathing is inhaling and exhaling air. But what actually went on in the lungs or what part of the air is drawn in was unknown. By means of experiments, buttressed by his oxygen theory, Lavoisier showed that burning and respiration are alike in kind—one a quick and the other a slow process of oxidation each leading to an increase in weight equal to the weight of the oxygen combined. Breathing, in other words, is a form of combustion. So too combustion and calcination are only different terms to express the general idea of oxidation.

13

Before the advent of Lavoisier chemistry could be described as "a collection of facts loosely strung together upon a false theory of combustion." With his demonstrations he re-ordered the tangled data of chemistry so that it became a true science (organized knowledge). In scientific theories we should be able to see not only the results of science but also the avenues of approach. The greatness of Lavoisier is to be found not so much in his originality as in his ability to rediscover and reinterpret facts. Other chemists must be ranked higher than he as original discoverers—men like Priestley, Cavendish, and Black. But no thinker of that age overshadows him as a theorist. It is now nearly a century and a half since Lavoisier gave to the world the many painstaking results achieved in his home laboratory. Since that day in 1794 when he was guillotined, eminent chemists have arisen and added their work to his. Notwithstanding the massive achievements of his successors the mind of Lavoisier soars over modern chemistry; he is its luminary.

Always a number of minds are very near a truth before any one mind fully comprehends it. Bryan and William Higgins were very close to the theory of the atomic structure of matter before Dalton published his explanations. Certainly Alfred Russel Wallace arrived at the theory of evolution just as Darwin proceeded to announce his own work. Nor will anyone acquainted with the facts deny that Augustin Fresnel in France, unaided and alone, reached the idea that light waves are a transverse vibration in the ether at the time that the celebrated Doctor Thomas Young in London achieved the same conclusion. Theories are often the culminating point reached through several lines of advance by widely separated and independent thinkers. Yet in each case some one individual achieves the final apotheosis. The predecessors and contemporaries of Lavoisier helped to make the time ripe; but the linking together of ideas whereby law and understanding supervene on chaos was an expression of his own creative genius.

Why did not Joseph Priestley (1733-1804) instead of Lavoisier overturn phlogiston and establish the correct theory of combustion? After all Priestley was the real discoverer of oxygen. When he visited Lavoisier in Paris, he explained to the Frenchman certain new facts about air. This information supplied Lavoisier with the right clue which led to the establishment of the correct explanation. How was it that Lavoisier succeeded where others failed? The answer is that Lavoisier had an architectonic mind, a mind capable of putting together facts and figures as an architect puts together plans and specifications. Priestley quarried the crude fact (dephlogisticated air); in Lavoisier's hands it became "oxygen." What was disconnected in Priestley's mind became an harmonious and consistent system in Lavoisier's. In no way was Priestley's skill in discovery equal to Lavoisier's ability as a theorist.

In the transformation of the raw material of facts into the finished product of a theory the personal factor of the theorist enters. Rightly did Lavoisier resent the attempt to deny him the honor of his achievement or to minimize his skill in bestowing comprehension. In his own mind he planned this magnificent temple of theory and every enduring stone of it he laboriously carved out of the sweat of his own struggle over a period of eleven intense years. "That theory," he stated emphatically, "is not, as I hear it called, the theory of the French chemists, it is my own; it is a possession which I claim at the hands of my contemporaries and posterity."

14

So far was Joseph Priestley from even the fringe of the new theory or a realization of the vast significance of his discovery that unto his dying day he stoutly upheld phlogiston. At the time of his death most chemists had forsaken the Stahlian doctrine. With his back against the wall Priestley fought bravely for a dead cause. One of his last memorable acts was to write a book to refute Lavoisier. It was entitled *Doctrine of Phlogiston Established* (1800).

Outworn doctrines and beliefs are like mandrakes; like those living plants of old and fabulous renown they utter their cries of pain when they are torn up. Yet it must be said in praise of Priestley that he refused to compromise. To those who attempted to sit on both sides of the fence he was rightfully contemptuous. In a letter addressed to Priestley, a certain Doctor S. L. Mitchell of Columbia made "An Attempt to Accommodate the Disputes among the Chemists concerning Phlogiston." He was willing to admit the truth of much of Lavoisier's work but wanted to retain phlogiston. Mitchell concluded his letter somewhat humorously: "Perhaps even now my labors are but of little avail; or if they are capable of bringing about a coalition of parties, I might say to you, after all, in the words of Prior in his 'Alma':

> " 'For Dick, if we could reconcile
> Old Aristotle with Gassendus,
> How many would admire our toil!
> And yet how few would comprehend us!' "

In reply to Mitchell, Priestley wrote that he thanked its author for his "ingenious and well-intentioned attempt to promote a peace between the present belligerent powers in chemistry; but I fear your labor will be in vain. In my opinion there can be no compromise of the two systems." Priestley was right even though he was wrong.

To return to Lavoisier.

The opinion of Justus von Liebig, one of the leaders of the nineteenth century and founder of German industrial chemistry, represents an accurate appraisal. "He discovered," says Liebig, "no new body, no new property, no natural phenomenon previously unknown; but all the facts established by him were the necessary consequences of the labors of those who preceded him. His merit, his immortal glory, consists of this—that he infused into the body of the science a new spirit; but all the members of that body were already in existence, and rightly joined together."

15

Lavoisier was that rare individual who could apply facts with telling effect. He not only revised and extended knowledge but altered its assumptions—its theoretical base. Why? Because he was possessed of a clear vision—*"pensées de la jeunesse, executées par l'âge mûr."* Take just such a simple fact as ordinary combustion. Lavoisier's handling of it was vastly different from all who preceded him. For centuries it had been known that neither lamp nor fire nor candle will burn without air. Stahl himself knew this; he knew, for example, that even soot (which he regarded as almost pure phlogiston) could not burn in the absence of air. Stahl, who was forever casting his facts in the mold of his dogmatic hypothesis, explained this on the assumption that phlogiston could not part from a substance unless it had somewhere to go. Both he and his followers regarded air as a kind of sponge which absorbed phlogiston. A candle, if placed in a closed vessel, will burn for a while and then go out. The phlogistonists explained this by saying that the air (acting like a sponge) could only hold a certain amount of phlogiston. Once the air was saturated nothing could burn in it. Lavoisier showed that this explanation was ridiculous for it took no cognizance of the fact that the volume of air actually becomes smaller during the burning process. So too in the calcination of metals: actually the volume of air decreases and the increase of weight of the metals is exactly equal to the amount of air that had disappeared.

When we glance back and compare Lavoisier's performance with the efforts of his predecessors, his achievements stand out in solitary grandeur. When he first began to experiment in his laboratory the knowledge of nature's laws was ragged and incomplete; when he died he left chemistry an unforgettable heritage of precision which has illuminated the whole realm of modern science. No theorist living or dead deserves more the name of experimenter in the sense in which Claude Bernard used it when he said: "To be worthy of the name, an experimenter must be at once a theorist and practitioner."

16

Equally as great as his oxygen theory is Lavoisier's incomparable generalization known as the law of the conservation of matter—a significant and imperishable contribution.

Vaguely the idea of the conservation of matter was entertained by some of the old Greek philosophers. Empedocles, for example, argued that in the universe there was no creation, neither was there any absolute destruction of the basic elements, but only changing combinations and transformations. With the introduction of the importance of weight in chemistry all chemists had more or less tacitly assumed that during a chemical reaction the sum of the weights of the reacting substances was always equal to the sum of the weights of the products. In other words, although the original substances apparently disappeared and new ones took their place, the weight of the substances always remained the same at the end as at the beginning of every operation.

Lavoisier performed very careful experiments to show that this was really so: (a) that there is not anything in the beginning which has not its precise quantitative counterpart in the end; (b) that weight is an immutable thing in nature; (c) that no matter was ever lost since all matter can be traced throughout and accounted for by weight. By the unanswerable evidence of the balance he demonstrated that every chemical operation ends in an equation, and although matter may be altered by whatever chemical process, still it does not change in amount.

This principle is stated thus: matter can neither be created nor destroyed.

17

Had Lavoisier been spared the revolutionary scaffold he would have cleared up a number of chemical problems that were perplexing the scientific world. He had planned for himself, with his wife as assistant, a series of experiments destined to extend the range of knowledge which he hoped would lead to an assured control over natural agencies beyond the dream of poets and seers. He was only fifty-one years old, in the prime of his experimental and theoretical powers, when the terrorists of the Revolution sacrificed him.

The leaders of the revolutionary proletariat in France saw in Lavoisier not a scientist, but a member of the odious and detestable *Ferme*. They spread the rumor that he was only masquerading as a savant. Was he not a rich man, having inherited two fortunes, married to a rich woman who was the daughter of that enormously wealthy and influential plutocrat, Jacques-Alexis Paulze? And was he not responsible for originating the proposal to build walls around the city of Paris in order to prevent smuggling? Lavoisier had estimated that approximately one-fifth of the goods entering Paris was brought in illegally. His suggestion was therefore sound; but the attempt to wall Paris proved unpopular. The project was interpreted as a design on the part of the *Ferme* to imprison the French people in their capital and, still more heinous, to prevent pure air from blowing over the city. To the revolutionists Lavoisier was a privileged person belonging to the upper crust of society, the lackey of the irresponsible nobility, member of the Academy (also controlled by the king and his henchmen) and head of the Powder Works—all for his own gain.

For a long time that frustrated bloodthirsty leader of the Paris mobs, Jean Paul Marat (1743-1793), had been deeply envious of Lavoisier. In 1780 Marat had written a chemical treatise devoid of merit and submitted it to the Academy. Lavoisier was on the committee that turned it down, despite the fact that the *Journal of Paris* had incorrectly announced that the paper had been approved. Marat, now editing a vicious underground sheet called *L'Ami du People*, kept up a brutal and relentless attack on Lavoisier. "I denounce to you the Coryphaeus of charlatans, the sieur Lavoisier, son of a land-grabber, pupil of the Geneva stockjobber, a farmer-general, controller of gunpowder and saltpeter, governor of the discount bank, secretary to the King, member of the Academy of Sciences"—so ran the article of January, 1791. And more, too: "Would you believe that this little gentleman, who enjoys an income of 40,000 livres and whose only claim to public recognition is that he put Paris in prison by cutting off the fresh air with a wall that cost the poor 33 millions and that he removed the powder from the Arsenal to the Bastille on the night of July 12 and 13, is engaged on a devilish intrigue to get himself elected as administrator of the department of Paris? . . . Would to heaven that he had been strung to a lamppost on August 6."

By a decree of the National Assembly on March 20, 1791, the *Ferme* was suppressed. Shortly thereafter Lavoisier resigned from the Arsenal and moved to 243 Boulevard de la Madeleine. He was now in constant dread for his life despite the fact that he had been using his private fortune to keep the Academy alive. In revolutions events move quickly. The king was guillotined in January, 1793. On August 17 the rooms of the Academy were sealed and within a few days Lavoisier's house was searched.

The suppression of the *Ferme* did not end Lavoisier's trouble. Neither his eminence as a scientist nor his services to the State could make a certain class of people forget that he had been a member of that much-hated company of tax gatherers. For many years the *Ferme* had been denounced as a den of robbers who despoiled the people; now in the heat of social upheaval it came in for terrific (and largely unjustifiable) attack. An angry speech delivered in the National Convention roused the people against the company. Its officials, called *Fermiers Généraux,* were ordered arrested. Lavoisier's appeal to the Committee on Safety went unanswered, and he was dragged into the cold and overcrowded prison of Port-Libre along with his associates of the *Ferme,* including his father-in-law Paulze.

Lavoisier wrote to Marie. They were separated now by the cruel hand of the Revolution. He advised her to save her strength and not wear herself out in useless attempts to gain his freedom. Despite the discomfort of the prison he wanted her to know that he was preparing his memoirs on chemistry. Several appeals were made for Lavoisier's release, but they were in vain. More doubtless could have been attempted in his behalf, but his friends, fearing their own safety, refused to act. Finally Madame Lavoisier made a last moment effort to save her husband from the Revolutionary Tribunal, in defiance of a law forbidding all ex-nobles from entering Paris, but to no avail.

The decree of May 5, 1794, demanded that the *Fermiers Généraux* be brought before the Revolutionary Tribunal. On the morning of May 7 these men were put through the empty formalities of being questioned—an exhibition of miserable knavery. The next day at ten o'clock they were brought before the tribunal, Coffinhal presiding. The jury lost no time in unanimously declaring the accused guilty. To Lavoisier, Coffinhal is reported to have said, *"La République n'a pas besoin de savants"* (The Republic has no use for men of science).

On a guillotine prepared in the Place de la Revolution the *Fermiers Généraux* were beheaded. Paulze was third, Lavoisier fourth. They died on May 8, 1794, and their bodies were thrown into nameless graves in the cemetery d'Errancis.

18

Two years after his death the French reversed the judgment of Coffinhal. True, the dismembered body of Lavoisier could not be brought back to life, but the nation solemnly strove to atone its error in an impressive funeral ceremony. Orations in his honor were publicly pronounced while friends at home and abroad mourned his death. "The gravest crime of the French Revolution was not the execution of the king, but the execution of Lavoisier."

At the time of his tragic death Lavoisier was preparing an edition of his collected works with the aid of his wife who had worked faithfully with him both on literary as well as on scientific problems. Theirs was a happy marriage, comparable to the productive happiness of that other great French theorist, Louis Pasteur, and the woman who shared his labors. What an unusual group of women they were, these wives of the classical theorists.

Lavoisier's justly famous *Traité Elémentaire de Chimie,* which appeared five years before his execution, has in it a series of diagrams and illustrations which were drawn and engraved by his talented and beautiful wife. Their marriage had indeed been an unusual partnership. And now that she was a widow, she alone gathered the papers he had prepared and presented them to the world under the title *Mémoirs de Chimie* (1805).

It was a tender tribute to the dead.

5. Rumford . . . . THEORY OF HEAT

FOR centuries fire and heat have been household expressions used to denote phenomena which appear alike but in reality are widely separated. So close has been the linkage between them that, long after the *phlogiston* of fire was acknowledged dead, its imponderable ghost survived in the so-called *caloric* of heat. As it took Lavoisier to demonstrate the nonexistence of phlogiston, so it took Count Rumford to demolish caloric. The theories of fire and heat are for this reason interesting parallels in the history of science.

2

On every issue about fire the phlogistonists took the opposite of the correct explanation. So did the calorists on heat. In both cases what was incomprehensible to a large group of men was understood by the lone individual who undertook to co-ordinate the data at hand by a bold stroke of genius, namely, a unifying process. Great theories are born in the minds of men of genius whose talents may be compared to that of an artist. No more can a work of art be produced by a committee of artists than can a great theory be evolved by a round-table conference of specialists.

No matter how iconoclastic, a theorist must be capable of taking all the past along with him. Legend says that Moses on the eve of his departure from Egypt to the Promised Land carried the bones of Joseph to symbolize continuity with the thought and personalities of an older generation. Since he believed in the life of the spirit he had reverence for the great spirits of the past. The theorist worships in a temple not easy to approach, a temple where the worshipers are few and the worship difficult. Over the portals of this temple are carved the favorite words of Vesalius, "One lives for the spirit, all else belongs to Death."

3

A crude heap of facts about heat was inherited by modern man from the dim notions of the ancients and the equally vague notions of medieval thinkers. To some of these men heat was a peculiar substance having no weight; hence it was called an imponderable. Others spoke of it in terms of a "fluid" which permeated the atomic spaces of matter and could be poured from a hotter to a colder body as water is poured from a higher to a lower level. Still others contended that heat was an indestructible substance and uncreatable by any process; bodies became warmer when caloric was added to them and grew colder as caloric left. Here they were, an erroneous huddle of ideas, mingled with all sorts of faulty observations and half-formed conceptions. One need not trace in detail the tangled channels through which these antiquated views have trickled down the long winding course of history. What happened is this: they became a part of the complicated network of traditional thinking. Popularity and acceptance regarded them semi-sacred. To doubt that heat was a material fluid was to doubt the wisdom of former generations.

When one lacks the data to lay an historical finger on the person who originated an idea, perhaps the next best thing is to choose that man in whom the idea, long in historical germination, finally awoke to full significance. The material conception of heat became a part of the scientific credo of an English doctor, William Gilbert (1540-1603), physician to Queen Elizabeth and a man of considerable importance in the history of science. Fellow of St. John's College, Cambridge, and President of the College of Physicians, he founded the sciences of electricity and magnetism. History justly ranks him with Galileo and Harvey as an early pioneer in the experimental method long before Francis Bacon wrote of it. As a matter of fact, Gilbert is repeatedly mentioned by Bacon, but since Bacon rejected Copernicus, ignored Kepler, and seemed unaware of Harvey, it is no wonder that he depreciated Gilbert.

The necessary combination of subtlety and vigor that makes a man a theorist of great acumen is rare. We recognize these talent in Gilbert notwithstanding the fact that his views on heat were in error. In the circumstances of his time he could not succeed in arriving at the true explanation. Yet Gilbert was fully conscious of the scientific value of experiment as a positive thing that links together the process of thought and the process of action. "In the discovery of secrets, and in the investigation of the hidden cause of things, clear proofs are afforded by trustworthy experiments rather than by probable guesses and the opinions of ordinary professors and philosophers." These sound like tame words to us but in the day when Gilbert wrote them they were upsetting to time-honored ideas.

To Gilbert we owe many things: he gave us the word electricity which he coined from the Greek word meaning amber; he wrote a book called *De Magnete* in which he collected all that was known about magnetism and added many fresh observations of his own; he pointed out the importance of the magnetic needle for navigation, and finally he theorized about these forces in an effort to see them bound together in a unitary structure. Many of his views were medieval, half-formed mystical notions, such as his belief that magnets possess some sort of soul or spirit. But these views, it seems, were apparently unavoidable to one who embodied in his struggle the emergence of science from the dark ages of superstition into the modern spirit.

Gilbert regarded heat, light, electricity and magnetism as forms of matter—excessively subtle and refined, capable of freely pervading and combining with all ordinary bodies. This notion of the materiality of heat (or *caloric* as it is frequently called) was almost universally accepted and taught until Sir Benjamin Thompson, Count Rumford (1753-1814), demolished it. "I am thoroughly satisfied," declared Rumford in a letter to his friend Professor Pictet of Geneva, "that I shall live a sufficiently long time to have the satisfaction of seeing caloric interred with phlogiston in the same tomb."

4

Like those two famous Italians, Christopher Columbus and Leonardo da Vinci, Benjamin Thompson and Benjamin Franklin were born only a few miles apart, Thompson in Woburn, Massachusetts, a little village not more than twelve miles from Benjamin Franklin's native Boston. These two American Benjamins were among the outstanding scientists of the age; yet there is no indi-

cation that they ever knew or met each other. Curious. Both were
young men of unusual mental power, both were wondrously successful in business and public affairs, both were scientists of rare
distinction—and yet there is not a shred of evidence to indicate
that they were even interested in each other's work. Apparently
their paths never crossed, although Franklin visited Lavoisier in
Paris, and Rumford, after the death of his first wife, married the
great chemist's widow.

Thompson's early training was gained in a piecemeal fashion;
first there was John Fowle, a graduate of Harvard College, who
tutored him as a boy; then came a short session at a provincial
school which was followed by another brief tuition under a certain Mr. Hill and still another under the Reverend Thomas Bar-
nard of Salem. From the scraps of information that have come down
to us it appears that young Thompson possessed an unusually
active mind so that from the varied personalities of his tutors he
absorbed many different kinds of interests. When he was only
sixteen his search for comprehension of natural phenomena led
him to request a friend to "give the nature, essence, beginning of
existence, and rise of the wind in general, with the whole theory
thereof, so as to be able to answer all Questions relative thereto."
There is no indication that the friend was able to oblige him.

At an early age he gave evidence of being able to do three things:
think for himself, experiment, and theorize. By self-practice he
became an able and accurate draughtsman and something of an
artist, too. In a prankish mood he sketched a group of spirited cari-
catures which he called "A Council of State" and which cleverly
depicted a jackass with twelve human heads.

The versatility of these men of theory is a continual surprise;
Thompson takes his place among them in the classical stream of
their manifold accomplishments. As he grew in mental stature, his
ingenuity was sufficiently large to meet every practical and theoretical problem in the long catalogue of his achievements. Without relying on the aid of a single person he designed his own inventions. In
those early years he undertook in a boyish way to experiment with
fireworks. This interest marked the auspicious beginning of a line
of thought which eventually led him to the discovery of the correct
theory of heat.

Both physically and mentally Thompson matured early. Before he was eighteen he was appointed teacher in Concord where he was described as "of a fine manly make and figure, nearly six feet in height, of handsome features, bright blue eyes and dark auburn hair. He had the manners and polish of a gentleman, with fascinating ways and an ability to make himself agreeable." Recognizing these qualities, the rich widow of Colonel Rolfe accepted him. She was thirty-three, Thompson only nineteen. Many years after, to his friend Professor Pictet, Thompson (then Count Rumford) remarked somewhat ungallantly that she married him, rather than he her.

5

Proud of her acquisition, Mrs. Thompson committed her new husband to the care of the best tailor and hairdresser in Boston. With a rich wife and good clothes the striking personality of the young man was bound to be noticed—especially when he made his appearance on horseback. And so it happened. In 1772 there was held near Portsmouth, New Hampshire, a large military review. Thompson was among the soldiers who rode, and Governor Wentworth was among the notables who were watching. Wentworth's eye was so charmed by the handsome equestrian figure that he invited Thompson to be his guest on the following day. Pleased as the governor was with the young man's physical appearance, he was equally impressed with Thompson's mind. He immediately assigned him to public service; and from that day to the end of his long career, which took him to England and the Continent, Thompson was a man of public affairs.

In the ferment of discontent which preceded the American Revolutionary War, Thompson was on the side of the Government, a Tory. His royalist sympathies on these controversial matters brought him into sharp disagreement and conflict with members of those pre-revolutionary clubs and committees which had been formed on the eve of hostilities to protect the interests of the colonists. Everywhere feeling ran high; it was a critical and anxious stage before the outbreak of armed conflict and it was particularly dangerous for those suspected of Toryism. Thompson, the friend of the Colonial Governor and the recipient of Wentworth's favors, fell under strong public disapproval. After several exasperating episodes

with the "Sons of Liberty," he decided it would be safest to leave
the country rather than submit to further inquisition and continued
threats of mob attack. "I have done nothing that can deserve this
cruel usage. I have done nothing with any design to injure my
countrymen, and cannot any longer bear to be treated in this bar-
barous manner by them." This is a part of a farewell letter he
wrote to his father-in-law, the Reverend Timothy Walker. But it
is not altogether true. His connections with the British General
Thomas Gage in Boston revealed definite royalist activities which
his incensed fellow-Americans sharply resented. Events finally led
to his arrest and, what was still worse, a humiliating experience
in being confined in Woburn. A "Committee of Correspondence"
was formed to review his case, and they discharged the prisoner.
Within a few days he was again examined by the Committee who
recommended him to the "protection of all good people in this
and the neighboring provinces." "Our candor," says George Ellis,
his biographer, "must persuade us to allow that there were reasons,
or at least prejudices and apprehensions, which might lead honest
and right-hearted men, lovers and friends of their birthland, to
oppose the rising spirit of independence, as inflamed by dema-
gogues, and as forboding discomfiture and mischief. They feared
that we should suffer the worst of the strife, and that the sort of
government we should be likely to have as the alternative of a
monarchy would probably make us largely the losers. Yet the utterance of said views, if only as misgivings, might in many places be
equally impolitic and dangerous."

Accordingly, on the 13th of October in the year 1775 this young
American of great promise sailed to England and expatriated himself, leaving his wife and infant daughter behind and his property
confiscated. In the letter to his father-in-law he expressed the devout
wish "that the happy time may soon come when I may return to
my family in peace and safety, and when every individual in America may sit down under his own vine and under his own fig tree and
have none to make him afraid."

6

On his arrival in London he quickly attached himself to the
service of the British Colonial Office where he became its expert

on American affairs. But always while busy with public matters
Thompson found time to experiment. Thought alone was never
sufficient for him—he felt the need for verification which guarantees thought. As a youngster he had been interested in fireworks,
guns, and gunpowder; these things fascinated him not alone as
toys or sport, but because of their importance in world affairs. Up
until now his life had been one of close association with them
and, as far as he could see, it was destined to continue that way.
The adolescent interest now ripened into a mature search for accurate knowledge. He began in earnest a series of experiments on
gunpowder. In addition to this he turned his attention to improvements in military matters and promoted several new devices. Recognition of his ability was brought to the attention of the Royal
Society. In 1779 he was elected a Fellow. In 1784 he was knighted
by the king.

How often did Thompson think of his wife and daughter in
America? Unfortunately we don't know. Many theorists have been
bachelors—Boyle, Hutton, Dalton, Cavendish, Huygens, Newton;
many have been happily married men—Lavoisier, Darwin, Pasteur,
Marx; and not a few have been celibates for the sake of the Kingdom of Heaven such as Copernicus and Gregor Mendel. But in
Thompson we meet a man who could find no peace or happiness
with the two women whom he married, or in any of the women he
chose for part-time affairs. When he left America he parted from
his wife; he never saw her again. Nor did he ever write to her.
When Mrs. Thompson died in 1792, Sarah Thompson, their only
daughter, was a grown young woman of eighteen years.

7

Shortly after receiving these English honors Benjamin Thompson,
now Sir Benjamin, was on the Continent. Unerringly he seemed
to know the way to his own advancement and to the distinctions
of Europe. No man ever lived who loved medals, decorations, honors, titles and rank more than he. He was recommended to the
Elector of Bavaria by Prince Maximilian who saw him on horseback, just as Governor Wentworth had seen him. On learning
that Thompson had served in the British Colonial Office and was
an expert on guns and gunpowder, as well as a Fellow of the Royal

Society of London, the prince invited him to meet his uncle, the Elector. Out of this meeting came a unique proposal: that this newly knighted American-born British subject be offered military and civil posts in the Government of Bavaria with full powers to reshape and reorganize the army and to initiate important social and economic projects. Thompson accepted. He became minister of War, minister of Police, and grand Chamberlain to the Elector. Reminiscent of the Biblical story of Joseph, it so happened, stranger than fiction, that the once poor farmer lad from faraway New England moved into a palace in Munich to exercise an authority second only to the king's. He was now on the road to world honors and immortal fame.

With resolution he faced the difficult tasks of government, managing to come through each project successfully by his genius for organization. A man of method, Thompson approached every problem in terms of a scientific inquiry. So remarkable and varied were his reforms in the fields of military, social and civic affairs, as well as in education, sanitation, housing, land reclamation, hospital work, poor-relief and food supply problems, that the Elector conferred upon him the glittering title *Count Rumford,* nobleman of the Holy Roman Empire. This official recognition was enhanced by a vast popular mark of esteem displayed during Rumford's absence from Munich in 1795-6. Without his knowledge a monument was erected in gratitude for those manifold and superlative accomplishments which he achieved for the people of Bavaria. On one side of the monument, which was composed of Bavarian freestone and marble, is a dedication to "Him who eradicated the most scandalous of public evils, Idleness and Mendacity; who gave to the poor help, occupation, and morals, and to the youth of the Fatherland so many schools of culture. Go, Wanderer! Try to emulate him in thought and deed, and us in gratitude."

While public applause was still warm in enthusiasm for the elegant Rumford monument on the Maximilianstrasse in Munich, Miss Sarah Thompson sailed for England to see her father. The Count had been ill, and when Sarah arrived, she was greatly disappointed in his appearance. He was not at all the handsome knight she had read about. There were other disappointments, too, for Rumford was far from being an affectionate father.

Not that he was ungenerous, but his mind was cold and impervious to feminine claims. It may well be that he was too self-centered, too demanding and impatient. At any rate his interests were in other directions. While Sarah was with him he founded and endowed the historic *Rumford Medal* of the Royal Society of London, and on the same date he presented a like amount to the American Academy of Arts and Sciences. Both endowments were identical in terms.

Early in 1796 Sarah was asked to accompany her father to Germany. Shortly after their arrival in Munich she was made a Countess of the Empire with a handsome pension conferred upon her by the Elector, who stipulated that she was at liberty to enjoy it in any country she chose to live in. What with the aloofness of her father and her intense dislike of the noisy life of Munich and London, she decided to return to America as a place more suitable in atmosphere and tranquillity for one of simple tastes in living. She reached Boston in the fall of 1799, "being then just twenty-five years of age."

8

The road to ultimate success is most often the road of trial and error, and the observer or investigator must always analyze the observational process itself. Does he really see what he thinks he sees? As a philosopher Rumford was aware of the dangerous tendency of the human intellect to accept as valid a plausible explanation and then look for facts in support of that explanation. In his experiments on heat he was constantly on his guard to avoid this error.

What led Rumford to heat? He had long been concerned with military problems and had regarded gunpowder as an important factor in the affairs of men and nations. The head of the British Colonial Office at the time of his expatriation was Lord George Germain who took a strong liking to this youthful expatriated American. Germain frequently breakfasted and dined with his new employee and invited him to his' county seat, Stoneland Lodge. It was here in 1778 that Rumford continued his scientific inquiries into guns and gunpowder and the enormous amount of heat generated in their construction and use.

What he began as a boy in Woburn and continued in England

under Lord Germain he now carried on in Bavaria as Minister of War to the Elector. "Being engaged, lately, in superintending the boring of cannon in the workshops of the military arsenal in Munich," he says, "I was struck with the very considerable degree of heat which a brass gun acquires in a short time in being bored." With these words Rumford begins the story of how he gave to the world the first experimental demonstration of the immateriality of heat.

By the upholders of the caloric theory it was believed that friction merely rubbed or squeezed out the heat from the interatomic spaces of the bodies, just as water is squeezed from a wet sponge. Rumford set out to prove that this sponge idea and all that it implied was ridiculous. He did it by a few simple boring experiments in the munition workshop. First he took a very blunt tool (a borer) and arranged that the metal cannon should be surrounded with water so that all the heat produced would go into the water. Then he got a pair of horses to keep turning this blunt borer round and round on its axis in order to generate heat by friction.

What happened?

The water got hotter and hotter. After tramping the circle for two and a half hours the horses had generated enough heat to boil the water. To the great amazement of the spectators the water continued to boil just as long as the horses continued their boring. "One horse," declared Rumford, "would have been equal to the work performed, though two were actually employed. Heat may thus be produced merely on the strength of a horse, and, in a case of necessity, this heat might be used in cooking victuals."

This was the first time on record, at any rate, that water had been made to boil without the use of fire. "In reasoning on this subject," Rumford said, "we must not forget *that most remarkable circumstance*, that the source of the heat generated by friction in these experiments appeared evidently to be *inexhaustible*." (The italics are Rumford's.) "It is hardly necessary to add, that anything which any *insulated* body or system of bodies can continue to furnish *without limitation* cannot possibly be *a material substance;* and it appears to me to be extremely difficult, if not quite impossible, to form any distinct idea of anything capable of being exited and communicated in those experiments, except it be MOTION."

With regard to the favorite illustration of the calorists, who compared heat to water contained in a sponge which could be "squeezed out" or "rubbed out," Rumford replied: "A sponge filled with water and hung by a thread in the middle of a room filled with dry air communicates its moisture to the air it is true, but soon the water evaporates and the sponge can no longer give out moisture." Such is not at all the case with heat; the boring experiments showed that the supply of heat was inexhaustible. The sponge idea was an erroneous illustration of what happened. In place of the evaporating sponge Rumford suggested a vibrating bell. "A bell," he declared, "sounds without intermission when it is struck, and gives out its sound as often as we please, without any perceptible loss. Moisture is a substance, sound is not."

Rumford recorded his experiments, his observations and his theory in a paper entitled *Enquiry Concerning the Source of Heat which is Exited by Friction*. The net result of his work was to destroy the entire conception of the corpuscular view of heat which regarded heat as a substance. The long-vexed questions over the supposed existence of an *igneous fluid* or a something called *caloric* (heat stuff) came to an end. Rumford's experiments were conclusive; he established for all time that heat is not a species of matter but a species of motion and that no body either gains or loses weight by virtue of being merely heated or cooled.

His theory became an effective formula to work with, a key which no lock refused.

9

A scientific hypothesis is more than a guess—it is a preliminary supposition which, lacking full proof, nevertheless leads to better understanding. Count Rumford began his work on heat with only a tentative hypothesis; this he passed through the purgatory of experiment before he announced to the world the proof of his theory. To experiment means to start out from ideas as well as facts. "Science walks on two feet—theory and experiment. Sometimes it is one foot which is put forward first, sometimes the other, but continuous progress is made only by the use of both."

In every arduous enterprise it is pleasanter to look back at difficulties overcome than forward to those which seem insurmountable. The principles announced by Rumford are now clear, but they were hidden by many deceptive veils. Robert Boyle experimented on heat problems before Rumford was born. He too generated heat by friction. But his explanations were false for he believed in the materiality of heat. Simple as facts are, they are nevertheless notoriously difficult to find. A trained observer is often slow to recognize them even when they stare at him. Indeed, it is surprising how simple all great discoveries in science are, after somebody else has made them.

Besides Boyle, one could mention at least five illustrious thinkers who had the germ of Rumford's idea—Hooke, Locke, Descartes, Newton and Hobbes. The vague hypothesis that floated in their minds was incubated and nourished by Rumford until it developed into a mature and self-sustaining doctrine. From a hypothesis barren of results it became in his hands a theory fertile beyond expectation. In a book entitled *Heat as Mode of Motion* John Tyndall summarized the work of Rumford in one sentence: "When the history of the dynamical theory of heat is completely written, the man who, in opposition to the scientific belief of his time, could experiment, and reason upon experiment, as Rumford did in the investigation here referred to, may count upon a foremost place."

The memorable paper on heat was submitted by Rumford to the Royal Society after he had left Bavaria. He was now living again in England. With advanced ideas on the practical aspects of heat, Londoners kept him busy telling them how to remodel their fireplaces and chimneys, how to save on fuel and at the same time get better results. Those who took his advice were amazed at the increased efficiency achieved at small costs. He could have kept himself occupied with these practical·problems to the end of his days had he been so minded, but he had been thinking about the possibility of returning to America. Rufus King, then United States Ambassador in London, offered Rumford an exalted position. "I am authorized," said Ambassador King in the name of the newly established republic, "to offer you, in addition to the superintendence of the military academy, the appointment of Inspector-General of the Artillery of the United States; and we shall moreover be disposed to give to you such rank and emoluments . . . as would be likely to afford you satisfaction, and to secure to us the advantage of your service." Despite his nostalgia for America and the allurements of the position offered Rumford did not go. Another project laid hold of his imagination—a project into which he poured his rare genius for organization and for science. This was the creation of the Royal Institution of Great Britain (not to be confused with the Royal Society) in which he took the leading part.

10

That the Smithsonian Institution should have been founded by an Englishman is no more curious than the establishment of the Royal Institution by an American. Did Smithson receive his inspiration from that pamphlet of fifty pages wherein Rumford set forth the purposes of the Royal Institution? The pamphlet carried a rather lengthy title: "Proposals for forming by subscription in the Metropolis of the British Empire, a Public Institution for diffusing the knowledge and facilitating the general Introduction of Useful Mechanical Inventions and Improvements, and for teaching, by courses, Philosophical Lectures and Experiments, the Application of Science to the Common Purposes of Life." Upon examination the title not only sets forth the purposes of the Royal Institution, but it seems to be a lucid statement of the personal vision and ideas of Rumford's life.

Among the many notable things that this intensely practical theorist did for the Royal Institution was to call to its service the talents of a young chemist Humphry Davy. In the story of theories we constantly witness the interlocking of great minds. Stimulated by Rumford, Davy was anxious to supplement the experiments on heat which had been carried out in Munich. This eager desire to confirm Rumford's theory led Davy to enrich the subject with a very simple but beautiful demonstration in which he rubbed together two pieces of ice until they were completely melted by friction. According to the old caloric theory two pieces of ice when rubbed could not melt because there was no "heat substance" in them. But Davy showed that they did melt and the change from a solid to a liquid form was generated by friction which did not come from any outside source. Thus without any difference of temperature (and therefore no flow of caloric from the temperature into the ice) Davy produced melting simply by rubbing. Why? Because rubbing "stirred up," as it were, the atoms in the ice causing them to be less cohesive. If, argued Davy, it is clearly possible to melt ice by friction from within, why believe in caloric from without? Other experiments added further confirmation to Rumford's views. Having with his own wings soared over the newly discovered ocean of truth, Davy announced in 1812 the following statement in his *Elements of Chemical Philosophy:* "The immediate cause of the phenomena of heat, then, is motion, and the laws of its communication are precisely the same as the laws of the communication of motion."

11

The last years of Rumford's life were spent in his mansion at Auteuil on the outskirts of Paris. He was a lonely man for his marriage to Madame Lavoisier had not been successful and they were now separated. In these declining days the thought that he had been responsible for Davy's enormous success at the Royal Institution gave him cheer, especially since Davy had so beautifully confirmed his own theory of heat.

It is sad to think that Rumford could not live happily with the widow of the great French chemist. Had he been able to adjust himself to her, his remaining years might have been full of radiant sunshine. Their courtship gave every promise of such an outcome— both were intelligent, interested in science, both possessed social distinction and great wealth. But—each had too much temper.

Before his marriage to Madame Lavoisier he wrote a letter to his daughter extolling her virtues. She was all that a man could wish for—"very pleasant in society, has a handsome fortune at her own disposal, enjoys a most respectable reputation, keeps a good house, which is frequented by the first philosophers and men of eminence in the science and literature of the age . . . what is more than all the rest, is goodness itself." They were married in Paris October 24, 1805.

"My dear child," wrote the Count to his daughter, "this being the first year's anniversary of my marriage . . . I am sorry to say that experience only serves to confirm me in the belief that in character and natural propensities Madame de Rumford and myself are totally unalike, and never ought to have thought of marrying. We are, besides, both too independent in our sentiments and habits of life to live peaceably together—she having been mistress all her

COUNT BENJAMIN THOMPSON RUMFORD

After the portrait by Gainsborough

Courtesy *of the Fogg Museum of Art, Harvard University*

days of her actions, and I, with no less liberty, leading for the most part the life of a bachelor. Very likely she is as much disaffected towards me as I am towards her. Little it matters with me, but I call her a female dragon—simply by that gentle name! We have got to the pitch of my insisting on one thing and she on another." Matters grew even worse. He did not like her parties, those large open house affairs where Madame Lavoisier de Rumford (she refused to drop the Lavoisier) ruled in queenly style over her own hand-picked court of admirers. And when she poured boiling water on his beautiful flowers in retaliation of some petty annoyance, he declared that his habitation was no longer an abode of peace. "*Lady* I cannot call her." After four years of marital unpleasantness they separated. Rumford said it was unavoidable; he could no longer live with a person "who has given me so many proofs of her implacable hatred and malice." He leased the villa at Auteuil and left her.

Rumford needed his wife. It is true he was miserable with her, but without her he was a defeated man. She retained her friends, kept her social contacts, entertained as usual, happily and gaily, while Rumford, cut off, sank deeper each day into an engulfing gloom. The distinguished French statesman François P. G. Guizot, one of Madame Lavoisier's most intimate friends, was astonished at the transformation that had come over Rumford. When the Count first courted her, "his spirit was lofty, his conversation was full of interest, and his manners were marked by gentle kindness. He made himself agreeable to Madame Lavoisier. He accorded with her habits, her tastes, one might almost say with her reminiscences. . . . She married him, happy to offer to a distinguished man a great fortune and a most agreeable existence."

Toward the end of 1811 his daughter Sarah, Countess de Rumford, joined him. It is not hard to understand why they did not find a great deal of pleasure in each other's company, for Rumford was selfish and Sarah, after all, was a woman. Moreover, she had been twice blocked in love by her father's interference. Sarah earnestly wished matrimony, and but for Rumford's arrogance, she would have been the wife of Sir Charles Blagden or Count Taxis. She never married, and as the years went by she became eccentric.

Occasionally Madame Lavoisier visited them. While Rumford

frequently declared, "I believe *that* woman was born to be the torment of my life," Sarah, with a woman's keener sense of appraisal, had quite a different estimate. From her we learn that Madame Lavoisier's character was admirable. Their difficulties she ascribes to too much independence and hypersensitivity: "One wanted this, the other wanted that, Madame loved company, the Count loved quiet." And so on. Two extreme individualists tried to live under one roof and could not make a go of it. Sarah's point of view is summed up in one very brief observation: "It was a fine match, could they but have agreed."

On August 21, 1814, after a brief illness which lasted only three days, Count Rumford breathed his last. He was not an old man, not quite sixty-two; yet into those years he had packed the experiences and achievements of several ordinary lives. His knowledge of men and nations, his command of many languages, his powers of imagination and creativity, his striking ability to put into operation difficult social, civic and military enterprises present to us, after the passage of more than a hundred years, an immortal figure of singular impressiveness. History has sustained him.

In his death he did not forget America. He executed his last will and testament in the presence of La Fayette, who was one of the witnesses. After providing for his daughter he left an annuity to Harvard, "for the purpose of founding . . . a new institution and professorship, in order to teach by regular courses of academical and public Lectures, accompanied with proper experiments, the utility of the physical and mathematical sciences for the improvement of the useful arts, and for the extension of the industry, prosperity, happiness and well-being of society."

12

Upon the dethronement of the material theory of heat a new era began, an era open for the acquisition of significant knowledge which led to results greater than at any previous epoch in the history of man on earth. Under the new rule of the dynamical theory of heat it only remained for the successors of Rumford and Davy to enlarge the domains bequeathed to them.

The region of discovery proved rich beyond the power of conception.

Within less than a century there was erected the science of thermodynamics. Once it became understood that mechanical energy and heat are identical and convertible, the rest was comparatively easy. Striking achievements came thick and fast, all to illustrate that great practical consequences are bound to flow from correct views. A host of men of various grades of genius carried the new science to unbelievable heights—Sadi Carnot in France, Joule in England, Helmholtz in Germany, not to forget Rankine, Clausius, Lord Kelvin and their co-workers.

But the supreme genius of them all was that peerless theorist, Robert Mayer of Heilbronn.

13

In approaching the life and labors of Robert Mayer (1814-1878) we are conscious of dealing with a wondrous field of knowledge of which no previous generation had even the slightest inkling. Under the genius of this thinker the new theory of heat was elaborated in such a way as to show links and similarities where people had imagined separation and differences. To perceive is to see what we do not see—to grasp the subject as a whole, so that greatly differing phenomena are understood as manifestations of one principle. Truth of this sort is not easily come by, and in Mayer we see a genius-theorist whose life was embittered by long years of misunderstanding which almost ended in suicide.

There is a little town in Germany, not far from Heidelberg, named Heilbronn. Here lived the young physician, Doctor Robert Mayer, who in 1841 had just returned home to begin the practice of medicine after having spent a year as ship's physician on a Dutch East India vessel. What Charles Darwin owed to the voyage of the *Beagle* Robert Mayer was to owe to an experience on board the *Java* which sailed from Holland to Batavia with a captain and crew of twenty-eight.

Mayer noticed that the blood drawn from the arm of a patient in the tropics was much brighter in color than that of an inhabitant of a colder country. He pondered this seemingly insignificant fact, recalling what Lavoisier had written about the relationship between oxygen and heat—the physiological aspect of combustion. Considering the body as a machine, Mayer concluded that the cause of the brighter color of the blood was due to the lesser amount of oxidation required to keep up the body temperature in the tropics. "Heat produced mechanically by the organism," he declared, "must bear an invariable quantitative relation to the work expended in producing it." This conclusion led to a train of thinking that kept Mayer busy on the subject of heat to the end of his days.

What started out in its embryonic stage as a vague intuition in the brain of a ship's doctor ended in the announcement of the law of the conservation of energy, conceded to be the greatest nineteenth century generalization in the domain of science. It is amazing to think that Mayer's initial interest in heat arose out of this experience and that from it, unaided, he should have been able to see that a definite relationship exists between the heat developed by mechanical action and the force which produced it. Many months after his return to Heilbronn he wrote about this lone experience on the *Java* in a letter to his friend Griesinger, the neurologist. "I hung on the subject with such delighted interest," wrote Mayer, "that I—and many may laugh at me for this—asked little concerning those far parts of the earth, but preferred to remain on board where I could work without interruption, and where during many hours I felt so inspired that I can remember nothing like it before or later. Certain lightning flashes of thought that went through me—it was in the roadstead off Surabaya—were at once eagerly followed up and led to new subjects. Those times are past, but a quiet examination of what came to the surface in me at that time has convinced me that it is a truth which is not only felt subjectively but that can be proved objectively. The day will come, that is certain, when these truths will become the common property of science."

The day did finally come when the world recognized Mayer, but it came after long years of abuse and torture which led him to an insane asylum, to brutal treatment, and finally, in a fit of uncontrollable bitterness towards the injustice of the world, to an attempt at suicide. What a contrast to the life of Rumford, whose path led him into the high places of the world, to fame and early recognition! No such good fortune came Mayer's way. The first significant paper that Mayer wrote was sent to *The Annals of Physics and Chemistry* at Leipzig. It contained the great principles of the law of the conservation of energy: "motion, heat and electricity are phenomena which can be converted into *one* force, and can be changed into one another under definite laws." There was also stressed the doctrine that energy, like matter, cannot be destroyed or lost. This unique and priceless paper reached the editor of *The Annals*, Professor Poggendorff, but Mayer did not receive even the courtesy of an acknowledgment. After making several fruitless inquiries, he was forced to let the matter drop. Many years later, when Poggendorff died, Mayer's paper was found in an envelope among the professor's effects, unopened and unread.

14

True, Rumford had arrived at correct views on the nature of heat (which Mayer after long and careful thought accepted), but he did not fully appreciate or understand that an exact quantitative relationship existed between the mechanical work expended (as when the cannon was bored by horsepower) and the amount of heat produced by such action. But Mayer did. And his comprehension was the necessary element in the permanent foundation of the completed theory. It was a rare achievement not only to be able to follow out and check this relationship in its many and varied aspects—organic and inorganic—but to understand its calculable mathematical nature, a relationship imposed upon perception by an act of the mind which is different from anything which our senses directly offer us.

A year after the Poggendorff miscarriage there appeared in print Mayer's paper entitled *The Forces of Inorganic Nature* (1842). Again he told about the conservation of energy: "A force once in existence cannot be annihilated." Mayer was familiar with various kinds of forces—magnetic force, electrical force, chemical force, the force of gravity. All these forces he saw gave rise to one and the same thing which we now call energy. Whenever one of these kinds of energy disappears, one of the others always appears in its place. When heat appears during friction, it is because the energy of motion has been transformed into heat.

This memorable paper of 1842 is remarkable in that it contains the first calculation of the mechanical equivalent of heat, the numerical relationship between heat and work. It grew out of a

word of advice received from Doctor Norrenberg, professor of
physics at Tübingen, to whom Mayer went seeking counsel. "Yes,"
declared Norrenberg, "if you can base a new experiment on your
theory, then your case is established." Mayer lost no time; he
returned home to experiment, to find out how much energy is
necessary to produce a unit of heat. Successfully arriving at the
coveted numerical relationship, he proved that the fall of a unit
of weight from a height of 365 meters is equal to the heating of
a like weight of water from 0° to 1° centigrade. It was a brilliant
and truly epoch-making achievement that interested nobody. The
world gave him indifference and drove him mad.

15

Chemistry has mostly to do with the transformations of matter;
physics with the transformations of energy. To Lavoisier we owe
the doctrine of the conservation of matter which teaches the impos-
sibility of either creating or destroying matter. Man can only rear-
range it. To Mayer we owe the doctrine of the conservation of
energy, which explains that energy is always changing from one
form to another, but none is ever lost. To illustrate this energy
law take a machine. Not quite so much work can be got out of
it as is originally put in. There is an apparent loss of a certain
amount of work because a machine while working develops heat
due to friction. Actually however, declared Mayer, the "loss" is
only apparent not real, for this certain amount of heat is the exact
equivalent in energy of the work which had been lost. Every experiment that Mayer carried out proved conclusively that the heat
formed and the work lost were proportional to each other.

Just as matter exists in various forms so does energy; and energy
may be changed from one form to another in various transformations. So much energy of one kind produces so much energy of
another kind. There is, for example, mechanical energy, electrical
energy, heat energy, chemical energy—all capable of being transformed one into the other in such a way that the quantitative value
always remains the same. A bank draft may be converted into notes,
gold, silver, or bullion, all interchangeable. In like manner there
exists a corelation of the different forms of energy mutually convertible. Any form capable of producing another may reciprocally

be produced by it; hence these forms of energy are known to be mutually and constantly convertible.

The conservation of energy at first regarded from the point of view of the reciprocal transformations between heat and work was vastly extended in Mayer's mind to cover the entire cosmos. One need only glance through his essay *Organic Motion* (1845) to realize how audaciously he advanced his energetics to embrace the most varied phenomena which at first appear to have no connection with each other. Here he tells how the sun pours out its vast solar energy, how this energy is taken up by plant life which in turn supplies the energy of food for the complex physiological processes of man and animals. But solar energy is also stored in the earth in vast coal beds which are the remains of ancient plant life. This coal can be used for fuel, thereby releasing energy which can be transformed into heat which supplies steam wherewith to generate electrical energy which can be used for many purposes. Thus one form or manifestation of energy generates another so as to bring together into the same series of effects physical actions and changes seemingly dissimilar. One form of energy disappears (is transformed) as another is evolved. Thus energy is protean in its nature for it may be converted directly or indirectly into any other form.

The existence of different forms of energy had been known for centuries, but Mayer was the first to establish their essential identity and interaction. This had not even been suspected. His achievement proved to be one of the grandest conquests of contemporary thought. What were indefinite general notions in the minds of other men became in Mayer's a clear and certain piece of knowledge. The forces of the universe were brought together into a unity, and understood now as never before.

16

Mayer was a man whose intellectual fabrics were steeped and dyed in the seething vat of his emotions. A little kindly encouragement, such as he received from Karl Baur and Justus Liebig, elicited tremendous creative energies, whereas rudeness and indifference tragically unbalanced his mind. It is unfortunate that his work met with such little response in the early years of his life. This in itself was enough to embitter him. What made matters infinitely worse, however, was the attempt later on to rob him of his honors when the scientific world at long last finally awoke to the significance of his discoveries.

James Prescott Joule of Manchester (a pupil of Dalton's) and the illustrious Professor Herman von Helmholtz of Berlin both behaved unfairly toward Mayer; both claimed for themselves his honors. It is true that Joule wrote a paper of unquestioned importance entitled *The Calorific Effects of Magneto-Electricity and the Mechanical Value of Heat,* which was wonderful in its detailed knowledge. Heat was long suspected of being a form of energy and this was now verified. But Mayer had arrived at the mechanical equivalent of heat before Joule. He justly resented Joule's claims to priority: "Mr. Joule had made no discoveries regarding heat and energy without knowing mine. The numerous services of this eminent physicist move me to the highest esteem. Nevertheless, I believe I am within my rights when I repeat that I was the first in 1842 to publish the law of the equivalence of heat and energy as well as its numerical expression."

Joule was never magnanimous enough to acknowledge Mayer's rights. He wrote a letter of disapproval to Professor John Tyndall for acknowledging the greatness of Mayer. Tyndall replied: "I believe he deserves more praise than I have given him. It was he who first used the term 'equivalent' in the precise sense in which you have applied it; he calculated the mechanical equivalent of heat from data which, as I have said, 'a man of rare ingenuity alone could turn to account,' and his calculation is in striking accordance with your own experimental determinations."

With Helmholtz it was an even sadder case. Men of science like to be thought devotees of truth uninfluenced by personal prejudice. In an exalted mood a utopian dreamer once wrote: "The true man of science worships but one god—truth. He despises the ecclesiastic for teaching half-truths for the sake of moral influence; the politician for dressing up truth in a partisan guise; and the business man for subordinating truth to personal gain." Splendid words! But where is that marvelous abstraction "the *true* man of science"? Science is a part of the universal biography of man and shares too often, alas, the crude anthropomorphism of his life. How else can one account for the petty hostility of Helmholtz, who sat in the seats of the mighty at Berlin begrudging Mayer recognition? There was no fierce denial on Helmholtz's part of Mayer's great work—only indifference and a desire to claim the discovery for himself. He too had been working on the law of the conservation of energy; he knew it was the greatest vivifying generalization since Lavoisier had established the law of the conservation of matter. But it annoyed him to think that it was conceived and worked out by an unknown physician whom he chose to ignore. Helmholtz went so far as to allow himself to be called the "father of the law of the conservation of energy."

Had it not been for the eminently fair-minded John Tyndall, Mayer in all probability would have died without a word of recognition. Tyndall literally came to the poor man's rescue. In that brilliant London lecture of June, 1862, he acknowledged the genius of Mayer and called to the world's attention the surpassing significance of his work. It often happens that he who is stoned in one country is enthroned in another. Mayer's recognition in England immediately spread to Germany. The man who was ignored by his colleagues, flouted by his townsmen, tortured in an asylum by morons, and actually declared dead by vicious gossip and newspaper reports, came to life. High honors were now showered upon him by governments and learned societies at home and abroad. Even Helmholtz had finally to admit him as his equal. Mayer wrote John Tyndall a touching letter of appreciation for calling the attention of the world to the gross injustice of his case. "Your kindness," wrote Mayer, "impresses me all the more from the fact of my having, for many years, been forced to habituate myself to a precisely opposite mode of treatment." A year later Tyndall met Mayer in Switzerland.

In the little town where he was born this illustrious theorist passed quietly away. His last years were long days of rest and peace —and recognition, too. The King of Württemberg ennobled him, and in his hands were placed the Copley Medal and the Poncelet Prize. Death came to him peacefully in his sixty-fourth year in the month of March, 1878.

"Simplex Veri Sigillum"—Simplicity is the Seal of Truth.*

* The motto of one of Mayer's books.

6. Huygens . . . . THEORY OF LIGHT

THE story of light, the discovery of its principles, its laws, and its behavior, revolves around the names of a small group of uncommonly erudite men. After the passage of centuries, much of what they thought still remains a part of the unshakable basis of our modern knowledge. Theorists of light, they themselves are luminous figures whose work has been undimmed by the passing of years. And this despite cycles of revision and reformulation. They literally saw light while to other eyes all was yet darkness.

Not that people in all ages were not cognizant of this daily display of nature. They were. But they did not understand it. They knew a few elementary things: that light streamed to the earth principally from the sun, that it was reflected from polished surfaces such as metal mirrors, marble, glassware. They saw reflections in the water, too; but beyond knowing that light travels in straight lines their knowledge was fragmentary and absurdly limited. Phenomena such as the rainbow, the aurora borealis, the shooting star, the mirage were baffling mysteries. A great deal of outright superstition was connected with the appearance of comets, meteors, and eclipses. During the fifteenth century a comet made its appearance at the time when the Turks were fighting the Christians. In keeping with medieval ideas Pope Calixtus III decreed several days of prayer for averting the divine anger: "From the Turk and the comet, good Lord, deliver us!"—so ran the litany. As comets were believed to be fire balls flung from God's angry hands, so eclipses were equally ominous as tokens of some terrible trouble about to happen.

2

The emancipation of the human mind from grotesque medieval ideas about light and related subjects developed very slowly. No thinker can be credited with more careful spadework than Christiaan Huygens, the so-called "Dutch Archimedes," whose *Treatise on Light,* published in Leyden in 1690, remains one of the classics of science.

Huygens was born in the Hague in 1629, just three years before Spinoza was born in Amsterdam. He came of an old aristocratic Dutch family of wealth and distinction. His father, Sir Constantijn Huygens, was the *grand seigneur* of Dutch culture and an influential statesman. For his son he had marked out a literary and diplomatic career; but the early and extraordinary exhibitions of talent in mathematics and the sciences indicated the direction into which the future theorist would turn his abilities.

After attending the Universities of Leyden and Breda, he went to Denmark for a brief visit in the retinue of Henry, Count of Nassau. On his return the youthful Huygens gave himself over to a detailed consideration of the problems of mathematics and astronomy. His early essays on these subjects, written when he was only twenty-two years old, evoked enthusiastic praise from René Descartes who saw in them evidences of the greatness that was to follow.

The prodigious mental vitality that characterized the youth of Huygens never forsook him. To his last breath he was a man of plans, inventions, and ideas. After startling Descartes in mathematics, he turned his attention to the advancement of astronomical knowledge, but he was hampered by poor equipment. Thereupon he promptly devised ways in which to improve telescopes and clocks, so that he became the world's greatest authority on these subjects. Then he turned to the problem of manufacturing better lenses, and hit upon new methods of grinding and polishing. Out of these improvements came his famous discovery of the rings of Saturn.

Recognition of his abilities was not by any means wanting. Spinoza, who was a lens-grinder, found a common bond with this man, still in his thirties, who knew so much about the world and all things in it. They appear to have met with some frequency up until Huygens began to travel. He went to France to receive from the University of Angiers an honorary degree. On the occasion of his second trip to England in 1663 the Royal Society elected him a Fellow. Such distinguished honors brought him world recognition. To crown it all, King Louis XIV, the Grand Monarch, invited him to live in Paris and become a member of the newly organized French Academy of Sciences with the promise of a large stipend and many advantages. Huygens accepted.

It was here in the seclusion of the *Bibliothèque du Roi* that the Dutch philosopher spent fifteen years in study, experimenting, inventing, writing, and theorizing. These were the great productive years that witnessed the development of several mechanical inventions, including the pendulum-clock (an honor which he shares in part with Galileo), and the writing in 1673 of that remarkable treatise called *Horologium Oscillatorium,* in which he worked out the mechanics of the pendulum. This treatise Huygens dedicated to his royal patron. Isaac Newton in England read it and was so profoundly influenced by its concluding pages that it is not too much to say that the greatness of Newton's *Principia* finds its prelude in this work.

3

The remarkable thing about Huygens is that he had a mind that could voyage alone and unaided through strange seas of thought. He is one of the pre-eminently versatile thinkers of all time, a man who made lasting contributions to the sciences of mathematics, astronomy, optics, and physics—demonstrating an exceptional combination of mathematical power and practical ingenuity. He invented the micrometer (an instrument for the precise measurement of minute distances), the pendulum-clock, the spiral watch spring, improved the air pump and was among the first to discover the phenomena of the polarization of light. But that is not all. He constructed unusually powerful telescopes, developed lenses, and devised an almost perfect achromatic eyepiece, which still bears his name.

Then toward the end of his career he wrote in Latin a remarkable little book, published posthumously, which he called *Cosmotheros.* It was translated into English under the title: *The Celestial Worlds Discovered Or, Conjectures Concerning the Inhabitants, Plants and Productions of the Worlds in the Planets.* It is fanciful, and a delight to read. Here is the real precursor of Jules Verne and H. G. Wells. And yet what a new range of possibilities such conjectures brought to the scientific imagination and daring of that early day! After the long and dreary winter of the Dark Ages, the liberated spirit of man needed just such thoughts as Huygens gave it, in order to sense the vastness and yet the interrelatedness of the universe. His views stimulated the rising intellect of the time, turning science into the channels of rapid growth and boundless aspiration.

It is easy to understand how an astronomer would inevitably come to grips with the subject of light. The stars in their courses blinked from their immense distances—what was the nature of their light? And the light of the moon? And above all the light of day issuing from the sun? This Dutch scientist, at work in Paris, answered these questions and, out of it all, he evolved the wave theory of light.

4

Perhaps some brief comment ought to be made here on the theory of probability and Huygens' relationship to it. A bowing acquaintance with it will be of great help later on when a modern scientist like Heisenberg stresses the principle of indeterminism. Perhaps it seems a long way from the subject of light to the mathematical theory of probability. Yet in this world of speculations one must always be prepared for a strange inbreeding of ideas.

A pioneer contribution was made to the theory of probability by Huygens in a small pamphlet published in Leyden in 1657. It was the first attempt at a systematic treatment of a subject that had an unsavory beginning nearly four centuries ago in the activities of a professional gambler, Chevalier de Mere. The purpose of the theory is, of course, to enable the scientist to deal with cases involving a very large number of possible events. Every insurance company in the world bases its operations not on the life of any one man but on probability applied to large numbers. So many thousand people die of certain diseases each year, at certain ages, and in certain trades or professions. It is on the basis of these studies that insurance policies are written. In many fields where statistics are used, probability enters into the situation with tremendous importance as a powerful aid to investigation and analysis. Later on in this chapter it will be seen how heavily the modern scientist in dealing with the quantum theory leans upon "probability concepts" in order to understand the fundamental nature of the universe. It is now an inescapable fact (repugnant, indeed, to a great many people) that quantitative science is at bottom a situation ruled by probabilities—by the goddess of chance just as she rules at Monte Carlo. One of the fundamental considerations now uppermost in science today is that all data is of necessity probability data.

Huygens' insight into probability vaguely foreshadowed this.

5

With solid achievements in science already attesting his genius, this gifted thinker was now prepared to frame his theory of light. From his earliest days as an astronomer he had studied this phenomenon and now he was ready to tell the world about it. Not all about it. Only as much as he felt sure of; for Huygens was a modest man, and he well realized how much research remained to be done before the subject could be fully understood. Yet he knew that his wave theory of light was essentially correct, and that it could be given to the world in anticipation of much that would be discovered by future scientists. All these thoughts he set forth in a brief essay begun in 1678 but actually not published until 1690. He called it *Traité de la Lumière*—Treatise on Light.

Huygens' preface to this brief essay is a charming bit of writing. "If in the following treatise," he says, "all these evidences of probability are present, as it seems to me they are, the correctness of my conclusions will be confirmed; and indeed it is scarcely possible that these matters differ very widely from the picture I have drawn of them. . . . I trust also there will be some who, from such beginnings, will push these investigations far in advance of what I have been able to do; for the subject is not one which is easily exhausted. . . . Finally, there is much more to be learned by investigation concerning the nature of light than I have yet discovered; and I shall be greatly indebted to those who, in the future, shall furnish what is needed to complete my imperfect knowledge." Here is the modesty that makes science truly great.

The essence of the message contained in the famous *Traité de la Lumière* is that light, like sound, is essentially a form of wave motion. For a long time it had been known that sound was conveyed in waves through air. When, for example, a bell is struck its vibration is communicated to the surrounding air. Because of the elasticity of air this vibrational energy is swiftly carried in the form of waves to regions more and more remote. Like a stone dropped into a quiet pool of water, sound waves spread out from the center of the disturbance in ever-widening circles. Gradually, of course, they decrease in amplitude and die out. Now, in order to explain light as a wave form, Huygens had to postulate the existence of a medium through which light could act. For how could light come to the earth in the form of waves without some medium through which these waves could travel? This medium Huygens called the *ether*.

Ether is not air. Air exists only in very limited quantities, apparently not at all in the vast depths of interstellar space through which light must travel. Then again, air could not possibly be the transmitting agent, for light is capable of passing through a vacuum. (Sound waves however cannot be transmitted through a vacuum.) Ether is therefore something supersensible; it cannot be seen or weighed or isolated. It pervades all space throughout the universe and permeates all material things.

This in brief is Huygens' theory; and it is not to be wondered that, despite its explanation of the phenomena of reflection and refraction, it was not immediately accepted. After all, no one can see a light wave, any more than one can see an atom. So much of theory is in the realm of the invisible. The word theory (compare it with the word *theater*) means to see; it is the supreme co-ordinating act of the mind. As the mental process involved in a scientific generalization is not easy, it can readily be understood that the simplest and most familiar explanations are always the most quickly believed.

6

It was not because a light wave is invisible that Isaac Newton (1642-1727) repudiated Huygens' theory. He fought it on other grounds, and came to the conclusion that light is not a wave form at all, but a stream of minute particles, like a flight of arrows, emitted from the source of luminosity (sun, moon, stars, etc.). Newton's theory is therefore known as the corpuscular theory of light.

What led Newton to disagree with Huygens is the fact that sound (also a wave phenomenon) can bend around corners, while light is propagated in straight lines. On the basis of his own corpuscular theory, Newton found that he could more easily account for rectilinear propagation. If light consists of waves (as sound consists of waves), then luminous objects should be visible—Newton argued— even when an obstacle is between them and the eye, just as sounds are heard even though a dense body may be placed between them and one's ear. If light waves, unlike sound waves, do not bend, then why not abandon the whole wave-concept and regard light as streams of exceedingly minute corpuscles which fly through the air with inconceivable swiftness? Furthermore, Newton regarded the ether-concept as something superfluous and not to be reconciled with his celestial mechanics which showed no signs of resistance due to a medium filling all space.

In 1704 Newton published his *Optics*. He had been professor at Cambridge and was now in the full zenith of his powers—Member of Parliament, Warden of the Mint of England, and a great favorite at court. His pronouncements in science were regarded with awe. To question Newton was to question the dominating scientific personality of the world. By the weight of his great authority the corpuscular theory of light ruled for a hundred years. It was the "Age of Newton."

But accumulated knowledge refused to adjust itself to Newton's particle theory. That it would have to be overthrown was evident to several thinkers. Newton's theory, for example, led to the conclusion that velocity of light in air must be less than the velocity through a transparent medium such as glass or a liquid. But just the very opposite was eventually proved true. At first thought, it would seem unbelievable that Newton should have advocated such a view. But to Newton it was not absurd, for he reasoned like this: a beam of light is made up of particles, therefore they are subject to the attraction of gravitation; therefore when light approaches a more dense medium the increased attraction should hasten its speed. And it was not until 1850 that the French investigator J. B. L. Foucault was able to demonstrate conclusively to the satisfaction of the scientific world that the velocity was less in water than in air.

7

The man who did more than any other person to overthrow Newton's views and establish the truth of Huygens' conception was a young Quaker physician who was just beginning the practice of

CHRISTIAAN HUYGENS

medicine in London at the time Rumford was establishing the Royal Institution. It was in 1801 that Doctor Thomas Young (they called him "Phenomenon Young" at Cambridge) took up the fight against Newton. In that year he delivered a lecture entitled *The Theory of Light and Colors* before the members of the Royal Society and staunchly declared that light is not a particle but a wave form, a pulsation in the all-pervading ether, just as sound is a pulsation in the air. This declaration against Newton was based upon very careful experiments dealing with the subject of *interference.*

Take, for example, just such a simple problem as this. In certain circumstances light meeting light results in darkness at certain points, and double illumination at points in between. Even a schoolboy who sees such an experiment performed for the first time asks: How does it happen? Young answered that light is a wavelike process, and waves always and everywhere lead to so-called interference. By a tremendously important experiment Young showed that two beams of light incident upon a single point can be added together to produce darkness at that point. The explanation to him was as simple as it was obvious, namely, that two light waves can meet so that the crest of one combines with the trough of another. When that happens the entire wave is destroyed and darkness results. Why? Because the waves have annulled (interfered with) each other.

Many of the experiments which Young undertook were beyond the capacity of Huygens. It must be remembered that a full century had intervened between them, with increasingly better scientific methods and more instruments of precision, so that Young became the first of those men of the future who Huygens prophesied in 1690 would arise to "furnish what is needed to complete my imperfect knowledge." It was the ability of the wave theory to give a satisfactory explanation of interference that turned the scale against Newton's corpuscular views.

8

There is much in the mental stature of Young that reminds one of Huygens. Like his Dutch predecessor, Young was a child genius. At the age of two it is said that he was able to read fluently. At six he learned by heart the whole of Goldsmith's *Deserted Village.*

His was a remarkable memory, combined with a rare aptitude for learning the most amazing variety of things. Before he reached his fourth birthday he had read the Bible twice from Genesis to Revelation and had begun to take an interest in languages. His early mastery of more than a dozen tongues, including Arabic, Persian, and Ethiopic, eventually led to his interest in archaeology and a partial decipherment of the Rosetta Stone.* From his ability to read Egyptian hieroglyphics came the enormous scientific interest in digging up the records of man's prehistoric past.

Like Huygens, Young entered into manifold fields of thought—mathematics, botany, literature, painting and philosophy. Before he was twenty-one he had produced a work on the eye which resulted in his election to the Royal Society. In addition to this, he was an excellent physician, an accomplished musician, a recognized art critic and a splendid athlete. The full list of his accomplishments seems incredibly fantastic. He could turn his mind on the subject of tides and write a learned treatise about it, and at the same time illuminate problems in navigation; then he could fulfill the request of an important insurance company seeking extensive actuarial studies. Such a supreme exhibition of mental power in the life of one person gives some evidence of hope for the race of man.

9

What was clear in the co-ordinating mind of Thomas Young was far from acceptable to his contemporaries. The renowned Marquis de Laplace, known as the "Jupiter Olympus" of the French Academy, was particularly bitter in his opposition. Young was distressed that one so eminent in science should disregard the facts in the case and use his influence to block progress. Truth is seldom born without the pains of parturition. Confronted by phenomena and explanations that are unpalatable, most men immediately de-

---

* This Stone was found by the French in 1798 near the mouth of the Nile and passed, by treaty, into British hands. For a long time most people believed that Champollion (1790-1832), the French archeaologist, deserved sole credit for having been the first man to decipher this important record. Actually, however, Champollion based his readings in part upon the discoveries of Young and then claimed for himself all honors. The Rosetta Stone is now in the British Museum in London.

clare the new inadmissible and therefore feel safe in rejecting it without examination. It is hard to believe that this serene aesthetic student of nature could actually have aroused a hostile controversial spirit over the truth of his ideas. And yet that is exactly what happened.

Unable to understand the far-reaching nature of Young's work, Lord Brougham, editor of the *Edinburgh Review*, undertook to ridicule him. Brougham was vicious in his attack, asserting that he could not find in Young's scientific papers anything "which deserves the name either of experiment or discovery." In fact, Brougham deemed them "destitute of every species of merit," and thereupon took the Royal Society to task for its stupidity in printing such "paltry and unsubstantial papers." Of course (and here is the tragedy) few people could read Young's scientific document, but they could and did read the *Edinburgh Review*. Sidney Smith once remarked that Lord Brougham had discovered, in the course of his editorship of that paper, two important things: first that Byron was no poet and second that Young was no scientist.

Oftentimes a great mind comes too soon. The age in which he lives is not prepared for him. The philosopher Kant is reported to have said to Stägemann in 1797: "I have come too soon; after a hundred years people will begin to understand me rightly, and will then study my books anew and appreciate them." Robert Mayer felt exactly that way about his work and so did Gregor Mendel. Young realized that the prestige of Newton was too firmly rooted for men to give his ideas a fair hearing. He knew he would have to bide his time. "He was one of the most clear-sighted men who ever lived," once declared Helmholtz in a tribute to Young, "but he had the misfortune to be too greatly superior in sagacity to his contemporaries. They gazed on him with astonishment, but could not always follow the bold flight of his intellect, and thus a multitude of his most important ideas lay buried and forgotten in the great tomes of the Royal Society of London, till a later generation in tardy advance remade his discoveries and convinced itself of the accuracy and force of his inferences."

10

Progress is always by stages, each advance being one step at a time. In 1815 a young French military engineer, Augustin Jean Fresnel (1788-1827), became interested in the subject of light. Unaided and quite unaware that his experiments on interference had been anticipated by Doctor Young, Fresnel communicated his results to the French Academy, supposing them to be absolutely novel. Luckily his papers fell into the hands of that fine soul, Dominique François Arago (1786-1853), who headed the committee to which Fresnel's papers had been referred. Like Descartes, who recognized the brilliant work of the youthful Huygens, Arago was thrilled by Fresnel's achievements "which appear to be destined," he declared, "to make an epoch in science." Here was a young man who achieved much in the gathering and crowding details of a vast subject.

Arago told Fresnel that he had been anticipated by Doctor Young of London, but asked him to continue his researches on light because so much remained to be accomplished. He congratulated Fresnel on discovering independently and fully proving the ideas established fourteen years previously by the learned British physician. Then to show Fresnel that his words were no mere empty sounds, he generously offered to help him, suggesting that the two of them be associated in the furtherance of future experiments.

Research is search. It is a search for new ideas and an examination of the validity of those already advanced. This Fresnel did. It was in order to explain the phenomena of polarization that he introduced the idea of *transverse* vibrations in the ether. It is true that Doctor Young simultaneously arrived at the same idea. But Fresnel, by his greater mathematical ability, carried this joint discovery to tremendous heights. He found that light waves are not longitudinal, like sound waves, but definitely transverse like waves on the sea. By the union of Huygens' clear conception of the wave form (especially the wave front as the envelope of an infinite number of elementary waves) with Young's principle of interference, Fresnel gave the first satisfactory explanation of rectilinear propagation of light. Newton's prime objections were now answered.

Arago brought Fresnel's papers to the attention of his colleagues at the Academy, together with his own personal endorsement of their truth and value. At once a bitter controversy broke out, led by Laplace, Poisson and Biot. The opposition raged for several years and yielded only after hostility gave way to reason.

Despite neglect and opposition from the intellectual giants of the Academy, Fresnel followed his own course. Doctor Young was particularly pleased with the progress this eager Frenchman was making and cheered him on. Finally, in 1823 the opposition weakened and bowed to the profound mathematical insight and experimental resourcefulness of the engineer whom they had belittled. Fresnel was elected a member of the Academy.

And now came further recognition. Through the efforts of Doctor Young, Fresnel was voted the Rumford Medal of the Royal Society in 1825, and two years later he was chosen to be one of its honorary foreign members. It fell to the lot of Young, as Foreign Secretary of the Royal Society, to inform Fresnel of these distinguished honors. To add still greater satisfaction to this turn of events, it now fell to Arago, as secretary of the French Academy, to notify Doctor Young that he had been honored by the savants across the channel.

The wave theory and its champions had come into their own.

11

Following the death of these three exponents of light—Young, Fresnel, and Arago—the wave theory moved on to splendid conquests and remarkable confirmation. As new discoveries in light were made, as the phenomena became more various and complex, the wave theory grew in stature and acceptance. It accounted for and explained an increasing number of significant observations and experiments. Especially after the work of Foucault on the velocity of light, the cumulative evidence against the corpuscular theory was so overwhelming as to confirm the wave form concepts. All in all, it proved to be a great victory for Huygens, even though it took fully two centuries to consummate the triumph.

12

The immediate effect of Fresnel's work was to focus the attention of the scientific world upon the ether, that universal medium for the transmission of light which Huygens had assumed and

L

Young had adopted as a necessary part of the wave theory. Fresnel's brilliant mathematical demonstrations on light, coupled with his belief in the ether with its strange and paradoxical characteristics, drew a group of noted investigators into this intriguing field.

One of these was Michael Faraday (1791-1867), who, at the age of twenty-two, became an assistant to Humphry Davy at the Royal Institution and immediately entered upon a triple career of discoverer, experimenter and theorist. His researches on electricity and magnetism brought him face to face with the question of a universal medium through which these phenomena express themselves and convey their forces from one point to another. He brooded over these ideas until there dawned upon him the one big concept that co-ordinated all the lesser ones. It was this: that the phenomena of magnetism and electric induction indicate that there must be an invisible universal medium everywhere in space and that this medium is very probably the same that transmits the waves of light. In other words *one* ether is concerned in the transmission of all these phenomena. Faraday demonstrated that electricity, magnetism and light are, in some way, intimately interrelated. Just how he did not know.

But others followed Faraday who made it their supreme business to know. And now we turn to those personalities whose researches constitute the most penetrating attack man has yet made into the delicate and minute secrets of nature. "The world little knows," once declared Faraday, "how many of the thoughts and theories which have passed through the mind of a scientific investigator have been crushed in silence and secrecy by his own severe criticism and adverse examination; that in the most successful instances not a tenth of the suggestions, the hopes, the wishes, the preliminary conclusions have been realized."

13

James Clerk Maxwell (1831-1879) began where Faraday ended, not all at once but by gradual degrees of approach. He was born to wealth in Scotland and early trained in scientific subjects. It was especially in mathematics (the subject in which Faraday was weak) that Maxwell was overwhelmingly brilliant.

Profoundly impressed with Faraday's unusual views, Maxwell was

determined to master completely his predecessor's ideas. He became
convinced that those strange flashes of Faraday's mind were not
whimsies but significant insights, faint stirrings toward the next
steps that Maxwell was now destined to take. Maxwell set himself
to the task of converting into exact terminology many of Faraday's
observations. By superb mathematical analysis, he was able to prove
that electromagnetic disturbances and waves of light are transmitted
by one and the same medium and with the same velocity. In fact,
the only difference between electromagnetic waves and light waves
is that light waves are shorter. In their fundamental nature all forms
of wave radiation, radiant heat, X-rays, gamma rays emitted by ra-
dium, ultra-violet rays used therapeutically are the same. Maxwell
formulated a celebrated equation of the electromagnetic field which
applied to light no less than to electromagnetism. In other words,
he did not hesitate to declare that light waves are short electromagnetic waves. This led Maxwell to announce to the world in 1873
the electromagnetic theory of light, in which light is regarded as an
electrical phenomenon in the nature of a transverse vibration in the
ether.*

Maxwell's development of the wave theory proved to be a line
of thought productive of astonishing energy and foresight. As a
result of his efforts, the story of the wave now becomes the story
of a steady advance from point to point with tremendous practical
results. The history of science does not present a more bountiful
flowering of achievements than emerged from Maxwell's theory.

See what happened:

Maxwell declared that his electromagnetic theory of light implied the possibility of producing waves of a similar sort, but longer
than could be seen by the eye. Nine years after Maxwell's death,

* No concept in the history of science has had a stranger or more checkered
career than the concept of ether. Nor has any concept been more the subject of
bitter controversy. It has been killed and revived numerous times, especially
since the days of Huygens. Even its bitterest enemies recognize that it has played
a helpful rôle in the development of science. Einstein, however, in the main,
threw it overboard and thereby opened the way to his discovery of the special
theory of relativity. Looking at the work of Maxwell from our more modern
vantage ground, it can be said that Maxwell's results remain even though the
picture underlying electromagnetic phenomena is destroyed. Nevertheless, Eddington in his *The Nature of the Physical World* says, "We need the ether."

his prophetic prediction came true in Germany through the efforts of Heinrich Rudolph Hertz (1857-1894), in the course of new experiments on electromagnetic waves. Hertz was unquestionably the first man to demonstrate the existence of electric waves. He showed that light and electricity possess the same wave properties, the difference being one of length—that is, the rate of vibration of the ether. Moreover, Hertz discovered the means of increasing the amplitude of these waves, which are now called in his honor Hertzian waves (that is, radio waves).

Then came Marconi (1874-1937), who saw that these Hertzian waves might be put to practical use. He adapted them to a system of telegraphy, and in 1896 (at the age of twenty-two) took out his first patent for wireless based on the use of electric waves. His success in transmitting messages startled the world, for it was at first incredible that such a practical "wonder" could be realized out of the realms of theory. In 1900 Marconi used these words in which he acknowledged the work of his predecessor: "The experimental proof of Hertz, thirteen years ago, of the identity of light and electricity, and the knowledge of how to produce, and how to detect, these ether waves, the existence of which had been so far unknown, made possible wireless telegraphy."

The romance of science is no fiction. Out of the highly theoretical work of Maxwell came another triumph—radio. Those dry and forbidding equations of this Scottish physicist now bring voices out of the ether pulsating from station to station round the world. But perhaps the most sensational result to date of Maxwell's unification of light and electricity is television.

14

At the turn of the century Doctor Max Planck (1858-   ), professor of theoretical physics in the University of Berlin, gave to the world the quantum theory. While dealing with the many complex aspects of energy, this theory has a great deal to say about the nature of light, which is also a form of energy. Planck's theory is in itself a generalization independent of classical physics, and its success has led to new knowledge already fruitful of profound consequences.

The important thing about the quantum theory is that Planck insisted that energy is granular in its structure, just as Dalton insisted that matter is atomic. Planck claimed that all energy is emitted not in a continuous flow, but in tiny bundles called *quanta*, the energy of which depends upon the wave length. Thus all energy is emitted and received in definite individual proportions or "quanta"-wise, just as the chemical elements occur "atom"-wise.

Planck's thought applied to light means that it too is atomic and discontinuous, just as matter is. A beam of light leaving its source is in reality a stream of small entities (quanta). There is associated with each light-quantum a certain amount of energy and a certain velocity and momentum, just as we associate these concepts with a bullet or cannonball.

Does the quantum theory therefore mean that Newton was not wrong after all? Does it hold that light is essentially corpuscular in its nature, and that Huygens, Young, Fresnel and Maxwell were not altogether right in their wave contention?

Yes, it does!

There is no denying that Planck's theory has been greatly strengthened in the broad fields of physics. The experiments of the last twenty years have added enormously to its prestige and influence. Planck received the Nobel Prize for Physics in 1919. Together with Einstein he has headed the greatest revolt in modern science.

But the quantum theory cannot, like the classical theory of continuous waves, explain easily and naturally the facts of diffraction and other phenomena due to the interference of light. Having revived corpuscular ideas, which were admittedly dead for a whole century, the quantum theory has caused a peculiar impasse. Here then are two theories, each surprisingly successful in explaining a variety of phenomena, yet presenting two distinct pictures of light: a particle-picture and a wave-picture.

Since 1926 (the date which marks the rise of the school of wave-mechanics) experiment, debate, and investigation touching the dual aspect of light have been extended to the entire domain of nature. Men like Louis de Broglie, Erwin Schroedinger, Werner Heisenberg are the wizards in this new development. We met these men in the concluding paragraphs of the chapter on John Dalton, and here we meet them again, for they are pioneering in incredible truth on the remote frontiers of the universe.

As a result of wave-mechanics, we are stepping into a new and different kind of an order, quite unlike that which we were taught to believe under the discipline of the older concepts of physics, but nonetheless a rational order capable of mathematical formulation. For example, the classical notion of cause and effect (the principle of causality) has had to yield in these days to probability. More refined measurements, instruments of greater precision, have forced this change. And it is a revolutionary one at that. To deny the universal validity of the principle of causality (which means that under like circumstances, like results will follow) is to strike at the very roots of science as humanity has known it since the days of Galileo and Newton. Yet this is exactly what has happened. In its stead, the quantum-wave-mechanics has placed its reliance on statistical averages (probability). Causality as a dogma, however, is so deeply entrenched that it will be a long time before people will accustom themselves to think in these newer probability terms.

15

The purpose of theory is to give us a view of the whole in the truest sense of the word. But the new abstruseness is such that it leaves the mind of the average man more than a little bewildered. It is true that the latest advances of science, bound up with a terrifying revision of the facts, make our understanding of the universe not easier but harder. Yet those who stand on the sidelines, and can only touch these subjects with padded fingers, ought to rejoice in the challenge of new ideas and not protest against them. "Men are not animals erect," said Francis Bacon, "but immortal gods." See how the theorist approaches his facts. He has no ready-made scheme in his hands, nor does he attempt to force facts by Procrustean torture to conform to an arbitrary situation. He does not distort the facts or throw them away in disgust because they are too hard. On the contrary, he rejoices in their complexity; and despite their seemingly incomprehensible bulk and endless detail he finds satisfaction in attacking the problems of the universe with man's growing capacity for penetration.

In disdain of these newer and upsetting advances in science, someone composed a satirical quatrain:

"Little by little we subtract
Faith and Fallacy from Fact,
The Illusory from the True,
And starve upon the residue."

But the main thing is that man has not starved! The abundance of
the world is the achievement of science alone—against the fallacious
and the illusory. By revealing the nature of the world around us,
men of science have given a new curve to hope and to the increasing wealth and happiness of nations. "Primitive man," declared
Frederick Soddy in keen appraisal, "actually froze on the site of
what are now coal mines, and starved within the sound of water-
falls that now are working to provide our food."

16

Essentially, the scientific mood is a seeking after clearness, a
dislike of blurred vision and obscurities. Yet modern science con-
forms neither wholly to the corpuscular theory nor wholly to the
wave theory. Up to the present no one has bridged them. Apparently, the two theories throw light upon two quite different aspects
of nature, and as such may be compared to two different languages
for deciphering the same problem. As Sir William Bragg so well
expressed it in his presidential address to the British Association in
1928 at Glasgow: "On Mondays, Wednesdays, and Fridays we adopt
one hypothesis, on Tuesdays, Thursdays and Saturdays the other.
We know that we cannot be seeing clearly and fully in either case
but are perfectly content to work and wait for complete understanding."

It now appears that both Newton and Huygens are right; that
the entities which the author of the *Optics* considered corpuscular
may under circumstances behave like waves. And this dual nature
is not only true of light but of every atom in the universe.

Among themselves the early pioneers in science tore up the
foundations of the comfortable little old static world in which they
lived. To us they have bequeathed a vast, restless dynamic universe
whose ultimate nature consists of something which must be described partly in terms of waves and partly in terms of particles,
and governed by the laws of probability—a certain element of pure

chance intrinsic in the very structure of the atom. The real world apparently is so unimaginable, unpicturable, in terms of what we know, that it may forever be beyond the grasp of the human mind. Just how to get at the inscrutable hiddenness and unity of nature is a staggering problem.

Do you remember Alice in *Through the Looking Glass?* "She went on and on, a long way, but wherever the road divided there were sure to be two finger posts pointing to the same way. One marked TO TWEEDLEDUM'S HOUSE,' and the other 'TO THE HOUSE OF TWEEDLEDEE.' 'I do believe,' said Alice at last, 'that they live in the same house! I wonder I never thought of that before.' "

7. Malthus . THEORY OF POPULATION

IN 1798 when Malthus was thirty-two years old, there was published anonymously *An Essay on the Principle of Population, as it affects the future improvement of Society: with remarks on the speculations of Mr. Godwin, M. Condorcet, and other writers.* The intellectually wide-awake world took an immediate and passionate interest in it. Overnight it was a sensation and instantly recognized as a significant piece of writing.

Here was a bold and brilliant treatise that did not shrink from the risk of sailing in uncharted seas, nor did it fear to touch strange and unfamiliar shores. Not every man is able to leap from a floating island of conjecture to a continent of fact. Did the author of this *Essay* do it? Some said "Yes"—definitely, unmistakably. Others said "No" with loud and angry insistence. No one was more surprised than Malthus himself at the storm which instantly raged about his theory. The notable reception which greeted his ideas, debatable in the extreme, made the author increasingly conscious of their vast significance.

2

Very quickly people learned that the anonymous essay was the work of a minister, the Reverend Thomas Robert Malthus, curate at Albury in Surrey. He was the second son of Daniel Malthus, a liberal-minded, independent, small landowner, who had been the friend of David Hume, the philosopher, and of that eminent French thinker Jean Jacques Rousseau who visited the Malthus home in March, 1766.

The theorist-to-be was reared in an atmosphere of culture and refinement in a "small elegant mansion" near Dorking known by the name of Chert-gate Farm (also as "The Rookery"), surrounded by beautiful country of hills and dales, water and wood. It was here on February 13, 1766, that Thomas Robert Malthus was born. Three weeks later, Hume and Rousseau called together and, like the Wise Men of old, paid the babe a visit in his nursery.

What early education Malthus received was given to him by his father, who took a keen interest in this boy of rare promise. And partly too by private tutors who continued the intellectual stimulation his father had initiated. No course of study was more calculated to make a young man think for himself than the private tuition he received from Gilbert Wakefield, an heretical clergyman, who was described as "wild, restless and paradoxical in many of his opinions, a prompt and hardy disputant." Wakefield's views were in accord with the advanced ideas of Rousseau's *Émile*. The unorthodox minister held that "the greatest service of tuition to any youth is to teach him the exercise of his own powers, to conduct him to the hill of knowledge by that gradual process in which he sees and secures his own way, and rejoices in a consciousness of his own faculties and his own proficiency."

From Wakefield's excellent tuition, young Malthus went on to Cambridge where he found himself in the center of a small group of brilliant students. The years he spent there (1785-1796) were fruitful, full of study, discussion, and unending conversation. By 1788 he had taken holy orders, and after 1796 he divided his time between Cambridge and a curacy at Albury.

3

In 1793 intelligent Englishmen were reading and discussing a new book entitled *An Enquiry Concerning Political Justice, and its Influence on General Virtue and Happiness* written by a philosophic radical, William Godwin (1756-1836). Godwin, who had been in the ministry, was deeply interested in the regeneration of society. With a new and almost fanatical evangelistic zeal he wrote this book in which he advocated a theory of human perfectibility to be arrived at by means of a gradual equalization of all wealth. The Marquis de Condorcet (1743-1794), and other utopian writers of the era of the French Revolution, had unmistakably influenced him—men who were chiefly enthusiastic for the overthrow of all existing institutions which they claimed shackled the human spirit and distorted reason. All control of man by man was considered intolerable; they preached about the Day when each human being, free from restraint, would live by the principles of pure reason alone, which would be sufficient to guide him in all that was good for himself and the community.

Godwin was the type of radical who wants to tear things up by their roots. Only he did not advocate violence. Calm discussion, he believed, was the only measure necessary to awaken people and bring about change. The power of Truth would in itself be sufficient to permeate society so that every form of force, including government, would be unnecessary. "There will be no war, no crime, no administration of justice, as it is called, and no government," wrote Godwin. "Besides this, there will be neither disease, anguish, melancholy nor resentment. Every man will seek with ineffable ardor the good of all."

Through his book, Godwin not only created a vast audience that listened to him as though he were the prophet of a new dawn, but he also became a strong personal influence in the lives of not a few impressionable young men, particularly Percy Bysshe Shelley, Samuel T. Coleridge, William Wordsworth and Edward Bulwer-Lytton, afterwards Lord Lytton. Godwin was indubitably influential. "He blazed up as a sun in the firmament of reputation; no one was more talked of, more looked up to, more sought after, and wherever liberty, truth, justice was the theme, his name was not far off." So wrote William Hazlitt. Shelley, who repudiated all outward authority and the despotism of custom, was swept off his feet. Godwin became to him the most honored of all oracles, until he eloped with the prophet's seventeen-year-old daughter Mary, notwithstanding the fact that about eight weeks previously Shelley had remarried Harriet Westbrook.

The book and its author who had so ably formulated the philosophy of anarchism, and had so powerfully influenced and inspired other young men, left young Malthus singularly unenthralled. In several conversations with his father touching on Godwin's ideas (particularly those stated in the essay on *Avarice and Profusion* in a volume entitled *The Enquirer*), Malthus marshaled several arguments against Godwin's entire system of thought which he regarded as naïve and based upon a distortion of history and economics. To Godwin's thesis that a utopia could be achieved by the mere removal of all restraints Malthus replied that these restraints were necessary to save society from its worst horror: the unlimited increase in population. The removal of all restraint would permit men to spawn beyond the ability of the earth to feed and support their offspring. This condition would give rise to vast miseries which would not only prevent the realization of any such happy utopia as Godwin had in mind, but also might easily end in the complete disintegration of society as we know it.

Daniel Malthus was so impressed with the weight and originality of his son's argument that he urged him to publish it. And that is how the famous *Essay on Population* was given to the world to puncture the gorgeous bubble of Godwin's *Political Justice*.

4

The first edition of the *Essay* is a pamphlet of about 50,000 words divided into nineteen short chapters. To those who habitually swallow everything and chew nothing, the *Essay* came as a distinct shock. Godwin's book had been written knee-deep in lush optimism. But here was a pamphlet in stinging refutation that fairly dripped with pessimism. "The view which he [the author] has given of human life has a melancholy hue," acknowledges the anonymous Malthus in his own introductory remarks, "but he feels conscious that he has drawn these dark tints from a conviction that they are really in the picture; and not from a jaundiced eye, or an inherent spleen of disposition." Those who first read the *Essay* found that all their standards and landmarks were suddenly blown about. When the air is full of unknown quantities men are uncomfortable and—very often—angry. Godwin, in particular, brooded in bitterness.

The fields of sociology and economics are cluttered up with so many theories, singularly sterile and paraded with a pretense at wisdom, that one must be on guard against absurdities. "A writer may tell me," says Malthus cautiously in the first chapter of the *Essay*, "that he thinks man will ultimately become an ostrich. I cannot properly contradict him. But before he can expect to bring any reasonable person over to his opinion, he ought to show, that the necks of mankind have been gradually elongating; that the lips have grown harder, and more prominent; that the legs and feet are daily altering their shape; and that the hair is beginning to change into stubs of feathers." In these words we discover the beginnings of the modern effort to bring scientific method into a field where nothing but vague general ideas had prevailed. It is the temper of his inquiry that makes Malthus so important. His outlook was truly scientific; he did not wish to consider man as an object for praise or blame. That kind of approach, he felt, had long hampered a fair and unshackled appraisal of the facts. If reputed facts come heavily encrusted with emotional charges of one kind or another, then conclusions drawn from them are not science but a masquerade of science. Malthus' great merit lies in considering man objectively, as a part of nature, a creature possessed of a certain characteristic behavior from which certain consequences must follow as day follows night. No amount of disagreement as to the validity of his theory can impair the value of his method.

5

"I think I may fairly make two postulata," he announces to the reader as he calmly begins the really significant part of the *Essay*. "First, that food is necessary to the existence of man, secondly, that the passion between the sexes is necessary, and will remain nearly in its present state."

In bringing together the necessities of food and sex, Malthus upset Godwin's most important assumptions. The powerful and intimate linkage between these two factors, so real to Malthus and apparently so elusive to others, proved to be blindingly simple. One likes to think of that character in Molière's play *Le Bourgeois Gentilhomme* who expresses unbounded delight on being told that he has been talking prose all his life. Without perhaps even realizing it people began to find out that food and sex were inescapably what Malthus said they were: namely, the two basic "postulata" of existence. He ridiculed Godwin's idea that the passion between the sexes may in time be extinguished. "These two laws ever since we have had any knowledge of mankind, appear to have been fixed laws of our nature; and, as we have not hitherto seen any alteration in them, we have no right to conclude that they will ever cease to be what they now are."

Having thus established the pivotal basis of his argument, Malthus then proceeds to show the significance of these two forces:

"Assuming then, my postulata as granted, I say that the power of population is indefinitely greater than the power in the earth to produce subsistence for man. Population, when unchecked, increases in a geometrical ratio. Subsistence increases only in an arithmetical ratio. A slight acquaintance with numbers will show the immensity of the first power in comparison with the second. By that law of our nature which makes food necessary to the life of man, the effects of these two unequal powers must be kept equal. This implies a strong and constantly operating check on population from the difficulty of subsistence. This difficulty must fall somewhere; and must necessarily be severely felt by a large portion of mankind. Through the animal and vegetable kingdoms, nature has scattered the seeds of life abroad with the most profuse and liberal hand. She has been comparatively sparing in the room, and the nourishment necessary to rear them. The germs of existence contained in this spot of earth, with ample food, and ample room to expand in, would fill millions of worlds in the course of a few thousand years. Necessity, that imperious all-pervading law of nature, restrains them within prescribed bounds. The race of plants and the race of animals shrink under this great restrictive law. And the race of man cannot, by any efforts of reason, escape from it. . . . This natural inequality of the two powers of population, and of production in the earth, and that great law of our nature which must constantly keep their effects equal, is the great difficulty that to me appears insurmountable in the way to the perfectibility of society. All other arguments are of slight and subordinate consideration in comparison with this. I see no way by which man can escape from the weight of this law which pervades all animated nature. No fancied equality, no agrarian regulations in their utmost extent, could remove the pressure of it even for a single century. And it appears, therefore, to be decisive against the possible existence of a society, all the members of which should live in ease, happiness, and comparative leisure; and feel no anxiety about providing the means of subsistence for themselves and families. Consequently, if the premises are just, the argument is conclusive against the perfectibility of the mass of mankind."

The rest of the *Essay* is a detailed examination of the truth of this paragraph.

6

Six editions of the *Essay* were published during Malthus' lifetime. Five years passed before the second edition appeared in 1803. In the meantime a hot stream of vituperation poured down upon him. The modest country parson was accused of defending wars, famine, plagues because he had claimed that these agencies have always stepped in to reduce overpopulation. More than a score of formal replies were shot at him in refutation. Where there was no understanding of his ideas, his opponents resorted to execration and abuse. He was condemned for having denounced soup kitchens, early marriage and parish allowances. And above all things, for having the impudence to marry, after preaching the evils of families.

The objections that were made to his doctrine when it first claimed public attention—that it was gloomy, depressing, and horrible—implied an unscientific attitude of mind. Malthus wished to study man as a natural phenomenon, utterly divorced from emotional considerations. In order to do that he was prepared to have himself called the prophet of pessimism.

In the warfare of debate that has raged over his theory for almost a century and a half, Malthus has never been without enthusiastic supporters. Prime Minister William Pitt, who in 1796 thought that any man had "enriched his country" by producing large numbers of children, even if the whole family were paupers, abandoned this idea on reading the *Essay*. Thus did Malthus' theory, early in its career, affect legislation; for Pitt dropped his Poor Bill of 1800 and stated in the House of Commons that he did so in deference to the views of "those whose opinions he was bound to respect."

Pitt's conversion was not more important than that of Archdeacon William Paley, England's most popular theologian. Paley, who had once argued that "the decay of population is the greatest evil a State can suffer, and the improvement of it the object which ought in all countries to be aimed at, in preference to every other political purpose whatsoever," was now prepared to say that he had been in error. The *Essay* had awakened him to the danger of a tumorous overgrowth of population.

At a time when people everywhere believed that a nation's strength and its economic prosperity depended entirely on the number of its inhabitants, when statesmen, poets, philosophers and economists held that public welfare, national wealth, and census figures were axiomatically interdependent, Malthus arose and exposed the error of such teaching.

As we have seen, every great theory brings to an end some curious belief. With his inquiry Malthus killed the doctrine that under all circumstances an increasing population is desirable. It took courage to take this stand; Malthus anticipated only too well that his ideas would not be the sort people wanted to hear, any more than they liked reading Voltaire's *Candide*. But the frontal attack upon unwarranted optimism made it no longer possible for mankind to be lulled into the apathy of believing that all is for the best in this "best of all possible worlds."

Malthus now became the most talked of man in England. An avalanche of replies and refutations, some of them from Godwin, were indicative of widespread hostility; for he was accused of favoring vice and misery, hardheartedness and oppression. Karl Marx and Henry George denounced him bitterly. Nonetheless, his views were swiftly being adopted by an increasingly large and influential circle—economists, editors, educators. Malthus soon came to occupy a unique position as the most rejected and the most accepted man of his age.

It has been claimed that Malthus was dogmatic. The tone of the *Essay* is both reasonable and elevated. Perhaps its cool scientific objectivity was too great a chill to the ardor of those who believed so zealously in the perfectibility of mankind. Godwin claimed that Malthus had forsaken the protection and assistance of the poor, that his theory was "un-Christian," tainted with a strong upper-class bias. A man who projects a theory is necessarily a man of strong convictions. Indeed, the most interesting part of his mind is the sum total of his convictions. Such a man is not reactionary or dogmatic because he says, "I believe." Certainly Malthus was not. He had none of Godwin's conceit, nor that tone of finality which Thomas Love Peacock so well expressed in the following doggerel:

> "Not a scheme in agitation
> For the world's amelioration
> Has a grain of common sense in it
> . . . Except my own."

7

A year after the appearance of the first edition of the *Essay*, Malthus spent several months in travel on the continent in search of statistical material to buttress the basic elements of his theory. He visited Sweden, Norway, Finland, and a part of Russia, "these being the only countries at the time open to English travelers." Three years later he spent some time in France and Switzerland gathering additional data for his second edition. More than ever was he convinced that he had found the clue to human misery.

When the second edition finally appeared, the *Essay* had been expanded into a lengthy treatise. "In the course of this inquiry, I found that much more had been done than I had been aware of when I first published the essay. The poverty and misery arising from a too rapid increase of population had been distinctly seen, and the most violent remedies proposed, so long ago as the times of Plato and Aristotle."

Within a few months after the appearance of the second edition, Malthus married his cousin Harriet Eckersall of Bath, England. He was now thirty-eight years old, a tall man of a ruddy complexion, with red whiskers, bright darkish-blue eyes, auburn hair, and a distinguished figure. His portrait by John Linnell hangs at Dalton Hall, Albury, together with a companion portrait of Mrs. Malthus. The picture shows a handsome, kindly philosopher, quite in contrast to the gloomy and vicious monster created by his intemperate opponents of pamphleteering controversy. He had a keen sense of humor, a gift his calumniators lacked; and those who knew him attest by general acknowledgment that he was a good father, a devoted husband, a pleasant companion, and always a charming host.

In the same year that he married Miss Eckersall, Malthus was appointed to the professorship of modern history and political economy at the newly founded East India College, located at Haileybury in Hertfordshire, about twelve miles from London. This unique institution was established by the East India Company to train its young men for Oriental civil service, as a gateway to a lucrative career. Until his death in 1834, Malthus occupied this post which was the first of its kind to be established in England. Here for thirty years his students and his three children called him "Pop," and

M

his life was placid and cheerful. He was blessed also with an agreeable and understanding wife. "The tradition of Mrs. Malthus' delightful evening parties, at which the élite of the London scientific world were often present, lingered at Haileybury as long as the College lasted."

8

It is not the novelty of the facts but the powerful and smashing emphasis he placed on them that makes Malthus' theory memorable. To have hammered the truth of population into the consciousness of mankind was the great accomplishment of that simple generalization which he alone made the facts yield. Other men had written about population problems, but their approach was vague and clumsy. Malthus combined logic and intuition and a wide knowledge of social-economics with a clarity of presentation. In describing how the *Essay* was composed Malthus frankly states: "It was written on the spur of the occasion, and from the few materials which were then within my reach in a country situation. The only authors from whose writings I had deducted the principle, which formed the main argument of the *Essay*, were Hume, Wallace, Doctor Adam Smith and Doctor Price." Whereas his predecessors produced only lamentably meager results, Malthus, in his quest for relationship between facts, evolved a theory.

9

Malthus claimed that population, when unchecked, tends to increase in geometric ratio while the food supply increases only arithmetically. "Taking the population of the world at any number," argued Malthus, "a thousand millions, for instance, the human species would increase in the ratio of 1, 2, 4, 8, 16, 32, 64, 128, 256, 512, etc., and subsistence as 1, 2, 3, 4, 5, 6, 7, 8, 9, 10, etc. In two centuries and a quarter, the population would be to the means of subsistence as 512 to 10; in three centuries as 4096 to 13; and in two thousand years the difference would be almost incalculable, though the produce in that time would have increased to an immense extent."

Is this true? Is it true that human increase is geometric (by multiplication) while food is only arithmetic (by addition)?

Despite Malthus' strong emphasis, it must be admitted that the mathematical ratio as he originally gave it is not the essential point of the theory. When Malthus came to write the article on *Population* in the MacVey Napier Supplement to the Encyclopedia Britannica (1824), he leaned away from the mathematical aspect. This was his final, his best, and his most mature reflection. Dropping the geometric-arithmetic ratio, the theory still stands, for the law of population as Malthus enunciated it, shorn of its unnecessary secondary propositions, is this: *Life everywhere and always tends to exceed the warrant for it.* This stresses the differential nature of food and fecundity without contending for an exact mathematical statement of their relationship.

Yet calculations on the subject are helpful in illustrating the nature of human fecundity. "Let us," suggests Professor A. M. Carr-Saunders in his *Population Problem,* "consider a population of a million born in the same year, half of whom are males and half females. Let us suppose that they all marry, each couple before the age of twenty producing two children, half of whom are girls and half boys. For the sake of simplicity we may imagine that at the end of each twenty-year period the parents die simultaneously with the birth of their offspring. Then, if the children marry and produce offspring as did their parents, we shall have a standard population of 1,000,000 which will neither increase nor decrease so long as these conditions are fulfilled. If, however, the average number of children is two and one-half per couple, then in 100 years the population will be 3,000,000; if three, 7,954,000; if four, 32,000,000; if five, 97,650,000." These figures of Carr-Saunders' very simply illustrate how the Malthusian doctrine is based upon the enormous strength of human increase which is operative at all times, in all places, and under all conditions. There is no escaping it. Neither capitalism, fascism, democracy or communism can set it aside. This alone is the fundamental doctrine of Malthus, inescapable, irrepressible, incontestable. Those dreary and fruitless discussions that have raged over the inconsequentials of his theory are nothing more than a meaningless jousting with windmills.

Nor did Charles Darwin, the supreme theorist of biology, mistake this essential feature. Shortly after he had returned from the voyage of the *Beagle* he chanced to read the *Essay.* Its basic principle struck him with such overpowering force that it alone supplied him with the key to his own theory of natural selection. Malthus is the only thinker to whom Darwin was directly indebted. And this debt he acknowledges in the well-known passage in the *Autobiography:* "In October, 1838, that is, fifteen months after I had begun my systematic enquiry, I happened to read for amusement *Malthus on Population,* and being well prepared to appreciate the struggle for existence which everywhere goes on from long-continued observation of the habits of animals and plants, it at once struck me that under these circumstances favorable variations would tend to be preserved, and unfavorable ones to be destroyed. The result of this would be the formation of a new species. Here then I had at last got hold of a theory by which to work."

Independently of Darwin, Alfred Russel Wallace saw exactly the same thing. Wallace, the magnanimous colleague, was resting between fits of fever at Ternate in the Malay Archipelago. Something brought to his recollection the work of Malthus which he had read twelve years before. "I thought of his clear exposition of 'the positive checks to increase'—disease, accidents, war, and famine—which keep down the population of savage races to so much lower an average than that of more civilized peoples. It then occurred to me that these causes or their equivalents are continually acting in the case of animals also; and as animals usually breed much more rapidly than does mankind, the destruction every year from these causes must be enormous in order to keep down the number of each species."

Both Darwin and Wallace followed the clue which Malthus gave them. Both saw that every species gives rise to many more descendants than ever attain to maturity, and that, therefore, the greater number of all plants and animals perish without reproducing. Those that survive in the struggle of nature carry on; hence they are selected. This spells natural selection.

Having profoundly influenced two great theorists, Malthus was yet to influence another who, like Darwin and Wallace, saw clearly the basic principle of the *Essay* and was led by it, independently, from a social problem to a biological generalization. This thinker was Herbert Spencer (1820-1903) of whom Huxley once said that his (Spencer's) idea of a great tragedy was a beautiful theory killed by an ugly fact. In 1852 Spencer wrote an important essay entitled

A Theory of Population Deduced from the General Law of Animal Fertility. It was Malthus' influence that suggested to Spencer the idea that the struggle for existence leads to a survival of the fittest. Spencer himself coined these historic phrases. That is how the Malthusian theory became the interpretive formula of the doctrine of evolution.

10

Having established the thesis that the tendency of human beings is to increase beyond the available food supply, Malthus next investigated the "checks" that everywhere restrict population growth. In the first edition of the *Essay* the checks are very simply stated: whatever tends to produce a smaller number of births is a preventive check; whatever leads to a greater number of deaths is a positive check. Plagues, famine, war, infanticide are definitely the larger positive checks. The fear of falling into poverty causes untold thousands of young people to postpone marriage until they can safely provide—this is a typical preventive check. In other words, the positive checks are death-producing; the preventive checks are birth-limiting. "To these two great checks to population, in all long-occupied countries, which I have called the preventive and the positive checks, may be added vicious customs with respect to women, great cities, unwholesome manufactures, luxury, pestilence, and war. All these checks may be fairly resolved into misery and vice. And that these are the true causes of the slow increase of population in all the states of Modern Europe, will appear sufficiently evident from the comparatively rapid increase that has invariably taken place, whenever these causes have been in any considerable degree removed."

The ultimate check to population is, of course, the food supply. This Malthus showed to be basic. It arises from the different ratios according to which population and food increase. The severe pressure of human mouths on the means of subsistence gives rise to all sorts of situations which operate ceaselessly and cruelly to keep down the number to the level of the supply. Without depopulation forces acting very sharply, every country would be subject to periodical plagues and famine.

With each successive edition the *Essay* was amplified. By the time the reader arrives at the sixth edition, he finds that the discussion of the checks to population has swollen into a torrent of two hundred and fifty-three pages. With incredible assiduity Malthus had examined the statistics of European countries and their colonies, in an endeavor to throw the maximum illumination upon the dark complexities of this problem. For this reason he kept on pouring an enormous amount of research, both historical and statistical, into his various editions. He considered the populations of India, China, Arabia, Japan, as well as those of Europe, in both the medieval and modern ages. In Africa, he saw the checks to population to be chiefly of the positive kind: incessant warfare, epidemics, famine and a high percentage of accidents. The struggle for food among the Negro tribes was so great that longevity was rare. After discussing the checks to population in Northern and Southern Siberia he passes on to consider the peoples of Persia and the Turkish dominions, then to Hindustan and Tibet. America, Europe, Asia, Africa, Australia—all come under his observation. The subject intoxicated him for a lifetime.

To supplement the checks to population arising out of misery and vice Malthus, in later editions, recommended "moral restraint." By moral restraint he meant postponement of marriage, and this, he said, if it did not lead directly to vice, was "undoubtedly the least evil that can arise from the principle of population." Malthus did not advocate birth control by contraceptives. By moral restraint he meant "a restraint from marriage, from prudential motives, with a conduct strictly moral during the period of restraint." He was opposed to the limitation of offspring once marriage has been contracted. Particularly did he denounce all methods applied by human effort for the mitigation of the evil of overpopulation. "Promiscuous intercourse, unnatural passions, violations of the marriage bed, and improper arts to conceal the consequences of irregular connections, are preventive checks that clearly come under the head of vice." Malthus advocated late marriage and strict continence until marriage as the best solution. He advocated nothing more than that.

Others, however, more daring than he (who likewise saw and assented to the basic principle of his *Essay*), advocated early marriage and instruction in the use of contraceptives. They called themselves Neo-Malthusians. Unlike Malthus, they preached the technique and practice of birth control which the reverend professor strongly repudiated. The founder and leader of this unorthodox movement was Francis Place (1771-1854), social reformer and theorist, whose significant international contribution, until very recently, remained in unmerited obscurity.

Place rejected the Malthusian remedy of moral restraint—that is, a long-delayed marriage with strict continence. He rejected the Malthusian barrier between single and married life which carried with it the idea that once people were wedded they should be left to propagate up to the physiological limit of their ability by the whimsical operation of the "laws" governing the consequences of their own acts. But the essential Malthusian doctrine that population has a capacity for increasing faster than subsistence was, for Place, a cardinal and indisputable proposition. "My attention was called to the principle of population," wrote Place, "soon after Mr. Malthus published the first edition of his *Essay* and I have ever since been a careful observer of and a diligent inquirer into the habits and circumstances of the working people, and especially in regard to the consequences of population amongst them."

11

Of all people in England at that time, how did it happen that Francis Place—a journeyman tailor—was able to see so clearly and courageously what others missed? The story of his life is an incredible record of a self-taught workingman.

Brought up practically in the gutters of London, Francis Place was the son of a drunkard and gambler who was a bailiff and keeper of a "sponging house" (private debtor's prison) in Vinegar Yard near Drury Lane. Left early to shift for himself, the boy was batted about among the low companions of the streets until, at the age of fourteen, he secured his first job as an assistant to a wretched and disreputable tailor. This marks the beginning of his great career, for the opportunity was now given him to learn the trade of a leather-breeches maker. In this business, after years of hard struggle, he was eventually to become one of the most successful tailors of the British metropolis with sufficient means to retire and devote himself exclusively to the lofty purposes of social reform.

In 1791, at the age of nineteen, Place married an unusual girl, Elizabeth Chadd. She too was of the very poor working-class, but she was possessed of a fine mind and a strong character with a determination to help her husband get on in the world. She proved the great moral influence of his life "and lifted him, smirched but not deeply stained, from the mire of his past surroundings."

The marriage that began so hopefully suffered a severe strain within two years. A strike forced the young husband out of work and left him and his wife and child on the verge of starvation for eight months. Those long cruel weeks of acute suffering brought young Place into close grips with misery, and the memory of its horror was never erased from his mind. Save for an insatiable desire to improve himself those months of unemployment would have demoralized him. But the encouragement of his wife and his own intense resolution for knowledge led Place to fill all these unhappy days with study. He read widely and deeply, but more especially did he concentrate on mathematics, law, history and philosophy.

Following his return to work, Place became secretary and organizer to several trade clubs; he frequently drew up their articles or rules, and spent much time attending meetings and delivering notices. This active participation in the stern struggle of the working-class stimulated the urge, greater now than ever, to read, to study, and to learn. He was troubled at this time by religious questions which were resolved by his mastery of Hume's *Essays* and Paine's *Age of Reason*. It was of course the era of the French Revolution, and no young man living in so great a metropolis as London and suffering as he had suffered, could avoid being influenced by the stirring humanitarian messages that flamed out of that social upheaval. Accordingly, he joined in June, 1794, the famous London Corresponding Society, whose originator and secretary, Thomas Hardy, had been arrested on a charge of high treason. The Society was a mildly proletarian organization, English working-class supporters of the ideas of the French Revolution. Its intentions were far from radical. Universal suffrage, annual parliaments, payment of members were some of the major reforms it advocated. The chief object of the Society was to enable working-class organizations to communicate with each other. "In this Society," wrote Place, "I met with many inquisitive, clever, upright men, and among them I greatly enlarged my acquaintance. They were in most, if not in all, respects superior to any with whom I had hitherto been acquainted. We had book subscriptions. . . . We had Sunday evening parties at the residences of those who could accommodate a number of persons. At these meetings we had readings, conversations, and discussions. There were at this time a great many such parties; they were highly useful and agreeable."

It was in 1795, while Place was chairman of the Corresponding Society, that he determined to go into business for himself. He felt that he had by now sufficient courage, sufficient experience, to alter his career from a journeyman to a master tradesman. A long period of suffering and privation gradually yielded to his indomitable spirit and prodigious industry. It is characteristic of Place that while he was passing through innumerable vicissitudes on his road to success, he spent several evenings of each week in study. He had determined to learn French in a well-thought-out plan to know Helvetius, Voltaire, Rousseau and other French thinkers at first hand. This knowledge of French helped form his social and political philosophy and proved to be immensely valuable in his business.

His first tailor shop at 29 Charing Cross was followed by a larger and more conspicuous store at Number 16 exactly two years later. "I put in a new front as elegant as the place would permit. Each of the panes of glass in the shop front cost me three pounds, and two in the door four pounds each. . . . Such shop fronts were then uncommon; I think mine were the largest plate glass windows in London, if indeed they were not the first." The alert modern businessman who understands something about the psychology of a store front can appreciate how far Place had advanced beyond his time.

In a room behind his prosperous shop, Place accumulated a library which became his retreat from the demands of business. In this sanctum he consulted his books, and into its privacy he admitted notable men, members of Parliament, and authors, among whom were William Godwin and Robert Owen, the father of British socialism.

After acquiring a sufficient competence, Place retired from business. He turned over the shop and its affairs to his oldest son. Now in his forty-sixth year, in the prime of his mental powers, relieved from economic pressure, Place boldly faced the new possibilities of his life. His labors, both theoretical and practical, which he himself initiated, alone and unaided in the face of relentless opposition, have commended themselves to posterity. The reward of his patient observation and persistent inquiry is that he has become one of the great benefactors of the human race.

12

The reforms that Place championed, until he died at the age of eighty-two, are legion: the education of workers, trade unionism, freedom of the press, penny postage, abolition of the Corn Laws and other notable endeavors. He drafted the People's Charter of 1838, prepared for publication Robert Owen's *Essays on the Foundation of Character* and Bentham's *Not Paul, but Jesus;* assisted Roebuck in editing the *Pamphlets for the People,* and directed the publication in cheap form of James Mills' *Essays.* Most important of all, he wrote that remarkable book to advocate birth control. It appeared in 1822 under the title *Illustrations and Proofs of the Principle of Population; including an examination of the proposed remedies of Mr. Malthus and a reply to the objections of Mr. Godwin and others.*

Place was deeply versed in the economic, political and social views of his day, and his book shows it. As it was an age which saw great recasting of men's beliefs and practices, the erstwhile tailor of Charing Cross was singularly prepared to render the molding process distinguished service. What seemed to him basic to all social reform was some effort at birth control. Population in England, he believed, was already too large for the welfare of the country, a heavy burden on the working-classes. Something had to be done about it. Here then was a particular work awaiting an intelligent crusader. And here was the man who did not shrink from it.

Malthus had expressed the hope that late marriages would be the solution to the problem. By practicing "moral restraint" people would wed in their late thirties rather than in their early twenties. Francis Place saw the problem far more realistically. He was convinced that the delay of marriage, even if it were possible, would be harmful and that the biologic urge was too strong and essential to life to be held in check by any such dream as "moral restraint." Certainly it was idle to expect that the working-classes would accept it or, even if they did, act upon it. Malthus' remedy was im-practicable and would never be adopted. "His [Place's] own early marriage," observes one of his biographers, "had been his salvation. He had failed to live decently in celibacy even to the age of nineteen; and, for the man of the laboring-class who awaited assured means of supporting a family before taking a wife, the horror of this youthful experience foretold to him hopeless immorality. But experience *no less* emphatically warned him that early marriage meant many children. He himself, it is recorded, was the father of fifteen [born between 1792 and 1817], of whom five died in childhood."

The epoch-making paragraphs of Place's book begin at the top of Page 173. Unequivocally he argues for birth control (contraception) as the best means of preventing the numbers of mankind from increasing faster than food is provided. His distinctive contribution is the high moral advocacy of the employment of contraceptive measures for reasonable and ethically defensible purposes. Within six and a half pages (pp. 173-179) he elaborates his theory which has resulted in one of the most profoundly significant movements of the modern world.

What did Place think of Godwin? For the most part he considered Godwin's ideas occult, based upon rhetoric and optimism instead of reasoned evidence. To expect human fecundity to "wear out," subsistence to be made to increase faster than population, man to become immortal *—all this was too much for Place to accept. A large part of *Illustrations and Proofs* is therefore given over to a thoroughgoing refutation of Godwin. When the reader finishes reading Place's complete demolition of Godwin's views he feels that the author of *Political Justice,* like Icarus, has fallen to his death because, though his wings were willing, the wax was weak.

The immediate influence of Place's book was not great; its appearance attracted little attention. But the pronouncement of the theory, so clear in Place's mind, galvanized him into fearless activity. Having written his theory into a book, it ceased to be for him a mere intellectual speculation. In his hands it became at once a powerful tool for social reform. Accordingly, Place set for himself

* That is, to argue that human life would eventually be prolonged indefinitely.

the task of public enlightenment. He organized a campaign to spread the doctrine of birth control and the use of contraceptives. "The author is perfectly aware that he has exhibited views and proposed remedies which will with some persons expose him to censure; but he is also aware of the utility of thus exposing himself."

A year after the appearance of *Illustrations and Proofs*, Place drafted and printed three dignified handbills addressed respectively: (1) *To the Married of Both Sexes*, (2) *To the Married of Both Sexes of the Working People*, (3) *To the Married of Both Sexes in Genteel Life*. They were anonymous documents and were circulated widely through various channels. Place, who knew more about the morals of the English working-classes than perhaps any other person in the kingdom, took a realistic view of the situation. Birth control could not possibly make matters worse, because little chastity existed anywhere, promiscuity, both premarital and postmarital being very general. Malthus' advocacy of deferred marriage introduced a new heartlessness into society and invited a coarser immorality than previously existed. It was perilous advice. Place argued that marriage, in order not to be an extravagant indiscretion for youth, had to be established upon the safe and sane practice of contraception.

In these handbills the retired tailor crystallized the mute longings of man's desire to limit human offspring by methods at once harmless and humanitarian. Undaunted by abuse, he continued to advance the cause of birth control until his death in 1854. Every workingman whose confidence he could gain, every newspaper or magazine that would print his letters or articles, every committee that would listen to him, heard the practical message of this theory expounded. Out of his own pocket he defrayed all costs. When he died it was written that he was "valuable in council, fertile in resource, performing great labors, but he never thought of himself."

13

The spark of living fire which Place set aglow gave light to other penetrating minds. The story of the birth control movement is a history of the triumph of an idea and a record of martyrdoms within the memory of living men and women. Not only was it nec

THOMAS ROBERT MALTHUS

Engraved by Mᶜ Fournier after a painting by J. Linnell

Courtesy of The Robert Fridenberg Galleries

ssary to anounce the doctrine to an apathetic world, but its
roponents had to battle the prejudices of orthodox religion, medi-
ine, and government. Richard Carlile (1790-1843), the advocate of
ree speech who at various times in his life spent over nine years
n different jails, was among the first to espouse the cause of Place's
neory. Carlile published a daring tract entitled *Every Woman's
look* which proved enormously popular. In addition to being an
uthor, Carlile was a lecturer and his speaking tours up and down
he country spread the new gospel throughout England.

The first tract on birth control to be published in America was
he work of Robert Dale Owen (1801-1877), son of Robert Owen,
n old friend of Francis Place. The younger Owen did not like
he "style and tone" of Carlile's book, and thereupon he wrote
*Moral Physiology, or, a Brief and Plain Treatise on the Population
Question,* which appeared in New York City in December, 1830.
t was an eloquent document, justly meriting the wide circulation
: enjoyed—approximately 75,000 copies—until Owen's death.

Moral Physiology was followed in 1832 by a pamphlet called
*ruits of Philosophy, or, the private companion of young married
eople,* by Charles Knowlton (1800-1850), a western Massachusetts
hysician. Knowlton had been deeply influenced by Place's hand-
ills and felt that the medical profession ought not to be silent in so
nomentous and far-reaching a concern. Shortly after its appear-
nce Doctor Knowlton was fined at Taunton, Massachusetts, and
vas sentenced at Cambridge to three months' hard labor.

More sensational than anything that had yet happened in the
irth control movement was the prosecution of Charles Bradlaugh
nd Annie Besant in England for republishing Knowlton's pamph-
et in 1876. Bradlaugh (1833-1891), who had long been the out-
tanding champion of freedom of opinion and liberty of the press,
ndertook the printing of the Knowlton pamphlet in order to
indicate the right of free discussion. "We republish this pamphlet,"
leclared Bradlaugh in his introduction to Knowlton's *Fruits of
Philosophy,* "honestly believing that on all questions affecting the
appiness of the people, whether they be theological, political, or
ocial, fullest right of free discussion ought to be maintained at all
azards. . . . We believe, with the Reverend Mr. Malthus, that
population has a tendency to increase faster than the means of

existence, and that some checks must therefore exercise control over population. The checks now exercised are semi-starvation and preventable disease; the enormous mortality among the infants of the poor is one of the checks which now keeps down the population. The checks that ought to control population are scientific, and it is these which we advocate. We think it more moral to prevent the conception of children than, after they are born, to murder them by want of food, air, and clothing. We advocate scientific checks to population, because, so long as poor men have large families, pauperism is a necessity, and from pauperism grow crime and disease. . . . We point the way of relief and happiness; for the sake of these we publish what others fear to issue; and we do it, confident that if we fail the first time, we shall succeed at last."

Both Mr. Bradlaugh and Mrs. Besant were arrested and brought to trial. In his speech in his own defense, Bradlaugh was fully aware that he was running the gauntlet of fierce and unbending hostility; "I ask you, then, to consider the issues which I have put to you already and which I put to you again—viz., Is overpopulation the cause of poverty? Is overpopulation the cause of misery? Is over-population the cause of crime? Is overpopulation the cause of disease? Is it moral or immoral to check poverty, ignorance, vice, crime, and disease? I can only think you will give one answer, that it is moral to check these evils. You may say: Try to restrain them, like Malthus, by late marriage. Aye, but even to get late marriage you must teach poor men and women to comprehend the need for it, and, even then, if you get real celibacy, Acton and others will tell you what horrible diseases are the outcome of this state of things. Really, you never can get even celibacy. You know what takes place in London and Paris. I have passed through Naples and Rome, and I have been shocked at being stopped by lads at night. In Florence, in Berlin, in Paris, you all know what arises from this pretense of celibacy. Even in our own large centers of population, such as Dublin, Edinburgh, and Glasgow, you know what this false pretense of celibacy means. Take the case of Birmingham as an illustration. Walk through the streets of that city between nine and eleven in the evening, and as the gaslight shows the flaunting shame, tell me whether celibacy is a reality or a sham. Tell me whether or not that terrible word 'prostitution,' written

:verywhere in letters of festering curse, is not a disfiguring scar
ipon the surface of society. It is said that this pamphlet tries to
defend immorality. You must contradict every page of it—ignore
·very word of it—to warrant that assumption."

The jury sentenced the defendants to six months' imprisonment
ind a fine of two hundred pounds. But on Bradlaugh's appeal to a
iigher court the indictment was quashed. Bradlaugh won the battle.
Hundreds of thousands of copies of Knowlton's pamphlet were now
sold, together with other birth control literature, including Mrs.
Besant's *Law of Population*. What had for so long a time been a
feeble movement suddenly became the vigorous world-wide possession of Anglo-Saxon civilization.

Present day accomplishments strike their roots deep in the sub-
soil of earlier efforts. What began in the mind of an unknown
tailor, struggling in the back room of a store at Charing Cross,
grew and finally emerged through this trial from darkness into the
sunlight of a modern triumph. His theory, in our age, has become
the scientific, moral, and humanitarian answer to the vast irrepressible spawning of mankind.

14

The work of Malthus and Place dealt essentially with the problem of numbers. Both agreed that, however perfect the social system
might be, unrestricted population must reduce the majority of
humanity to the frightfulness of misery and poverty. Their attention, therefore, was most naturally focused upon the quantity aspect
of population, a subject that had been discussed in piecemeal fashion
as far back as the days of Plato and Aristotle. But what of *quality?*
Does not the population problem involve both considerations?

Owing to the work of Darwin and Wallace, both of whom acknowledged their debt to Malthus, the problems of man soon began
to be viewed from a biological angle. It fell to Francis Galton
(1822-1911), a cousin of Charles Darwin, to see clearly the full
significance of the qualitative side of population and to undertake
a scientific investigation of the factors that would lead to its improvement. "I always think of you," wrote Galton in a letter to
Darwin dated December 24, 1869, "in the same way as converts
from barbarism think of the teacher who first relieved them from

the intolerable burden of their superstition. . . . Consequently the appearance of your *Origin of Species* formed a real crisis in my life; your book drove away the constraint of my old superstition as if it had been a nightmare, and was the first to give me freedom of thought." Galton saw that, just as animals breed, man breeds; and the laws of selection that lead to an improvement of, say, a flock of sheep or a herd of cattle are basically the same laws that must be called upon to produce a better quality of human beings. Man can elevate man.

The Darwinian impulse flowered in Galton's mind, after long years of exceptional and original work, into the science of eugenics which is built upon the theory that human reproduction can be controlled in order to benefit the race. Galton himself coined the term eugenics from a Greek word meaning *wellborn*. He employed it for the first time in 1883 in his book *Inquiries into the Human Faculty*. In this book he showed on biological grounds (heredity) that Godwin's no-restraint thesis was untenable. All views of the social visionaries that stressed with incorrigible optimism mankind's improvement by environmental changes, Galton called theories of "nurture." While nurture is important, and Galton did not in the least underestimate it, he saw that *Nature* was infinitely greater. Environment is only a part of the story of man. By far the more important part is heredity. It is not enough to improve the outside of man; efforts must be made to improve what is going on inside of him. The population problem, rightly considered, therefore embraces two necessary procedures which must develop together— environment and heredity. The theory that Galton worked out and the program of eugenics which he projected rest upon the facts of heredity. "Eugenics," declared Galton, "is the science which deals with all influences that improve the inborn qualities of a race; also with those that develop them to the utmost advantage."

All theories have their share of cranks and extremists. Galton foresaw that eugenics would have its quota; for this reason he warned against haste and lack of restraint. He knew that he was a pioneer in a campaign that would have to be laid out over long decades. To discover the best human strains and perpetuate them is the task which makes eugenics "the science of rearing human thoroughbreds." Stern compulsion, he declared, ought to be exer-

cised to prevent the free and easy propagation of those who are
seriously afflicted by lunacy, feeble-mindedness, habitual criminality
and pauperism.

Since the turn of the century, the science which Francis Galton
initiated and christened has brought to the conscience of mankind
the need to *civilize* the reproductive instinct so that, in the interest
of better human beings, there should be birth *release* as well as
birth control. Not indiscriminately more children, but certainly
more children from the best stocks and fewer from the worst.

15

Long before the death of Galton in 1911, it was felt by many
people that the tremendous growth of modern industry, with its
world transportation, immigration, and general technological advances, had invalidated the Malthusian doctrine, and that consequently the theory of overpopulation was nothing more than a
scare. It is true that Malthus did not live to see the new era ushered
in, bringing a season of prosperity and plenty which seemed to
belie his gloomy forebodings. However, within a hundred years
after his death the population of the world has actually doubled.
How did this immense increase come about? The answer is not
far to seek. The industrial changes that transformed the age of
Malthus into our own (the Industrial Revolution) gave a tremendous impetus to population growth, simply because machinery
applied to agriculture resulted in greater cultivation of old lands
and in the development of new and distant virgin soils. World
population, consequently, spurted ahead at an enormous rate until
mankind in our day again confronts the Malthus doctrine with
a situation unique in history: there are practically no more virgin
soils to conquer.

What is to be done? Modern theorists take divergent points of
view. The optimum size of a population is a highly controversial
topic which demands many more years of investigation and research
before anything like a truly scientific opinion may be ventured.
Population studies, in other words, are just in their infancy. Yet the
unmistakable tendency in all advanced democratic countries is
to pursue a policy of restriction of growth based upon the Mal-

N

thusian belief that life will be more desirable if numbers are limited in accordance with the *available* means of support.

Malthus pointed out a very interesting difference between human increase and food increase; human fecundity is enormous because it involves a pleasurable experience whereas the acquisition of food is based on irksome labor. Contraception alone enables man to adjust this important difference.

Apparently no population policy can be comprehensive that does not take into account Malthus' warning, Place's suggestion, and Galton's insistence. It seems therefore that the scientific approach to mankind must be woven of these three considerations, remembering, of course, that the economic structure which underpins any given society determines the optimum—that is, how many human beings can live in comfort upon the available means of supply.

8. Schwann . . THEORY OF THE CELL

THE majesty of modern science owes much to the telescope and the microscope, two instruments whose histories are closely interconnected. It is certain that without the microscope the theory of the cell could never have been formulated.

Moreover with each succeeding improvement of the lens the focus of human curiosity sharpened into impressive new knowledge.

2

The use of a lens for magnifying purposes goes back to antiquity. For this reason no historian can say who first conceived the idea of an instrument for magnification. Simple "magnifiers" such as burning glasses, spectacles, and other lenses were in constant use during medieval days. Somewhere between 1590 and 1609 a Dutch optician, Zacharias Janssen, placed a concave and convex lens at the ends of a tube and produced a crude microscope, prophetic of an unseen world. The same principle of compound lenses was used by another Dutch scientist, Johannes Lippershey, to magnify objects at a distance. The idea of combining lenses so as to add new dimensions to the human eye reached Galileo in Italy, as we have seen. His success with the telescope established the Copernican theory. Then came the invention, about 1639, of the micrometer which enabled an observer to adjust a telescope with excellent precision. Soon other developments followed until the telescope brought the heavens of the mythical gods down to earth.

Unfortunately, the microscope failed to match these spectacular strides, although the early advances in the history of both instruments are interrelated. For a long time the microscope was held back by a serious difficulty known as the chromatic aberration of the lenses which Isaac Newton declared insoluble. The story of the cell theory follows the growth of the mechanical perfection of the microscope. All those early speculations and discoveries, which belong to the pre-Schwann period, were made possible by such crude developments of the microscope as were then available. The second period, however, followed immediately upon the solution of the problem that Newton had seriously believed would forever block the hopes of the pioneers. The way out was discovered by a Swedish scientist, Samuel Klingenstierna (1698-1765), professor of physics at Upsala, who succeeded in showing how achromatic glass should be made. Opticians in Holland, Paris and London began at once to follow Klingenstierna. The microscope which had long been an imperfect instrument suddenly gave new impetus to research. Besides Klingenstierna, there was Dolland in England, Chevalier in France, Amici in Italy who made the new world of improved microscopical visibility the heritage of man.

3

Limited as they were by the imperfections of the microscope, the scientists who were first privileged to look through it produced results that have become a part of the permanent fabric of knowledge. However faulty, their pioneer observations are of tremendous historical interest. Revealing the hitherto unseen world of minute organisms and cells is the pre-eminent achievement of Hooke, Grew, Malpighi, and Leeuwenhoek. Their inquisitive eyes saw nature more scientifically than any of their predecessors, and their rapturous endeavors led to the formulation of one of the most profound generalizations of knowledge—the universal cellular organization of living matter.

The history of a theory is the theory itself. For this reason the wonder world of the cell begins with the adventure of that ingenious and accomplished Englishman, Robert Hooke (1635-1703), who was the first man to discover the cellular structure of living things. A man of prodigious industry, Hooke among other things was interested in lenses. He was eager to show how much more the human eye could see when aided by glasses. With delight he turned them upon everything within his reach. He looked at raindrops, insects, snowflakes, feathers, scales of a moth's wings—and one day upon finely cut sections of cork. To his amazement he found cork to be composed of tiny boxlike compartments which he likened to a honeycomb. He called these compartments "cells" after the Latin word *cella*, which means a small room. In 1665 he published his *Micrographia*—the first book devoted exclusively to microscopical observations. Aside from its unique assemblage of facts, the *Micrographia* is illustrated by drawings memorable for their beauty and accuracy. Perhaps they are, as experts now believe, the work of Sir Christopher Wren. But their unmistakable inspiration is the encyclopaedic Robert Hooke.

The incidental observations on the cellular structure of cork and other vegetable products which Hooke gave to the world in his heterogeneous collection stimulated a fellow Englishman, Nehemiah Grew (1641-1712), to carry on an extensive search into the microscopic structure of plants. Grew's first publication on the subject, *The Anatomy of Vegetables Begun*, appeared in 1671. Ten years later came his revised observations in four books with two hundred and twelve folio pages, eighty-two plates and five hundred and thirty-eight figures! A massive study executed by a man of large and rugged competency.*

The desultory character of Hooke's observations and the lack of connection between the topics he discussed prevented the *Micrographia* from attaining high scientific value. But with Nehemiah Grew it was different. As a scientist Grew concentrated with almost religious zeal upon vegetable anatomy. Organ by organ he describes his plants with a fascinating wealth of detail, suggesting the sexual character of flowers: that the pistil corresponds to the female, and the stamen with its pollen to the male. While Grew was more concerned with the vessels and fibers of plants than with the cells, he was well aware that the tissues of plants are spongelike in character, or, as we should now say "cellular." He frequently spoke of the cells of plants as "bladders" and seemed to recognize that they play an important part in nutrition. But he did not understand their origin, their composition, the nature of their growth or their complex function.

Closely paralleling the work of Grew was the microscopical research of a contemporary Italian, that lovable doctor, Marcello Malpighi (1628-1694), professor at the University of Bologna and

* While in the waters of Epsom, Grew discovered magnesium sulphate—Epsom Salts.

private physician to Pope Innocent XII. The high ideals of this saintly scientist and his devotion to the pursuit of truth lift his memory out of the melancholy dust of three centuries. Many of his discoveries bear directly upon anatomy and physiology. He was, for example, the first scientist to demonstrate the structure of the lungs and to indicate the nature of the papillae on the tongue. Medical men to this day still connect his name with the Malpighian corpuscles of the spleen and the Malpighian pyramid of the kidney. As a pioneer worker with the microscope, and more especially as a trail-blazer in the world of scientific theory, the acute Malpighi engages our attention; for he possessed greater genius, a higher fertility of ideas, and a much more penetrative insight than Nehemiah Grew. Like Grew, he too discerned the sexuality of plants and was one of the first to give an account of the development of the seed and embryo. Aside from Malpighi's studies on animal tissues, science is indebted to him for extensive work on anatomy of plants which he submitted to the Royal Society of London.

The writings of Grew appeared almost simultaneously with the work of Malpighi. Curiously enough, on the very day (December 7, 1671) that the Royal Society received in print Grew's first essay, the Secretary reported having received from Italy Malpighi's manuscript dealing with the same subject. The case of Grew and Malpighi bears a remarkable similarity to that of Charles Darwin and Alfred Russel Wallace, whose work on evolution arrived by mail from Ternate in the Malay Archipelago just as Darwin was almost to announce his discoveries. Grew, in his complete work, refers to Malpighi and tells how the manuscript of the Italian doctor was received by the Royal Society on the same day that his own contribution was published. The English botanist, conscious of the fraternity of science, voluntarily abandoned in Malpighi's favor any claim to priority. Matching this expression of magnanimity, Malpighi undertook a Latin translation of Grew's writings.

The sketches illustrating the microscopic observations of Malpighi and Grew were not more important than those of the Dutch investigator, Antonj Van Leeuwenhoek (1632-1723), the man who made the first studies in bacteriology. Leeuwenhoek was famous for having the largest collection of magnifying glasses in the world, most of which he had made with his own hands. He is the third member of that group of intense men, all belonging to the seventeenth century—one working in England, the other in Italy, and the third in Holland—who first described the cellular construction of plants with the crude microscopes at their disposal. Leeuwenhoek called the cells "globules," just as Grew had called them "bladders" and Malpighi had dubbed them "utricles."

Aside from the extraordinarily faithful representations of their drawings, these pioneers did not understand or even remotely guess that the cell is the uniform architectural element of all plant and animal life. Consequently, lacking this comprehension, they had no theory. Nevertheless their pre-vision reached ahead to foreshadow generalizations that were not established in biology until a century and a half after their labors. To these infinitely curious men belongs the distinction of laying strong foundations in science by breaking away from the thralldom of mere book learning. Time has shaken many of their opinions and loosened their speculations, but they relied upon their own eyes when most thinkers were still blinded by medieval dogmas.

4

A century after the labors of Grew, Malpighi, and Leeuwenhoek the world of biological discussion was ringing with a lively interest in the theoretical side of the youthful science. The air of intellectual Europe was full of theories; scientists were now eager to establish relationships between that huge mass of new facts made available by the advent of the microscope. The high purpose of theory is to help the human intellect clear its vision, for men too often look at nature through the very badly ground lenses of their preconceived opinions, their dogmas or prejudices.

Consider, just for illustration, the fanciful fiber theory of the pompous but gifted eclectic Swiss doctor, Albrecht von Haller (1708-1777), whom his unsympathetic critics called "that abyss of learning." It is a fine example of the statement that the path of science is strewn with the bleached bones of dead theories. Haller's doctrine declared that all tissues are reducible to fibers as their ultimate constituents, the fibers being cemented together by "organized concrete."

Half overshadowing Haller's doctrine was the globular theory

espoused by a number of men, including Henri Milne-Edwards
(1800-1885), a Belgian scientist of English ancestry. Fibers, Milne-
Edwards supposed, were made up of globules ranged in lines. All
tissues, whether in the embryo or later, he regarded as based upon
these elementary structures. Unfortunately for the globular theory,
there was so much confusion as to the use of terms and words
(globule, granule, molecule) that no systematic statement could be
made. Very frequently the word *globule* was used to indicate what
is now clearly recognized as the cell. Essentially, however, the Milne-
Edwards doctrine considered a cell to be produced by globules,
which, of course, was an erroneous assumption. A cell, we now
know, is never produced by anything other than another cell.
Where a cell arises, there a cell must have previously existed.

5

In the days of Haller men were also arguing the merits of the
preformation theory, loudly championed by the Geneva scientist
Charles Bonnet (1720-1793), which was foolishly believed superior
to the theory of generation propounded by the youthful Kaspar
Friedrich Wolff.

With the notable exception of Wolff's doctrine (which won the
admiration of Thomas Huxley in the nineteenth century) these
defunct biological theories possess only an antiquarian interest.
However, they show that the knowledge of the cell made slow but
steady progress, the botanists rather than the zoologists leading the
way. Still, no one had a theory about the cell, nor had its character
been closely determined.

No one but Kaspar Friedrich Wolff.

Recalling the story of Doctor Robert Mayer of Heilbronn, we
remember how John Tyndall in a lecture given in London brought
to the attention of the world the gross injustice done to the man
who conceived the entire sweep of the doctrine of the conservation
of energy. What Tyndall accomplished for Mayer, Huxley achieved
for Wolff. Only Wolff was long dead when Huxley published in
1853 an article entitled *The Cell Theory* in the *British and Foreign
Medico-Chirurgical Review,* which lifted the forgotten German scientist out of a frozen Russian grave into the light of world acclaim.

Born in Berlin in 1733, the son of a poor tailor, Wolff became a doctor first by attending the Medico-Surgical College of his native city and then by obtaining his degree from the University of Halle. There in 1759, at the age of twenty-six, he presented his doctor's thesis entitled *Theoria Generationis* (Theory of Generation). A copy was sent to Haller for review.

All that Haller and his eminent colleagues in medicine, anatomy, and biology stood for, this book denied. In it young Wolff demolished the doctrine of preformation—the belief that various forms of animal life existed in miniature in the egg, and that the process of development merely consisted of the unfoldment of the preformed embryo. An analogy to flower-buds was commonly used by the upholders of preformation to illustrate their doctrine. Just as in a small bud all the parts of the flower are already present, so in the animal egg, including the human, all generation was believed nothing more than the emergence (unfolding) of already existing parts. Haller passionately defended this view not only on scientific grounds, but he also claimed that the teachings of the Bible and revealed religion demanded that it be so. For the doctrine of preformation was essentially the dogma of *original creation,* according to which all formation of life was completed by God at the beginning of the world. The individuals of each species of animal and plants—so preformation claimed—had been created simultaneously for all time: the first female of every species contained within her all the individuals of that species (present and future) until the end of time. As for human beings, the forms of all men were contained in the ovary of Eve, placed there by the Deity. The lives of all unborn generations were pictured enclosed in the body of the First Mother in a series of incapsulated embryos (*emboîtement*), like Chinese boxes one within the other. It was estimated that, inasmuch as each female had necessarily one less egg, the original supply given to Eve would last only 200,000,000 generations. After that the race would be extinct.

What led Wolff to reject preformation? How did he know it was not the truth?

Wolff had been using the microscope and actually saw and distinguished cells in both plants and animals. He could find no trace of incapsulated embryos as Bonnet and Haller imagined. He saw only cells with not a sign of preformed organs. Cells, Wolff understood, assimilated food, grew, multiplied, and thus gradually bit by bit, cell by cell, produced the various tissues and organs of animal and plant life. Wolff's views were called epigenesis. To Wolff epigenesis was not simply an account of the early life history (embryology) of the individual, but a record of the annals of its race. That is why he called his book *Theory of Generation*.

In a world reeking with the dogmas of medieval past, it was comparatively easy for Haller to block the advanced teachings of this young doctor. The authority of the Swiss scientist exercised a paralyzing censorship over Wolff's ideas. It has been well said that an opinion is held with a violence inversely proportional to the amount of evidence which can be adduced in its support. What finally added to the young man's complete defeat was the impressive philosophical support given to the preformation doctrine by Leibnitz.

It took no small courage for so young and uninfluential a scientist to stand against the combined authority of Bonnet, Haller and Leibnitz. Wolff's opinions excited the most energetic opposition. One would like to think that in science there could be no blind adherence to previous conclusions. Unfortunately it is all too common. Not only did his opponents accuse him of irreligion, but they almost completely ruined his chances for a livelihood.

Despite his obscurity, Wolff was right and the opposition egregiously wrong. Not preformation but epigenesis approximates the truth. This is the doctrine that Wolff's book was the first to bring forth. It stresses as a fundamental procedure in all organic life, plants and animals alike, epigenetic growth—that is, a development in which something appears which was not there before even in rudiment. Or, to put the same thought in more exact language, the fertilized egg gives rise to the embryo little by little by the progressive production of new parts previously nonexistent as such. Having launched his work in an uncongenial atmosphere, Wolff was finally forced to leave Berlin. Ugly hostility prevented him from securing even as much as a small secondary post in any German university. Disheartened at such antagonism, he finally accepted an offer from Catherine the Great who invited him to live in St. Petersburg and become a member of the Russian Academy of

Sciences. Wolff left Germany never to return. He died in 1794 at the age of sixty-one, a mind sealed up in loneliness.

It was unfortunate both for the career of Wolff and the growth of science that his ideas met with such sharp opposition. Had it been otherwise, Wolff's teachings would have formed a valuable link in the actual development of the cell theory. His theory of epigenesis and his knowledge of the cell had to be rediscovered at a later date by other investigators. The penetrative genius that had enabled Wolff to attain so high a degree of clearness was lost. Science had to wait until the unwarranted exaggerations of Bonnet, Haller and Leibnitz, based upon an incomplete perception, died out before the threads of progress, which Wolff had so carefully held in his hands, could again be taken up and woven into the pattern of truth.

6

The predecessors of Theodor Schwann (1810-1882) helped to make the time ripe.

It is true that in the early decades of the nineteenth century the cell had come to be quite universally recognized as a constantly recurring element in vegetable and animal tissues. Biologists everywhere were groping after some unity underlying the varied phenomena of organic life. Nor was imagination wanting to furnish an interminable series of speculations. At last came a sharp moment, a profound comprehension that brought into focus all the preparatory knowledge that went before. This occurred in the mind of Theodor Schwann. Out of the meshes of faulty generalizations he disentangled the theory of the cell.

Schwann was born in Neuss, a little German town not far from Cologne, the fourth child of a family of thirteen children. The boy was practically brought up in his father's book store—a small shop but a happy place for a boy who loved the quiet calm of a library. Until the day of his death he kept the gentle and reserved disposition that he had shown in Neuss, avoiding the bitter academic controversies that made life unpleasant for his colleagues. After studying in a Jesuit school at Cologne he passed to the University of Bonn, where his thoughts were centered on the priesthood, until he met the anatomist Johannes Müller—a powerful personality sometimes compared to Haller but much greater as a teacher.

Müller (1801-1858) at that time was experimenting with the spinal nerves of frogs, and when he said to his pupil, "Herr Schwann, you may cut the anterior root," the youth's destiny was determined.

After two years spent in medicine at Würzburg, another great Catholic university of southern Germany, Schwann matriculated at Berlin. He was again attracted by Johannes Müller who had been invited to leave Bonn and accept a more distinguished chair in the Prussian capital. Immediately upon his graduation Schwann became Müller's laboratory assistant.

The assistant's job was an opportunity, but the salary was miserably small, less than ten dollars per month. Salary or no salary, Schwann was determined to forge ahead; the association with Müller was in itself sufficient compensation, for Müller's will-power spurred his easygoing and peaceful nature. Under the stimulus of the master the pupil grew. Possessed of a resourceful investigative spirit the youthful scientist from Neuss became the true experimentalist, the genuine man of research. His dissertation for the doctor's degree dealt with the respiration of the embryo of the chick. Long ago Malpighi had worked with the chick as a splendid research object, and now Schwann was carrying on the tradition. Experiment is a potent instrument to direct ambitions and exercise the reasoning powers. When it becomes the medium for a superior intelligence and an active and lofty mind, things are bound to happen. And they did in this case. Schwann began his excursions into a wonderland more strange than Alice had discovered. Only with this difference: the wonderland of Alice wasn't real.

A description of Schwann in these early Berlin days by one of his friends helps us to see and understand this serene student of nature: "He was a man of stature below the medium, with a beardless face, an almost infantile and always smiling expression, smooth, dark brown hair, wearing a fur-trimmed dressing gown, living in a poorly lighted room on the second floor of a restaurant which was not even second class. He would pass whole days there without going out, with a few rare books around him, and numerous glass vessels, retorts, vials, and tubes, simple apparatus which he made himself. Or, I go in imagination to the dark and fusty halls of the Anatomical Institute where he used to work till nightfall by the side of our excellent chief, Johannes Müller. We took our

THEODOR SCHWANN

dinner in the evening, after the English fashion, so that we might enjoy more of the advantages of daylight."

Before he announced to the world the theory of the cell, Schwann did some elementary work on the alphabet and grammar of biology. He discovered the ferment of gastric juice to which he gave the name "pepsin." He studied bacteria and experimented with the various phenomena of fermentation, the subject that was to mean so much to Pasteur in the establishment of the germ theory. No book on Pasteur fails to mention Schwann, for Pasteur himself very generously referred to the pioneer work of his German contemporary.

Both men had much in common, Schwann being Pasteur's senior by twelve years. The great theme of all theory is the search for relations between things apparently disconnected; in the pursuit of it men of widely different backgrounds are often brought together. Both scientists were university trained, sons of poor parents, the older born in a small German town and the younger in a French hamlet. Both men were Catholic—sincere, devout, pious. In them the ideal of religion came into rich fulfillment; for they were both possessed of a humility in the unselfish service of science that is as beautiful as it is rare.

Only once did Schwann clash with the Church. It came towards the end of his career when he was heavy-laden with honors and distinctions. Had not the clergy retreated, Schwann was prepared to face the consequences of his determined stand against superstition, despite a lifetime of unquestioned loyalty to Catholicism. The incident revolved around the case of Louise Lateau, the pious daughter of a Belgian miner. Louise became seriously ill and received the last sacrament. However, she did not die but fell into an ecstasy and developed a case of stigmatization—a pathological condition due, largely, to mental unbalance. It was claimed that she had been contemplating the bruises of Jesus Christ with such fervency that the injuries of her Savior miraculously appeared on her own body—a supernatural occurrence that excited considerable attention. A committee was appointed to investigate the Lateau girl to determine whether her stigmatization was due to natural or divine causes. Professor Theodor Schwann was asked to be a member.

After careful investigation it was found that Louise Lateau's recurring bleedings from stigmata were in no way miraculous. They were due to her own efforts: she frequently rubbed and scratched with her nails those spots on her body where the blood flowed and even during her sleep she kept up a highly nervous mechanical pressure with her fingers to maintain a condition of local congestion. Schwann quickly saw that the case was no miracle, and so did the rest of the committee. But the clerical press had already spread the report that Professor Schwann believed that divine forces were being displayed. Upon the publication of the biologist's report, denying the statements that had been erroneously attributed to him, there broke out a violent attack from the supporters of the Lateau miracle. They denounced him unmercifully and poured upon him an incalculable amount of abuse. They had assumed that he, being a loyal Catholic, would concur with the age-old belief that stigmatization was an evidence of God's favor toward his saints. Had not St. Francis Assisi received Christ's wounds? And what of St. Gertrude of Ostend, Rita of Cascia,* St. Catherine of Ricci, St. Lidwina? Church history abounds in cases of sacred stigmata. Was Schwann to deny this type of supernatural manifestation? He did.

Having made his report he refused to answer his critics or respond to the harsh and vile epithets hurled at him. And so the affair ended.

7

The linking together of ideas—even simple ideas—is a very complex thing. It is not in a laboratory that problems are solved: they are solved in the scientist's head. Other men working under better conditions than Schwann failed to grasp the full-rounded significance of the cell. But when he announced to the world—"There is one universal principle of development for the elementary parts of organisms, however different, and that principle is the formation of the cells"—scientific history was made.

In the hands of one man a fact may be comparatively inert, while another scientist, by the more vigorous activity of his mind, may em-

* The crown of thorns on Rita of Cascia's forehead was simply a circle of pimples due to smallpox.

ploy the same fact to effect a powerful comprehension. When Matthias Jacob Schleiden (1804-1881), professor of botany at Jena, visited Theodor Schwann in Berlin, he spoke enthusiastically about his
work on vegetable cells, especially emphasizing the significance of
the nucleus. (This was an idea he had absorbed from the work
of an English botanist, Robert Brown, who actually discovered
the cell-nucleus in 1831.) Schleiden's after dinner conversation on
the nucleated cells of plants stimulated Schwann to a quick in-
tegration of his own immense and detailed knowledge of animal
tissues. Schwann discovered that the animal organism also consisted
of nucleated cells. The cell, therefore, seemed to him to be the
basic element common to both forms of life.

Schwann was no botanist; he was an anatomist and physiologist
working on animal tissues in Müller's laboratory in Berlin. But his
specialized knowledge did not prevent his mind running through
the vast accumulation of facts in both fields of thought. With amazing swiftness and with deep philosophic breadth he formulated the
cell theory which brought together botany and zoology under one
significant generalization: namely, the principle of structural similarity. All organisms, declared Schwann, whether they be vegetal
or animal, represent in the final analysis either single cells or
association of cells. Everywhere in the biologic world the cell is
the unit of structure and the primary agent of biological organization. Beneath the unending diversity of form and function the
cell alone is the common denominator. It is the smallest complete
unit of structure, the brick from which all living buildings are
made. This doctrine Schwann announced in his now famous book
Mikroskopische Untersunchungen (Microscopic Researches) which
he published in 1839. It was the first clear expression of the cell
theory, thereby enabling Schwann to do for biology what John
Dalton had so memorably achieved, with the atom, for chemistry.
There was no necromancy in this accomplishment of Schwann's,
no supernatural inspiration, no flight of poetic imagination. Only
logical methods of thoughts which normal individuals regularly
use, so that the truth of it could justly claim universal assent. The
cell theory became at once more than an aid to comprehension. It
was comprehension.

The Schleiden and Schwann relationship presents a striking parallel to the episode of Priestley and Lavoisier. When Priestley visited the French chemist in Paris he spoke about his discovery of "de-phlogisticated gas." In Lavoisier's mind this gas soon became "oxygen" and formed the basis of a new theory of combustion, calcination, and respiration. Lavoisier therefore, not Priestley, became the father of modern chemistry. Schleiden suggested—Schwann executed. The cell theory is therefore Schwann's. Any other statement would be misleading. To write, for example, as Samuel Butler did of Darwin, that "Buffon planted, Erasmus Darwin and Lamarck watered, but it was Mr. Charles Darwin who said: 'That fruit is ripe' and shook it in his lap" is a specimen of erroneous appraisal.

Out of the chiaroscuro of the jungle Schwann stepped into a clear light. Not in the least is his theoretical ability impaired by an acknowledged indebtedness to Schleiden. More could be said about his predecessors than even these pages reveal. Schwann owed them much, yet he owed them only facts. The great vivifying truth of the cell is Schwann's own, the unmistakable result of the comprehensive fertility of his mind. "Science is built up of facts as a house is built up of stones," observed Poincaré in *Science and Hypothesis,* "but an accumulation of fact is no more science than a heap of stones is a house."

8

Shortly after the publication of his book Schwann was called by the University of Louvain to occupy the chair of anatomy. This recognition of his fame—especially coming from a Catholic institution—pleased him greatly and he accepted. He left Germany to spend the rest of his career in Belgium, occasionally visiting his Rhineland brothers and relatives. After nine happy years at Louvain, where he spent considerable time and effort learning French and practicing how to lecture in the adopted language, he was promoted to the University of Liége; the appointment was made in 1847. Here at Liége Schwann remained until his death in 1882, a span of thirty-five years. Again and again he had been offered posts in the leading universities of Germany, but he refused to leave Belgium. "It is not where you are but what you are."

Humanity advances on the road of progress by prodigiously unequal steps. Oftentimes in this upward march the world pauses to honor those who have been its truest benefactors. Rarely is it other than a posthumous tribute. But with Schwann it was different: while yet alive, humanity, with deep reverence, extended to him the laurel wreath.

It happened thus:

At Liége on the twenty-third of June, 1878, there was held in Schwann's honor *"une manifestation solennelle"*—a public demonstration in recognition of the fortieth anniversary of his book and the fortieth anniversary of his teaching career. A letter of invitation to participate in the festivities was sent early in January by the authorities of the University of Liége to the leading universities of the world and to all the learned societies of Europe and America. They were asked to send representatives to honor *le celebre auteur de la Theorie Cellulaire.*

After six months of intensive preparation the "manifestation" was ready. It began promptly at one o'clock in the afternoon of a beautiful June day in the auditorium of the university which was appropriately decorated and festooned for the *séance.* A distinguished audience was there to pay homage to this simple man and unveil his bust, which carried on the pedestal an inscription in Latin beginning with the words: *"Viro summo* THEODORO SCHWANN" —a professor in Belgium for forty years, celebrated author of the cell theory—*"qui inventa cellularum doctrina."* Three speeches were given that afternoon, the first by M. M. Stas, member of the Royal Academy of Sciences; the second by Doctor Edourd Van Beneden, professor of the University of Liége; and the third by M. Losson, a student of medicine representing Professor Schwann's pupils. In addition to these speeches, which reviewed the history of the cell theory and Schwann's leading rôle, tributes, honors, degrees were conferred upon him by representatives of foreign universities and learned societies. To all these expressions—*temoignages d'admiration, de respect, de reconnaissance*—Professor Schwann responded. And he did not forget to pay honor to Matthias Jacob Schleiden.

Of all the many tributes that were presented to him on that day none stated more clearly and cogently the reasons than those set forth by the faculty of medicine of the University of Edinburgh. It is too lengthy a document to quote in its entirety, but these words, in particular, cannot be forgotten: "We gratefully acknowledge the incalculable service that he rendered to biological science so long as half a century ago when he penetrated the then seeming chaos of animal histology, and revealed the great morphological law, that however diverse in structure and function the several tissues may be, they are all of them composed of cellular units variously arranged and variously modified, each with a vitality more or less independent. We are aware that in so doing Schwann elaborated and applied to animal histology the cell theory previously enunciated by Schleiden with regard to the tissues of plants; but we recognize how infinitely more difficult it was to prove that the theory also holds in the case of animal tissues for the investigation of which he had to rely on technical methods of a very primitive character. More refined methods of research have indeed led to different opinions regarding the essential constitution of the cellular unit, but this point of detail has in no degree shaken the fundamental principle of the cell theory."

9

The ultimate subdivision of living tissue into individual cells marked an entirely new departure in understanding the structure of plants and animals.* A grander era, studded by brilliant judgments brilliantly delivered, was on its way.

Hardly had the cell theory been formulated when its elaboration was begun by a group of research investigators who added new corollaries to the main thesis, thereby placing the theory in a far more significant light than either Schleiden or Schwann had dreamed of. These younger men succeeded in demonstrating that the key to every biological problem must finally be sought in the cell. This is an amazing disclosure when one stops to consider the range and diversity of phenomena they had to bring under a single point of view. Certainly it could not have been done had they not been in possession of Schwann's theory.

Once having discovered the universal importance of the cell the biologists undertook an attack upon its interior structure, in

* A group of similar cells devoted to a single use is called a tissue. There are many kinds of tissues such as bone, muscle, nerve, etc. The main idea of Schwann was to unify the plant and animal world by showing that cell structure is at the basis of all tissue.

much the same way that the followers of Dalton explored the realm within the atom.

What did they find?

They came upon a complex living system containing many structural components highly differentiated and of profound chemical diversity. Foremost, they discovered *protoplasm,* a translucent, grayish, slimy substance possessing extraordinary uniformity in both animal and plant cells. When stained and seen under high magnification, it appears to be somewhat granular or finely netted. Within the protoplasm is the denser central portion called the *nucleus,* separating itself by a recognizable membrane. Physically, it is much the same as the protoplasm; it differs only in its chemical constitution. Chemically, the protoplasm is three-fourths water. The other fourth is made up largely of protein, sugars, fats, and salts. It is in the protein complex of the protoplasm that scientific research is endeavoring to unravel the ultimate properties of that elusive thing called Life.

During the early period of exploration that was to reveal many new discoveries within the cell, one question always remained uppermost in the minds of biologists: "How does a cell arise—what is the true story of its origin?" Both Schleiden and Schwann bravely faced this problem, but their answer was erroneous and misleading. They declared that cells spring into being most commonly by a process of "free cell-formation"—that is, cells arise *de novo* by "budding" from the surface of the nucleus.

A versatile young Swiss botanist, Karl Nägeli (1817-1891), who had spent a part of his academic career working under Schleiden at Jena, undertook a microscopical examination of the processes of cell-formation in order to get light on the subject of the origin and growth of this universal biologic unit. By nature and cultivation Nägeli was an unrestrainable theorist. But first and foremost he was an investigator who had plunged deep into experiment. The question of the origin of the cell was just the kind of a problem to challenge his mind. After several years of close and incessant work Nägeli emerged from his laboratory in 1846 to tell the world that no such thing as "free cell-formation" takes place; on the contrary no nucleus buds from cells. All of his researches and observations, declared Nägeli, proved that a cell arises from another pre-existing cell by "division" only; that is, a cell by dividing into two halves forms two cells, where there had been but one before. The two cells become distinct. Then as growth proceeds, by a continuous process of subdivision, the two cells divide into four, the four into eight, the eight into sixteen, and so on, each resulting cell doubling in size and dividing in two, until the multitude of cells builds up the body of the embryo and finally of the adult.

Other men in the field of botany—scientists like Kölliker and Hugo von Mohl—arrived almost simultaneously at the same conclusion. And so did the zoologists. Within twenty years after Schwann had published his book, the universality of "cell-division" was established as the one and only process by which cells come into being. Never do cells arise *de novo*—that is, spontaneously out of some formless matrix.

10

Knowing that the cells of the body arise only by division of pre-existing cells, it is easy to understand the broad outlines of the theory of heredity: "A new life is only a piece of material separated from its parents—a chip off the old block."

In 1861 the German anatomist, Karl Gegenbaur (1826-1903), starting out from the doctrine *Omne vive e vivo*—"All life from life"—tore the veil from a mystery of nature which for thousands of years confronted humanity as unapproachable—the mystery of the ovum. Gegenbaur demonstrated that the fertilized egg is a single cell. (The human ovum is almost a thousand times the bulk of an average human tissue-cell.) Schwann had vaguely recognized this fact, but it was left for Gegenbaur in a new odyssey of discovery to establish it more carefully than any previous scientist.

Other observations on the cellular phenomena of sexual union showed that in both the plant and animal kingdoms the sexual process is nothing more than the union of a male cell with a female cell which creates the single new cell or fertilized egg. From this egg-embryo, formed by the union of ovum and spermatazoon, the organism develops. Consequently, within the microscopic compass of the single (ancestor) cell there is contained the total hereditary endowment of each individual—plant or animal—

which is transmitted from parents to offspring. Thus the continuity between generations is in reality a continuity of cells.

If the ancestor cell (the egg) contains no preformed embryo, what then does it contain? Surely it must contain *something* by which characteristics are transmitted. Kaspar Friedrich Wolff could not answer this question, neither could Schwann. But the answer is surprisingly definite. Within the nucleus there was discovered a substance called *chromatin,* particularly rich in phosphorus. When a cell is stained for microscopic study there can be seen in the nucleus strands of this material. At the time of reproduction the chromatin breaks up into a definite number of rodlike bodies termed *chromosomes.* Evidence points to these chromosome bodies as the express vehicles of heritage transmission.

The private affairs of the chromosomes, so long a secret, have yielded to tedious years of labor. Chromosomes have been tracked down; they occur in all cells of all plants and animals and they are constant in number and appearance for any given species. Moreover, they pass directly from parents to their offspring. Some creatures are provided with many chromosomes and some with few. Man, for example, has a set of forty-eight, a lily twenty-four, a mouse forty, a pea fourteen, the roundworm *Ascaris* only two, and a certain crustacean over a hundred. Every kind of creature has its own characteristic chromosome outfit. The set varies from species to species. In reproduction, half of the chromosomes are supplied by the father and the other half by the mother. This is accomplished by a remarkable process which prevents a doubling of the sets. Heredity is therefore a fifty-fifty proposition. Every human being starts life as a single cell—the center of him (or her) occupied by two complete sets of twenty-four of these chromosomes, one set transmitted from each parent.

The exploration of the cell has kept pace with the penetration of the atom. The search which started out centuries ago with a study of the tissues was transferred to the cell, then to the proto-plasm, then to the nucleus, which yielded the secrets of chromatin, and in turn made possible the discovery of chromosomes. The next giant step in biology was taken when the chromosomes were declared to be the habitation of *genes*—very small bodies having a definite serial arrangement within, or at least along, the chromosomes.

No one, of course, has ever seen a gene. Its existence is inferred, just as scientists infer the reality of the atom. Much is known about the nature of atoms even though they belong to a world beyond visibility. Similarly the genes. Unless their existence were assumed the facts of heredity could not be explained. There is indeed "a mask of theory over the whole of nature, if it be *theory* to infer more than we see."

1 1

The theory of the chromosome and the gene explains the experimental work of Gregor Mendel (1822-1884), cloistered scientist, who worked alone in the garden of the Augustinian Monastery at Brno in Moravia, which is now a part of Czechoslovakia. The intellectual curiosity of this remarkable man went beyond idle wonderment. Mendel experimented with plants, particularly the common culinary pea.

His procedure was to hybridize different varieties within a related species and note the results. He found that certain characteristics were transmitted from parents to offspring. Not haphazardly, but in definite numerical proportions.

Of the pea, Mendel had in his garden many varieties: one type had a relatively long stem while another had a short one, one was characterized by having a white flower and another a red flower; in one the unripe pods were green, in another yellow. By numerous and often-repeated experiments extending over several years Mendel produced results in crossing that were capable of statistical formulation. This method was an altogether new approach to the subject of heredity which no previous breeder of plants or animals had ever attempted.

It is one thing to utilize science and quite another thing to advance it. In order to explain the results Mendel assumed that somewhere in the plants' hereditary constitution there were "units" which controlled or determined this or that "character." If a pea plant, for example, was tall, Mendel reasoned that "tallness" as a unit character must be inherent in its endowment. When he crossed it with a short pea plant, all the offspring of the first generation turned out to be tall. These hybrids were then allowed to self-fertilize and their seeds collected. Some of the seeds produced tall plants, others produced short plants, in the ratio of three tall to one short.

What did this mean?

Mendel rightly reasoned that tallness was dominant—where two characters of a pair meet in an individual one of them masks or dominates the other. In this particular case "smallness" is therefore a *recessive* unit character—not destroyed but just held back. Further experiments with the offspring of the hybrids showed that smallness was there in a latent condition, for it appeared again and again in subsequent generations. In theorizing on these unit characters Mendel argued that, inasmuch as they did not mix with each other (that is, they did not in any way adulterate each other by intimacy), they must be self-perpetuating.

Mendel's discoveries apply not only to hybrids but also to all normal processes. The units which he discovered in the solitude of his garden are today known by the name of *genes*. It is because of the existence of the genes and their frequent mutation that nature is able to carry on (a) the process of heredity and (b) the process of variation. In other words, the gene is the smallest unit of continuity and change. Like the electron within the atom, it is, in our present state of knowledge, ultimate within the cell.

A very good example of how a Mendelian character operates in man is "night blindness," a peculiarity of the retina that makes it difficult for the human eye to see in twilight or in other dim light. This defect zigzags to and fro between the generations. In the time of Charles I one Jean Nougaret is known to have been afflicted with night blindness, and this trouble has recurred in his descendants for more than three hundred years. If a normal member of the Nougaret lineage married a normal type, none of the offspring were night-blind. But if a night-blind member of the lineage married a normal type, the night blindness cropped up in the descendants in definite proportions.

12

The basic laws of heredity discovered in the plant and animal world are, of course, applicable to man.

For man does not stand apart from nature, as was so long believed by the theologians, but he is a part of nature, as science has carefully and laboriously demonstrated. The cellular origin of all living things holds true for man as it does for all living things. Just as a geranium or a fish or a horse transmit to their offspring unit character through the chromosomes within the nucleus of the cell, so does man transmit his biological inheritance to his children.

Man, however, is a complex creature who, unfortunately, knows less about himself than he does of his corn and horses. More than half a century ago, Francis Galton perceived the fundamental importance of biological knowledge applied to a long range view of humanity and its future. But the innate conservatism of the human mind is such that we are pitifully small in the presence of great and new revelations.

Still, the foundations of this new temple of heredity have been laid. Some day it will be crowned with polished minarets.

9. Darwin . . THEORY OF EVOLUTION

THE question of the origin of life—perhaps the most primeval of all questions—is as old as man himself, for early in the childhood of the race there came the promptings of natural curiosity. Many of the answers that have come down to us, embodied in oriental myth and legend, are extremely naïve; they are the crude products of man's early thinking such as might be expected from infant peoples making the first tiny exploration of the complexity of the universe.

2

When we leave the Orient and come to the thinkers of ancient Greece we are in the presence of men who gave surprisingly good answers to this age-old question. Whereas the peoples of the far-eastern lands spoke of the origin of life in semipoetical terms full of racial and religious mysticism, the Greek attempts at explanation represent the very earliest beginnings of a scientific approach. Because of their genius these early Greek thinkers have been called "evolutionists before Darwin."

As a scientific theory evolution is essentially a product of the last one hundred years. It is, therefore, somewhat extravagant to call men like Thales and Anaximander evolutionists in our modern sense. While the best minds of antiquity made some splendid guesses, as, for example, Empedocles of Agrigentum who imagined (and rightly) that plants preceded animals in the evolutionary chain, and that less perfect forms gave way to more perfect, still even to these best minds there was little incongruity in the idea of animals and plants arising *de novo* from water or earth.

So illustrious a thinker as Aristotle apparently accepted with little reservation the statements of his predecessors that such highly developed organisms as worms, insects and some fishes could come into being from mud. This is the doctrine of "spontaneous gen-

eration," according to which fully formed living organisms sometimes arise from nonliving matter. It is also true of Aristotle, that
while he believed organic life is built upon a progressive scale of
complexity ranging from simple forms to highly developed ones
(with man crowning the whole system), he was unable to point to
any natural agency which could account for the interrelation of
living things.

3

Following the downfall of Greece the glorious period of speculative thinking came to an end. For more than twenty centuries
not a single new idea on the subject of the origin of life was brought
forward. Over and over again we find the scholars, theologians, and
poets of medieval Europe voicing the semioriental views of the
Bible: that all species are fixed (immutable), each having come into
existence by a special act of creation. Thus, in the second chapter
of Genesis, the Deity is pictured as taking a clod of earth in His
hands and, in a very literal way, holding it close to His nostrils so
as to breathe into it the breath of life:

And the Lord God formed man of the dust of the ground and
breathed into his nostrils the breath of life; and man became
a living soul (Genesis 2:7).

Inasmuch as the modern theory of evolution is based upon the
mutability of species, it can easily be understood that no one during
the long stretch of medievalism deserves to be called an evolutionist.
Throughout this period there was a complete stagnation of knowledge about nature. If men were not quoting the Bible directly,
they went about saying that various types of animals arise from
fermentation. Or they firmly declared that a dead horse breeds
wasps, a mule produces hornets, cheese gives birth to mice.

Such were the prevalent ideas on the origin of life before the
Renaissance.

4

One day in the year 1668 an Italian naturalist who was not at
all content with tradition began to put his faith in observation. Notwithstanding the fact that people had been saying for centuries
that decaying animal matter gives rise to life forms, this young

man thought that it would be best to test such a statement with a series of actual observations. One may well imagine how terribly silly it must have appeared to the sober-minded people of Tuscany to watch Francesco Redi toiling under the Italian sun with meat and maggots to satisfy a scientific curiosity.

But Redi was determined to know. He covered meat with fine gauze and exposed it to flies. The meat did not develop maggots, quite simply because the flies laid their eggs on the gauze, not on the meat: maggots could not develop on meat unless the flies' eggs were deposited directly on the meat!

Thus in one experiment the folly of centuries of belief was overthrown. Redi proved for all time that the supposed generation of life from putrefied matter was wholly untrue. On the positive side his experiment showed that no form of life arises except from preexisting life.

5

It would be a mistake to think that Redi's work was accepted all at once. His influence only gradually became apparent.

Slowly and very painfully the book of nature was being forced open. The sixteenth and seventeenth centuries saw the beginnings of embryology, which was to add conclusive proof to the doctrine of evolution; of comparative anatomy, the source of Darwin's earliest beliefs in the mutability of species; of microscopy, which would bring into the evolutionary spotlight more and more conclusive analogies of structure and function to fill out the vast picture of the unfolding of organic nature.

It was a period of hesitating progress.

Gottfried Leibnitz, the German philosopher, brought forward the idea of continuity, of a successive chain of species, ascending in direct line. This concept was to dominate evolutionary thought until Lamarck should realize that the ascent had been in branching lines. René Descartes, treading softly lest he should come under the iron hand of the Church, said that in all probability nature could be explained by natural laws instead of by divine revelation. Spinoza in Holland, Pascal in France, Newton and Hume in England, were the leaders of thought who saw that there had been evolution, but wondered how it had all come about. Men cannot advance much beyond the knowledge of their time, and the biological knowledge of those days was fragmentary, to say the least.*

But this state of affairs was not to endure. The eighteenth century marked the transition. It inaugurated a period full of important advances in the accumulation of facts with the consequent leavening of men's ideas. The scientific method of *observation* from *nature* and induction from observation was slowly infiltrating into the thought of the age. The real type of theorizing man, who would be content to let his speculation wait upon his knowledge, was in the process of becoming.

6

First there arose Carl Linnaeus, the Swedish naturalist, who bothered hardly at all with generalizations. He set for himself the prodigious task of systematizing nature, for he was a master in the art of classifying living things. No biologist before him possessed such a methodical approach. In his zeal for naming and classifying, the high goal of investigation was lost sight of. While he studied an extraordinary large number of animals, he unfortunately brought no deepening of our knowledge.

Linnaeus assumed that when the Deity created the world He stocked this earth with fixed and invariable species—that is, one pair of each kind of animals was created. Believing this, he assumed that existing species were the direct descendants without change of form or habit from the original pair. Because of the weight of his great influence this assumption helped to establish the dogma of the fixity of species. It is remarkable that, having been such a staunch believer in immutability, he veered toward the end of his career somewhat to the other side by admitting that a species might through hybridization degenerate into many varieties.

While Linnaeus was laboring at his tasks in Sweden and subsequently in Holland, there appeared in England a long didactic poem called *The Zoonomia* which created a minor sensation. It

---

* The word *evolution* itself was put into circulation in the eighteenth century by Charles Bonnet, who might have made significant contributions to biology if his eyesight had not failed him at the age of thirty-four, forcing him to abandon the direct observation of nature for the fanciful and deceptive paths of imagination.

was written by Erasmus Darwin, the grandfather of the future theorist. He had been profoundly touched by the newer attitude toward nature and in this poem boldly speculated on the origin and evolution of life. In many curious ways he anticipated the ideas of his famous grandson. He mentioned, for example, the struggle for existence, the origin of all nature from a single source, sexual selection of the stronger and most attractive males by the females, and the idea of mimicry or protective coloration. The chief factor of evolution according to Erasmus Darwin, however, was increased use or disuse of certain organs, the effects of which were transmissible to the offspring; and these changes were the consequence of the desires, aversions, pleasures, pains, irritations and other inherent propensities of the animals themselves. Unfortunately for Erasmus Darwin his views were far too advanced for his time. Those who ridiculed him, although now forgotten, were at least victors for a day.

What happened to Erasmus Darwin in England happened in France to George Buffon, who for fifty-odd years had been investigating the problem of the origin of species. Buffon promulgated a theory that declared for mutability, the struggle for existence, and the inheritance of acquired characters. Poor Buffon! His fellow members of the faculty of the Sorbonne turned on him; he was threatened with the loss of his position, with ostracism and ignominy. Finally he capitulated. He published a recantation ending with the words: "I abandon everything in my book respecting the formation of the earth and generally all which may be contrary to the narrative of Moses."

Despite Buffon's tremendous scientific influence the biblical doctrine of special creation had so strong a hold that as great a zoologist as Baron de Cuvier could not possibly shake it. While Cuvier recognized that there must have been successive geological epochs in the development of life on earth (catastrophic upheavals marking the separation between the successive epochs), he steadfastly refused to believe that there had been a mutability of species. Consequently he rejected and ridiculed the whole principle of evolution.

7

During those days in France there lived an obscure professor who was singularly untouched by Baron de Cuvier's ridicule.

Outside of his views on evolution there was nothing very eventful about the life of Jean Baptiste de Lamarck. Having arrived in his quiet way at certain very definite ideas on the origin of species, he was willing to endure ostracism, obscurity and poverty to promulgate what he felt to be the truth. The little recognition he received during his life was buried with him in a pauper's grave.

It is often asked why Lamarck met with such meager recognition. Why did the publication of his views excite only a flurry of comment, whereas Darwin's, published fifty years later, succeeded in arresting the attention of the entire world?

Lamarck's views were legitimate enough; in fact, Darwin adopted many of the Lamarckian arguments in the later editions of the *Origin of Species*. It was unfortunate that Lamarck's method of formulating his views was wrong; he failed to test his abstractions in the light of careful observation and experiment. His method frequently led him into ridiculous and weird deductions which canceled through their absurdity all the value his sounder work had for his contemporaries.

Lamarck postulated four laws in summing up his view of how evolution had come about. These laws are: 1. Life tends to increase the volume of each living body and of all its parts up to a limit determined by its own necessities. 2. New wants in animals give rise to new organs. 3. The development of these organs is in proportion to their employment. 4. New developments may be transmitted to offspring.

The first law may be conceded, although Lamarck adduced meager evidence for its validity. The third law, that the use of an organ causes it to increase in size (and its disuse to atrophy), Darwin later admitted as a factor in organic evolution. The fourth law, that of the inheritance of acquired characteristics, was at least as old as Aristotle, and this law Darwin also included as a possible contributing factor.

But it was the second law that was the keynote of Lamarck's

theory, and it was this law that was the occasion for the ridicule and the wholesale rejection of his entire scheme.

Simply put, this law means that a want, or a need, or a propensity in an animal causes the origin of a new organ. Giraffes, said Lamarck, acquired long necks because they "wanted" them, in order to browse off the high branches of the trees in the jungle.

The misinterpretation of Lamarck lay in the word "wanted."

What he intended to say was this: that the ancestors of the giraffes *needed* (*avoir besoin*) long necks, and that the gradual stretching of the neck towards the high branches finally produced this effect. But the critics of Lamarck were not kindly men. They were out to make their enemy look ridiculous and so they lost no time in assuming that Lamarck meant that the ancestors of the giraffes actually and consciously decided that they would be better off with long necks and thereupon went about acquiring them.

To make matters worse, Lamarck boldly insisted that it was a demonstrable fact that bulls originally acquired horns, because in anger they butted their heads together and that a rush of nervous fluid to the butted parts followed, in which there was secreted an osseous or bony material gradually resulting in the production of horns. Lamarck assigned a similar cause for the branching antlers of the stag. Snakes, he said, sprang from reptiles with four feet, but snakes grew longer because of continual effort to elongate themselves in order to push through narrow places.

In many respects Lamarck was a bad scientist: he gave more attention to *a priori* speculations and fanciful hypotheses than to the direct observation of nature. Yet Lamarck made a definite contribution to evolutionary theory.

He was the first evolutionist clearly to realize that the lines of biological descent were branching instead of a single chain. He was the first to publish a genealogical tree, showing that the relationships between present day species were not those of direct descent, but that they shared a common (extinct) progenitor. Lamarck also was the first to insist that for any sort of evolution, no matter what the factors, much more time must be allotted to nature to enact her laws than had been commonly assigned. He thereby demonstrated that the age of the earth must be much greater than any previous estimate had allowed.

But the chief glory of Lamarck is that of a lone man of science waging a battle against tradition, dogmatism and convention.

Nor is he to be condemned too severely for the fanciful nature of many of his hypotheses. Whatever checks an evolutionist, writing in 1800, might bring to bear upon his speculations necessarily had to come from himself. No careful scientific thinking existed in biology at that time to guide the theorizer. Lamarck is perhaps to be praised more for such restraint as he did exercise than to be condemned for the lack of it. Consider, for example, the ideas of some of his predecessors, such as Claude Duret, who described a tree that stood on the edge of a lake. Its leaves, as they fell, Duret tells us, were metamorphosed into either fishes or birds, according as they struck water or land! Or take Kircher of Amsterdam, who swore that he saw with his own eyes orchids giving birth to birds and "small men," through fertilization with a mysterious spermatic fluid given off by the ground. Compared to these and others of his sources in the evolutionary discussion, Lamarck was a veritable prodigy of self-restraint.

Although he had stated the concept of evolution in clearer terms than any man before him and marshaled in support of the doctrine more facts and logic, Lamarck died leaving virtually no impression on his own generation.

The reasons for this are not far to seek. Besides Lamarck's tendency to unscientific hypotheses, which we have already discussed, such evidence as he possessed was full of gaps. These gaps were to be largely filled in by a host of discoveries of the next few years in embryology, paleontology, comparative anatomy and botany. All these gaps in his evidence Lamarck unfortunately attempted to fill in with figments of his own imagination. The consequences were sad.

The *Philosophie Zoologique,* Lamarck's crowning work, was published in 1809. It appeared, but nobody read it. The date however is memorable for in that same year was born the classical theorist of evolution—Charles Robert Darwin.

8

After the death of Lamarck in 1829, evolution receded into disfavor and neglect. There were plenty of men, though, who bore in the corners of their minds a conception of evolution, or at least a queer feeling that all of nature was not quite as patly and easily explained as ecclesiastical authorities maintained. Thomas Huxley was assiduously at work trying to uncover a law of evolution he felt must exist. Charles Lyell, the geologist, was frankly puzzled by the conflict between his own observations and the prevailing belief in the biblical doctrine of special creations. Joseph Hooker, the botanist, was at a loss to explain the variety in the geographic distribution of plants by any other means than descent with modification; and even Richard Owen, successor of Cuvier, conceded somewhat guardedly the transmutation of species.

And it is important to remember concerning Charles Darwin that, before he conceived his theory, he was just another naturalist pondering the facts of the animal and plant worlds and wondering more and more why those facts should persistently run counter to current doctrines. Until Darwin's work had been made known, no evolutionist, no matter how convinced by the data collected, thought that there was sufficient evidence at hand to warrant any man's braving public disapproval. The storm winds of this disapproval would blow from two quarters: the theologians who were ready to hurl octavo Bibles at the heads of all who disputed special creation, and the contemporary scientists themselves who were waiting with that eternal question "What proofs?" So the evolutionists of the early part of the nineteenth century held their peace and cherished their hypotheses, hoping that the day would not be too far distant when some naturalist would present a fresh set of considerations and establish evolution upon a secure basis of fact.

In the meantime the foes of evolution were digging in and consolidating their position. Soon there appeared the *Bridgewater Treatises,* a series of essays by many prominent naturalists of the time who rationalized the viewpoint of special creation, pointing out the marvelous adaptations the Deity had created in nature. The authoritative work of William Paley on natural theology also concerned itself with this aspect of the creative process. Nothing seemed to the naturalist of the first half of the century more immutable than the belief in the immutability of species. Yet there can be seen even in these essays the germs of the inevitable triumph of evolution. The Bridgewater series stressed adaptation, as did

P

Paley, and such is the irony of things that the identical examples they gave to demonstrate special creation were to be repeated by evolutionists half a century later as evidence for the new doctrine!

9

The earliest record we have of Darwin's propensity for the investigation of nature tells us that at the age of ten he noticed the varying types of insects and contemplated collecting them. Some of his enthusiasm in this direction was dampened by an incident one day, when, with a newly caught beetle in each hand, he discovered yet another specimen of a rare and interesting species. He could not bear to give up either of his first two prizes, yet he had to have the third. Deciding quickly, he put one of the beetles between his teeth, holding it there as gently as possible. With his right hand he reached for the third tempting specimen and had it in his fingers when the beetle between his teeth inconsiderately squirted acid into his mouth and escaped with both his fellows, while the young entomologist frantically ran for a glass of water to cool his burning throat.

The profession of a naturalist appealed to Darwin as he grew older, but the prospect of finding a position where he might be able to do some really useful work appeared slender. His father thought the young man's bent just a hobby and wanted him to be a physician like himself and like old Erasmus Darwin before him. But he showed little inclination for medical work. The next, and inevitable, suggestion was the ministry. The problem rested there while Darwin went to Edinburgh and Cambridge where he continued in his apparently directionless existence observing the life of plants and animals, familiarizing himself with the facts of geology, finding his greatest pleasure in the study of outdoor things. Each day he showed less and less evidence of enthusiasm for the vocation of clergyman. When he reached twenty-two he was still undecided what to do with his life, so he had to accept tacitly his family's decision.

Then out of the clear blue came the offer of a lifetime: an appointment as naturalist to the government ship, H.M.S. *Beagle*, which was to make an extended voyage through the southern half of the New World. Anxiously he submitted the offer for his father's approval. It was not at once forthcoming; the senior Darwin thought that such a trip would hardly comport with the dignity of a clergyman-to-be. Fearing that the offer might be withdrawn, the youthful naturalist begged for quick acquiescence. At last consent was given, but only after Charles' uncle had interceded for him, saying that he thought the "pursuit of Natural History, though certainly not professional, is very suitable to a clergyman."

10

The *Beagle* sailed from England on December 27, 1831, made its way down the coast of Europe to Africa and arrived at Teneriffe on the sixth of January. Fear of the cholera kept the expedition from landing; but ten days later they disembarked at St. Iago, the chief island of the Cape Verde archipelago. During these first few days of the voyage the sea had been rough, and Darwin was experiencing the beginnings of the chronic nervous indigestion that was to torment him for the rest of his life. It took the form of violent seasickness which rarely left him for the rest of the five-year voyage. There were other discomforts that were to beset him on this trip —heat, bad weather, pestiferous insects, fatiguing expeditions and a growing homesickness—all of which were stoically endured for the sake of observation.

Toward the middle of February the *Beagle* made its way across the Atlantic and finally landed in Brazil. Here Darwin's real investigations began. At every anchorage, as the ship slowly worked its way down the east coast of South America to the Straits of Magellan and up the west coast to Valparaiso and the Galapagos Islands, young Darwin was among the first ashore with his butterfly net, geologic hammer, magnifying glass and other implements of the naturalist. Between ports, in spite of recurring spells of seasickness, he observed the sea birds and the marine animals that could be seen from the ship. Everything he came across he wrote down in his now famous *Journal* during those long evenings when his mind seethed with all manner of hypotheses and possible explanations in an attempt to arrive at a logical theory which would make understandable the interrelations among the many phenomena he had witnessed.

One particular point troubled him consistently. If these various

species he came across were the specially created offspring of
divine Hand, why then was there so much dissimilarity between
the individuals of each species? Why were there so many individua
differences? Why could he find no two members of a species exactl
alike? Could it be that each individual was created separately? How
else account for such variation?

Furthermore there was the puzzling matter of how to distin
guish between species and variety. What constituted a species
What a variety? Hitherto the consensus of opinion among natu
ralists had been that the matter of quantity must be the chie
criterion—that is, if the number of a variety was large enough
it constituted a species. But Darwin found variety and species s
interlocking that it was hard to discern the details that made them
distinct.

The next year, while on an expedition to the Andes Mountains
he discovered the mice on opposite sides of the range were quit
different. It did not occur to him then and there that such a thing
as the mutability of species was the explanation. But here was
puzzling problem! What caused variation? Why did the mice on
one side of the Andes vary in one way and the species on the othe
side in another? Here was a significant problem which could not b
solved with the meager facts at hand. He would have to leave th
solution of variation in abeyance until he could gather materia
to support an hypothesis.

Late in 1835 the *Beagle* left the shores of Peru for an excursion
to the Galapagos Archipelago, which lay about six hundred mile
west of South America. Several days were spent there while Darwin
gathered notes on the new species he came across. Sitting at hi
desk in the evenings, comparing his specimens with those he ha
collected on the continent, he was struck by the remarkable resem
blance between them. Were these birds and reptiles of Galapago
members of the same species, created simultaneously on islan
and continent? No, that couldn't be true, since the resemblanc
did not extend to all details, but only lay in the general form
But why would species be created so similar to each other, and ye
not the same? If the birds and reptiles of the islands were identica
with those of the mainland (or if they were completely different
then the conventional biblical doctrine of special creation woul

account for them. But neither was the case! These island forms
seemed *allied* to those of the continent, but were neither identical
nor yet distinct.

Here was a fine state of affairs! Neither identical nor distinct.
What was one to make of that? Obviously special creation was not
the answer. There must have been variations; these birds must
have migrated at one time or another from the mainland, and by
some sort of modification have diverged from their original character. Or else the islands had once been connected with the mainland only to be severed by geologic forces, thereby isolating the
animals. He could see no other explanation. For that reason there
was no other course left for Darwin but to abandon once and for
all the concept of the fixity of species and apply the hypothesis of
variability. "It was evident that such facts as these, as well as many
others, could only be explained on the supposition that species
gradually become modified; and the subject haunted me."

It turned out to be an excellent working formula. Observations
that had long puzzled him seemed to be adequately explained by
it. For example, there were the Andean mice. Nature had modified
them under different conditions; hence they had become diverse
in character. He remembered also that animals and plants on the
Cape Verde Islands, the scene of his first observations of the voyage,
showed the same peculiarity as the Galapagos group—that is, the
species were allied to but distinct from those of the mainland. Time
and again he pondered on the almost imperceptible gradation existing between the various species. Wherever he traveled he noticed
that one species graded into another. Added to all this was his
experience with fossil forms picked up here and there. The huge
fossils he had unearthed in Patagonia were strikingly similar to
living specimens. Obviously fossils must be ancestors of existing
life forms.

The swift joy of discovery now began to thrill him.

11

On his return home, there was no longer any question that his
would be the career of a naturalist. "The voyage of the *Beagle*,"
Darwin wrote in his autobiography years afterward, "has been by

far the most important event in my life, and has determined my whole career." And so it did.

The *Beagle* reached England on October 2, 1836. Darwin spent many long months preparing his "notes" for publication. In reality these notes were a journal, a day by day running account of his observations. What had been his private and exclusive property was now given to humanity under the title *Journal of Researches into the Natural History and Geology of the Countries visited during the Voyage of H.M.S. Beagle around the World.* The appearance of the *Journal* gave young Darwin a prominent position among men of science.

In January, 1839, the future theorist married his cousin, Emma Wedgwood, that wonderful woman who stood by him throughout the years of his illness. Almost immediately after the marriage the invalidism that dogged him all his life began to plague his health unremittingly. Rather quickly he gave up the idea of living in London and established himself in the small suburb of Down, in the county of Kent. It was here that he wrote the *Origin of Species* after twenty years of painstaking work in the face of chronic neurosis and chronic indigestion and long spells of nausea that confined him to bed for weeks at a time.

12

In spite of long periods of physical distress he managed to carry on investigations in many fields of science, never allowing any excursion into other domains to draw him from the one central job of his life: to seek for a natural cause to explain the origin of species. His passion was to collect facts bearing on the idea of modification.

It is said of Darwin that he found the world unexplored and with thoroughness explored it. Always the careful scientist, he took especial care to note the facts that seemed to contradict his theories; he had noticed that it was these unpleasant data that were most apt to escape the memory. But as the facts on variation came crowding into his notebooks the inevitability of the idea of evolution impressed itself on him with greater and greater force.

Already on the *Beagle* he had given the subject of modification a great deal of careful thought. Now that he was back in England he began to consider the vast amount of data that might be gleaned

from a study of variation under domestication,—that is, the differences between domestic and wild species of dogs, poultry, cattle
and plants. That should give him much material with which to
solve the problem of variability. Of course, modification in these
cases would be the result of selection by professional breeders, who
sought to perpetuate favorable variations by mating the animals
showing them. The whole problem of variations, their accumulation
to form modifications, and the adaptation of animals to their
environment through these modifications would repay his careful
study.

So Darwin went about the countryside talking to professional
breeders of domestic animals and plants, horticulturists, cattlemen,
farmers, cat and dog fanciers. He put questions to each of them:
what qualities did they breed for, how successful were they in per-
petuating them, what were the especial virtues of hybrids, how did
domesticated species differ from wild? He learned that it was comparatively easy for breeders to modify a domestic species within
a few generations (British cattlemen for example had improved the
quality of cattle and sheep to a marked degree within a short time
and race horse trainers had so improved the original stock of
Arabian horses that pure Arabians had to be given handicaps in
the races). Wherever he inquired he saw instances of man's ability
to improve nature by artificial selection. Domestic breeders had
produced better grades of cattle and sheep. So Darwin jotted down
in his notebook that "the power of this principle of selection is not
hypothetical."

Facts kept filling up one notebook after another, as Darwin
probed deeper into the mystery. "It is delightful to have many
points fermenting in one's brain." He could not escape mutability.
But still he jotted down every single item that might possibly disprove that view. Meanwhile, however, he searched for the explanation of modification and carefully examined the suggestions of his
predecessors.

Of all the thinkers who had preceded him in the study of the
origin of species, Lamarck interested him the most. It was in Lyell's
book on geology that Darwin came across Lamarck's theory in great
detail; and it was there that Darwin first examined critically the
Frenchman's idea that evolution was brought about through: (a)

the inheritance of acquired habits; (b) the use and disuse of organs; and (c) the expression of the wants of animals. Unfortunately for Lamarck, he gave out his doctrine of "habits-forming-new-organs" as fact instead of opinion or hypothesis. "Nothing of all this should be considered as an hypothesis or as a mere peculiar opinion; they are, on the contrary, truths which require, in order to be made evident, only attention to and observation of facts." Had Lamarck said something about natural selection as a factor in evolution, Darwin would not have rejected the Frenchman's ideas. But Lamarck missed the key of natural selection—completely! Repelled by the Frenchman's lack of adequate evidence, Darwin thrust aside the Lamarckian theory as meager and inconclusive and full of guesswork. "I have come not to care at all for beliefs without the special facts. I have suffered too often from this."

Returning to his own investigations he read book after book, performed experiment upon experiment, plunged deeper and deeper into the problem of artificial selection. He studied the doubtful species which naturalists found difficult to classify, and thought that these must be intermediate or transitional forms between two different modifications of a parent form. One hypothesis after another he tested after each ingeniously devised experiment. "I have steadily endeavored to keep my mind free so as to give up any hypothesis however much beloved."

In rejecting the doctrines of his predecessors, he slowly adopted a definite point of view as to the nature of this mysterious phenomenon of variation. The facts that filled his notebooks and whirled through his mind seemed to show that the means of modification were a product of the animal or plant itself, not of its surroundings. In other words, the organism adapted itself to the environment; it was not the environment that worked its will upon the organism. Certainly this was the case in artificial selection by breeders; these men did not cause variations to appear. Nature herself produced variations, yet man could (and did) select for his own purposes the most favorable variations that occurred.

Darwin now felt certain that it was by some sort of selection that modification of species took place. But how? Would he have to go back to the scientifically groundless hypothesis of a beneficent

Deity, a sort of Superbreeder improving the quality of his livestock? Or was there a natural agency which could adequately explain the causation?

13

During this period of intense mental activity, while he was preoccupied with the search for the key to the problem that was haunting him, he picked up a book to divert his weary mind. It was Malthus' *Essay on Population,* and it set Darwin afire. Here was his mechanism—the struggle for existence!

He knew that all animals varied from one another in greater or less degree; he knew that some of these variations were favorable and others not; he knew that artificial selection consciously chose the most favorable for its purposes. How easy it was to see now that this tremendous struggle for existence, which he knew from his own first hand observation of nature, was a continuous, vital phase of the organic world whereby *only the fittest could survive!* The stark necessity to live selected the more favorable variations in a state of nature, just as the desire for better stock determined their selection under domestication. "It at once struck me that under these circumstances favorable species would tend to be preserved, and unfavorable ones to be destroyed! The result of this would be the formation of new species. Here then I had at last a theory by which to work."

How different everything appeared under this new light! He thought: "We behold the face of nature bright with gladness, we often see superabundance of food, we do not see or we forget that the birds which idly sing round us live mostly on insects or seeds, are thus constantly destroying life; or we forget how largely those songsters, or their eggs, or their nestlings, are destroyed by birds or beasts of prey; we do not always bear in mind that, though food may be now superabundant, it is not so at all seasons of each recurring year." The struggle for existence penetrated every nook and corner of nature: insects, fishes, birds, fruits, animals—all competed bitterly with one another, fought for life, tried to survive in a world of tooth-and-nail existence. And out of this struggle for existence nature herself selected those whose organisms were better adapted to survive.

The rôle of the environment became clear now: varying environments did not produce varying modifications, but the modifications were accumulated by natural selection to fit the varying environments. That is, a species dies because it is not adapted to changing circumstances. A certain variety of ostrich, for example, may not be well adapted to survive and hence will perish; but another variety, being favorably adapted, will manage to live on and propagate. Thus, variations, or departures from type are the raw materials of all progress. If this were not so all life would be static, fixed.

Species without the capacity to vary swiftly enough were outstripped in the race for life. "Do or die" was the ultimatum of natural selection: and Darwin found among his geological notes scores of examples of varieties that had perished for want of variability. Obviously, a species that could vary itself had an advantage in the struggle for existence over one that could not. This too explains the likenesses and differences and the interrelationships of animals. The origin of new species by slow processes of descent with modifications from older species is evolution.

In addition to all this Darwin now began to understand more closely the nature of interlocking adaptations to be found everywhere in the organic world. He saw how flowers secrete the honey that bees use for their hives, and how the bees in return insure the fertilization of the flowers by bearing pollen on their sticky legs from one blossom to another.

"The web of life!"—the interlocking threads of adaptation, one organism's survival carrying with it the survival of another, the vital interdependence of different parts of nature. Remove from a certain environment a certain species of bird, and the insects it feeds on will increase in tremendous numbers. By removing a single plant or animal from an environment a readjustment takes place all along the line; for nature is full of complex ties, balances and checks.

14

It was not only his theory that occupied his mind; much of his time was devoted to the preparation and publication of monographs growing out of his general interest in natural history and geology. While he was investigating all these specialized subjects, the notes bearing on his theory accumulated and piled up. By the early summer of 1842 he felt the urge to put down on paper a short abstract of the theory of natural selection. This outline written in pencil covered thirty-five sheets; later in 1844 it was expanded to two hundred and thirty pages. Worried by incessant bad health, he hastened to complete his expanded abstract; he placed it in a sealed envelope, and entrusted it to his wife for publication in the event of his death. He also suggested several editors for the work and laid aside a sum of money to insure its publication. Had he died in 1844, the *Origin of Species* would not have been written, for he did not actually begin work on this major opus until 1854, after the publication of an exhaustive monograph on the lowly species of barnacles.

This work on the barnacles is significant in the history of his theory, more so perhaps than any of his previous publications, for in the careful study of these apparently insignificant little creatures he acquired a thorough training in biology and a full realization of the wisdom of a rigid control in his speculations. In a letter written to his friend Joseph Hooker in 1849 he tells the effect of this particular study on his theory. "I have been struck with the variability of every part in some slight degree of every species."

Nearly eight years were devoted to the examination of each and every sort of variety and subvariety and minor and major variation of function or structure that could possibly be located within the limits of this single but numerous species. The results of this cataloguing broadened the basis of his work; for he found that each characteristic of the typical barnacle varied to such an extent that there was between its extremes an extraordinarily large number of gradations exhibiting numerous shadings.

At last, in 1854, he was able to write to his friend Joseph Hooker, to whom he had confided the outlines of his theory, that his desk was now clear of the barnacle job and he was ready to get to work on his huge files of notes on the origin of species and varieties. To his friend Lyell he made the same confidence; and these two—his best friends—virtual leaders in their respective fields of botany and geology awaited with impatient interest the outcome of his labors.

Lyell, oldest and most experienced of the three scientists, saw the possibility of someone's anticipating Darwin and urged him to write his book as fast as possible. But Darwin could not hurry;

he must patiently pursue every conceivable line of inquiry; he must ferret out every fact bearing on his subject and accumulate his data almost as slowly as the mechanism of natural selection had accumulated variations to produce modifications. Nearly four years passed and he apparently seemed no nearer to publication than at the outset of his inquiry. To be sure, he had his theory definitely built with almost all the details filled in, but the fear of being premature or of giving insufficient evidence for his arguments made him heedless of the necessity to hurry.

However, something happened one day in June, 1858, which had an effect on Darwin far greater than the advice of his closest friends. On that memorable morning he received a letter from the other end of the world and it proved to be the most important letter ever mailed to him.

It was postmarked Ternate, an island in the Malay Archipelago. On the thick envelope was marked the name of the sender—Alfred Russel Wallace.

Darwin opened it. There was a letter and a manuscript. The title of the manuscript interested him—*On the Tendencies of Varieties to Part Indefinitely from the Original Type.*

15

Before thumbing the manuscript Darwin picked up the letter. It asked him to read the accompanying sketch, and if he thought well enough of it to pass it on to other naturalists—Lyell or Hooker —with a view to publication in the near future. Darwin remembered the last paper Wallace had written which Lyell had called to his attention. That was three years ago. In it Wallace had discussed modification of species as altogether probable, but he had not touched on an explanation.

But this paper was different! Wallace too had read Malthus' *Essay on Population.* During a period of intermittent fever at Ternate he was meditating on the problem of existence when the conclusion arrived at by Malthus suddenly illuminated the riddle. In two days he drafted a manuscript sketching a theory of adaptation through the elimination of the unfit in the struggle for existence. It was this manuscript that Darwin held in his hand.

When Darwin finished reading the Wallace sketch he was thun-

CHARLES ROBERT DARWIN

After the portrait by John Collier in The National Portrait Gallery, London

derstruck. Nothing had ever affected him so forcibly: right before his eyes was a statement of his own theory of natural selection almost word for word! The ideas upon which he spent a lifetime of labor were here set forth with amazing illumination.

What should he do about it?

Hurriedly he wrote a frantic letter to Lyell, put the case before him, and asked his advice. "I would far rather burn my whole book," he wrote, "than that Wallace or any other man should think that I behaved in a paltry spirit." It seemed that his work was to go for nought but to confirm Wallace's theories—theories which Wallace had formulated after investigations inspired by Darwin's own *Journal of Researches*. (Wallace was twenty-three years old when he read Darwin's *Journal.*) Unable to wait for a reply from Lyell he also wrote to Hooker, repeating his willingness to resign all credit to Wallace if it would aid the success of the idea.

But such a step was not necessary. At the suggestion of Lyell and Hooker and with the willing consent of Wallace, a short abstract of Darwin's theory was read in conjunction with Wallace's paper at a meeting of the Linnaean Society on July 1, 1858. There was added a letter Darwin had written in 1857 to Asa Gray, the American botanist, giving in detail the theory of natural selection.

Thus the matter was amicably settled. And thus there was written into the annals of mankind some of the most honorable pages in the history of science.

But the theory born of endless research and carefully shielded from possible disputes over priority seemed to be stillborn. True, the meeting of the society at which it was read caught something of its significance, for the discussion was intense and interested. Unfortunately, Darwin could not be present. Illness prevented him from attending, and Wallace was still in Malaysia. Had both men been there, in all probability a strong public interest would have been aroused; but beyond the rooms of the Linnaean Society nobody was excited.

Perhaps that was a good thing. Inasmuch as the theory had been placed before the leading body of English men of science, it was now left to Darwin to assemble the book he had been working on for these many years. "The one great result which I claim for my paper of 1858," said Wallace, "is that it compelled Darwin to write and publish his *Origin of Species* without further delay."

Throughout all his researches Darwin had been in the habit of methodically cataloguing and indexing not only his notes but also all the books containing passages relating to the subject of the transmutation of species. This habit proved fortunate for he was able to handle his material with facility. Here was an opportunity to review in a single sweep all the work of the past twenty years.

As he approached the end of the book, the potentialities of his theory overwhelmed him once more. What might not be discovered by scientists concerning the natural world now that they had this yardstick of natural selection to apply?

He tried hard to avoid a discussion of man as a product of the same natural forces that operate through the principle of natural selection. He realized that the origin of man was inextricably bound up with that of the animal world—"our fellows in pain, disease, suffering, famine and death—our slaves in the most laborious works, our companions in our amusements." He feared to do more than suggest a common origin, since it was abundantly plain that people were not prepared for any attempt to delve very far into the subject of man. Apparently, too, many cherished sanctities were at stake. For that reason Darwin restrained himself. Carefully choosing his words, he wrote on the last page of his great manuscript: "Much light will be thrown on the origin of man and his history." The implication was obvious.

Finally he was ready for the press. Lyell suggested John Murray of London as publisher. To him the manuscript was forwarded and in the early part of November, 1859, the first edition of the *Origin of Species* was presented to the world.

16

Darwin could hardly wait for the reviews and comments on his book, so anxious was he to learn how the world was receiving his theory. Reports were not slow in coming. The great naturalist had underestimated the eager interest his doctrines would arouse.

Never had a scientific work created such general interest. The first edition of more than a thousand copies was sold on the day of publication; Darwin had to get immediately to work on a new one. People were asking for the book everywhere, actually bewildering the booksellers who never dreamed there would be such a demand for a biological treatise.

Hooker was the first to announce his complete conversion. Lyell hastened to inform him that he planned to include Darwin's ideas in a new book he was preparing on the antiquity of man. From far and wide letters began to pour in. Besides Hooker and Lyell there was one other scientist whose opinion Darwin eagerly sought—a brilliant young zoologist, Thomas Huxley. Several days passed and when no word had come from Huxley, Darwin became uneasy and deeply pained. But in the meantime other letters flowed in: from Carpenter the physiologist, Sir John Lubbock the zoologist, Jenyns the paleontologist, H. C. Watson the botanist. All wrote to Darwin expressing their adherence to the new doctrine.

The clergy were not much slower than the scientists in learning about evolution. As expected, they were vehemently against it, rapidly forming an opposition headed by Samuel Wilberforce, the Bishop of Oxford. Seeing that the theory of natural selection invalidated the biblical account of creation, the clergy rightly sensed a dangerous attack on the dogma of the fixity of species. For that reason Darwin was loudly denounced; his work was called an "utterly rotten fabric of guess and speculation." Lesser men than Wilberforce asked Darwin how he dared to set up his doctrines over the teaching of the Bible.

Not all the churchmen in those days were antagonistic. While the vast majority were rabidly against Darwin, certain liberal theologians were inclined to see in the new theory a greater revelation of divinity. Charles Kingsley wrote to Darwin on November 18, saying that what he had thus far seen of the book awed him. Much that he had cherished would have to be swept away. But, he added, "in that I care little. Let God be true, and every man a liar! Let us know what *is*."

Strained from all the labor and excitement of getting his book ready for publication, Darwin decided to take a rest and accordingly left home on November 23 to take the water cure at Ilkley. He was sorry he had not heard from Huxley. But that very day Huxley, having cleared his desk from the mass of work upon it, wrote Darwin a note of sincere appreciation. The letter reached the theorist at Ilkley.

No testimonial could have been more pleasing to the weary naturalist than the hearty congratulations Huxley offered. With a few reservations and corrections (which Darwin eagerly incorporated into his theory) Huxley announced his wholehearted support.

He asked Darwin not to allow himself to become "disgusted or annoyed by the considerable abuse and misrepresentation which, unless I greatly mistake, is in store for you." It was good advice coming from a young man who declared he would take the field in controversy to defend the theory against the "curs who would bark and yelp" at it. "I am sharpening up my claws and beak in readiness," he wrote. Later he was to change the metaphor and refer to himself as "Darwin's bulldog."

With the evolutionary controversy raging stronger every day each side now had a leader: Huxley for Darwin, and Wilberforce for the clergy. In the churches throughout the land sermons were preached against the new monster and his associates. Darwin was denounced from pulpit to pulpit as an anti-Christ, a God-smasher, an enemy of the people.

It was to be expected that so revolutionary an idea would meet with emphatic public disfavor. It has always been the customary fate of new doctrines to be misunderstood and misapplied. One of the most prevalent of the misconceptions disseminated by the anti-Darwinians was that which misinterpreted the doctrine of evolution to imply that men are descended from monkeys. It is astounding how widespread this error is even today.

Darwin, to be sure, had avoided developing the application of his theory to man, but this policy turned out to be an error in judgment; for the public, lacking any studied investigation of this point, drew its own erroneous conclusion, namely, that man was descended from the monkeys. But evolution taught, not that men had monkeys for their ancestors, but that both men and the monkeys had a common origin in the remote depths of time and that both had branched out from a common progenitor of the prehistoric past. From this ancestor, who had been neither man nor ape, man had descended along one line of development and the monkeys along another. At no time did Darwin say that humans are descended from any of the various ape types. His claim was that apes are distant cousins —that is, allied to man—rather than ancestors of humanity.

Once having misunderstood the matter, the public was in no mood to change its views. The battle was now carried to the newspapers and magazines over the country. Most of the reviews were definitely against the new doctrine, although no clear or cogent argument was advanced by the opponents. For Darwin, by his careful and detailed elucidation of every possible objection to his theory, had forestalled his enemies. Every argument against his doctrine had been given in the *Origin of Species* so clearly and completely that there was little that his critical enemies could add. Nevertheless Darwin knew only too well that his work was in for a long campaign of misunderstanding and vilification. The *Athenaeum* led off with an anonymous review that ridiculed what it called the author's "evident self-satisfaction" and his airy manner of disposing of all difficulties. Other reviews accused Darwin of having made "an insane attempt to dethrone God"; he was called "an inhaler of mephitic gas"; his argument was a "jungle of fanciful assumption." Such was the tenor of the opposition that it carried little weight with those men of science who knew Darwin to be a painstaking, careful investigator and anything but cocksure.

It was difficult to get a correct exposition of the Darwinian point of view into any of the older papers, which were naturally conservative. A great coup however was scored by Huxley when he managed to obtain the assignment to review the book in *The Times*. The regular reviewer, Lucas, had been at a loss to know what to do with the *Origin of Species,* scientific books being out of his line. A friend suggested he ask Huxley to review it. Huxley did, giving a careful and lucid presentation of the theory. The review appeared anonymously in *The Times* of December 26. Lucas had made the formal gesture of writing a few introductory paragraphs; but the body of the long and widely read review was Huxley's (although this was not generally known).

Everybody was now talking about the theory of evolution, reviling Darwin for the most part. And yet, such was the intellectual climate of the age, one seemed to sense in the very air of the controversy the essential truth of the new teaching and the inevitability of its success.

17

While his friends were fighting for the new gospel, Darwin, prevented both by health and his naturally gentle disposition from active participation in the battles, went back to work. He gathered his notes on artificial selection into a book on *Variation under Domestication* whose publication added still more evidence to that of the *Origin*.

The *Origin* itself took a great deal of his time. As the editions mounted and suggestions and corrections continued to come in from naturalists all over the world, Darwin was supremely happy. Nothing was more characteristic of the man than his sincere humility which was based on the vast and haunting sense of his own ignorance. Anyone interested in learning the extent of Darwin's open-mindedness should compare the first and last editions of the *Origin*, and remember that nearly all the sweeping changes he will find are the direct or indirect result of outside information and advice offered to the writer.

While Huxley led the actual battle, Darwin himself won many converts. His reputation for accuracy, for scientific completeness, for generous and honest tolerance was gradually acknowledged even by his opponents. The stories of his kindliness and gentle character made a deep impression on those ordinary everyday citizens who were inclined at first to accept the verdict of their clergymen and condemn him as Satan's representative on earth.

Meanwhile his work advanced and with it the recognition of his theory. As early as 1863 the Reverend Charles Kingsley wrote to a friend abroad: "The state of the scientific mind is most curious; Darwin is conquering everywhere, and rushing in like a flood by the mere force of truth and fact." The flood had progressed so far that in 1871 Huxley was able to point to a complete revolution in biological science produced by the *Origin* and to compare it with a somewhat similar revolution produced in astronomy by Isaac Newton's *Principia*. This totally altered aspect of biology was of course due to Darwin's totally new point of view; and the research that was now being projected had a totally new and much more fruitful means of approach.

The stage in which Darwin found biology is comparable to the

Ptolemaic era in astronomy. The *Origin of Species* changed things completely. No such great body of evidence had ever been brought together before. Almost overnight the scientists who had been collecting and studying various species abandoned the old biblical doctrine and started to think anew in Darwinian terms of variation. There were, in Copernicus' day, many difficulties in the way of believing that the earth moved. So, too, in Darwin's day there were many obstacles to overcome before men could renounce the dogma of special creation. Most people were not prepared to think in transformation terms.

So profound and far-reaching was this new way of looking at nature that its influence was beginning to be felt far beyond the realms of biology. Progress in all branches of human learning was now accelerated. All the sciences were brought closer together, their interlocking relations being shown much more clearly under the light of evolution.

The theory of natural selection, besides placing upon its feet the mass of evidence for evolution, suddenly gave tremendous impetus to the search for new evidence. Men investigated geologic strata, established the immense age of the earth, and were able to ascertain at the same time the approximate age of the various fossils uncovered in these strata. The study of these fossils and the knowledge of their antiquity shed a bright light upon the meaning of evolution, for in these imperishable records of the past it was possible to trace the successive species of animal and vegetable life from the first lowly forms to the highly developed types of the present time. The quest for intermediate forms—the missing links— in the evolutionary tree became intensified, and before Darwin's death many such specimens were discovered. In 1880 the American O. C. Marsh bridged the gap between reptiles and birds by the discovery in North America of a large deposit of fossil-toothed birds, an indisputable link. Very significant discoveries were those fragments of early man which have been found in Java (1894); in Belgium (1886); in south Germany (1907); in England (1912). All these specimens were not identical, but represented varying degrees of advancement along the trail to modern man. The finds in each case were fragmentary, consisting often of no more than a portion of a jawbone, a few teeth, a part of a thigh. But so remarkable is the science of comparative anatomy that from these fragments the entire skeletons of our remote ancestors have been reconstructed. Thus man's antiquity has come to be measured not in centuries but in millions of years.

18

Not content to rest on his laurels after the publication of the *Origin of Species* and the collection of his notes on domestic variation, Darwin continued working up to the day of his death—still under the same conditions of poor health. One of the chief difficulties in his theory—the explanation of apparently useless parts of flowers—he met and solved by a monumental work on orchids, in which he was able to show that each ridge and projection in their elaborate blossoms had its own function in the struggle for existence.

In February, 1867, he had an interval of spare time. Anxious to write about the application of natural selection to man he began a "chapter," but soon found it growing. After several interruptions he sat down to continuous work and in 1871 there appeared *The Descent of Man*. The publication was Darwin's answer to those who had long taunted him with being afraid to apply the same natural laws to man's origin as he had applied to the origin of species. *The Descent of Man* aroused a tremendous interest throughout the world: it dispelled the fond dreams of sentimental idealists who had hoped that the belief in man's separateness and special creation might be preserved. In the closing words of this book Darwin said:

"We must, however, acknowledge, as it seems to me, that man with all his noble qualities, with sympathy which feels for the most debased, with benevolence, which extends not only to other men but to the humblest living creature, with his Godlike intellect, which has penetrated into the movements and constitution of the solar system—with all these exalted powers—man still bears in his bodily frame the indelible stamp of his lowly origin."

The uncertainties of humanity's pedigree and antiquity are still great, but it is not to be denied that the mass of evidence brought to light since Darwin wrote *The Descent of Man* sufficiently proves that man and ape are divergent offshoots of a common stock.

Each year Darwin came more and more to be consulted as a court of last resort in all matters of natural history. Young scientists sent their books to him for criticism; the mail from his readers assumed stupendous proportions.

19

Slowly the die-hard conservatives of the scientific world, realizing his importance, began to change their attitude toward the man and his theory. A growing crop of medals, honors, appointments, honorary degrees and other emoluments poured in upon Darwin as the years passed. As early as May, 1860, he had been elected a corresponding member of the Philadelphia Academy of Sciences. In 1864, to the horror of his enemies, he was awarded the Copley Medal of the Royal Society, the highest honor any scientist in England could attain. True, it was expressly stipulated that the award was for Darwin's work in geology, zoology and botany (the *Origin of Species* was only incidentally praised for the "mass of observations" it contained), but the recognition, however shamefaced, was there.

His honorary LL.D. degree from Cambridge broke that university's rule of never awarding honorary degrees to its own graduates. Other awards and honorary elections came to him from abroad, from Prussia, France, Italy and Holland. The Emperor of Brazil expressed a desire to meet him. Apparently everyone was now turning to him, praising the name of the man who a few years before had been reviled as an atheist and a degenerate.

Darwin took little notice of these honors other than to acknowledge them with a courteous expression of gratitude. He continued his researches, publishing a huge volume on earthworms in 1877. But now his research was more handicapped than ever by his malady; the constantly recurring attacks of nausea cut short his working periods; more and more frequent trips to the water resorts had to be made. But he never thought of easing his labors or abating a jot of the apparently endless energy that had carried him so far. In one of his works he casually mentions having counted under a microscope over twenty thousand seeds of a certain plant!

Toward the summer of 1881 the burden of his malady grew heavier; he felt he had not much longer to go. With his instinct for thoroughness he did not undertake any new line of research, fearing lest he might leave it unfinished. He grew weak and tired as the end of the year approached.

In December heart attacks began. The first came when he had gone to London. He was suddenly stricken on the steps of George Romanes' house. The butler saw his condition and wanted him to come in and rest; but Darwin, to the last unwilling to discommode anyone, protested weakly that he could manage by himself. The butler saw him totter down the street and get into a cab.

The attacks became more frequent in February. On April 15, 1882, he was seized while at dinner and was confined to his bed the next day. He got up toward afternoon and made some notes on the progress of an experiment. But this little effort seemed to have exhausted him again, for at midnight a severe attack gripped him and he realized he was close to the end. "I am not the least afraid to die," he whispered to his family gathered about his bed.

Next morning weariness crept over him and life slowly ebbed away. Soon he sank into unconsciousness and at four in the afternoon he died.

His family wanted him to be buried at Down where he had lived; but the pressure of public and scientific opinion caused the interment to be in Westminster Abbey. It was there, in the presence of representatives of the scientific societies of all the world, that Charles Darwin was laid to rest next to Sir Isaac Newton.

10. Marx . . . . . THEORY OF THE
ECONOMIC INTERPRETATION OF HISTORY

BEFORE the advent of Darwin all biology was in a stage comparable to astronomy before Copernicus. What Darwin and Copernicus did for their respective sciences Karl Marx accomplished in the domain of history. Few theorists have possessed so colossal a mind, especially in its ability to absorb the thinking of men of diverse nationalities.

Just as Darwin had his predecessors, so too had Marx; and just as Darwin was profoundly influenced by Malthus so Marx was influenced by Hegel.

It is therefore to Hegel—Georg Wilhelm Friedrich Hegel—that we must first turn in order to understand how Karl Marx arrived at his theory of the economic interpretation of history.

2

In the autumn of 1836, four years after the death of Hegel, Karl Marx came to the University of Berlin to study history and law. The figure of Professor Hegel was still considered the brightest star in all intellectual Europe. He had had the rare honor of being elevated within his own lifetime to the post of official philosopher of Germany. From far and wide students had flocked to his lectures, for it was conceded that he ruled the philosophic world as indisputably as Goethe dominated the world of literature and Beethoven the world of music.

Hegel was unquestionably the voice of the age. Not that he had expressed its spirit of revolutionary struggle and change (he was at heart too much of a conservative to do that), but he had given to his students and his readers a formula which he called a "dialectic" whereby all the many positive and negative aspects of history, ethics, law, politics and biology could be understood.

By dialectic Hegel meant a process of thinking which would give a complete insight into the dramatic conflict of ideas, institutions, and societies. Through it one could see with amazing clarity that a great harmonizing principle (synthesis) was also at work in nature and history, forever bringing unity out of the conflict. Dialectic, therefore, soon became the name of the process by which all things grow, change, and redevelop.

Consider an egg. It is something positive, but it contains within itself a germ which gradually changes the contents. This change (negation) is not destruction or annihilation: it results in a living thing. Thus Hegel taught that all things are not static but transitional. One sex is the antithesis of the other, yet out of the antithetical relationship there emerges the living individual. Hegel insisted that we must think dialectically because the facts which we think about develop dialectically. In this process every movement produces, by an automatic reaction, its opposite; and of the resulting conflict between opposites, between thesis and antithesis, is born the final synthesis.

Hegel's dialectic made a profound impression. Everywhere men were eager for just such an understanding. In an age of change it is marvelous to grasp large certainties. It was an era of movement, an age that had seen old states die and attempts made at the formation of new ones. The Industrial Revolution, which was to doom all previously existing forms of economic relations, had already begun its inevitable process. A static world had rapidly become a dynamic one.

Into this tumultuous age there had shot the mind of Hegel—a man with a formula. He saw all life as a process of change, of combination, of struggle and development. Because he was a philosopher, Hegel attempted to grasp history in an all-embracing system of logic. His attempt was a brilliant and profound intellectual feat which influenced a whole generation, including the mind of a young student who was to become not only a great theorist but also a great and original economist.

3

Hegel wrote many books and they are all difficult to read because his ideas are couched in language that is often obscure. It has long been claimed that when a man talks about what he does not understand to a lot of people who do not understand him he is talking "metaphysics." Such a charge, especially in Hegel's case, states a certain truth which is borne out in the story told about a French-man who asked Hegel to put his philosophy into one sentence. Hegel said he preferred to answer in ten volumes. When the vol-umes were published and all the world was talking about them, Hegel complained that "only one man understands me, and at times even he does not."

The most suggestive thing Hegel did was to explain the mean-ing of "relation." Hegel showed that everything in the universe is related or dependent; he showed that we cannot intelligently discuss anything except by reference to something other than that which we talk of. For example, we cannot talk about the floor without implying the walls, any more than we can talk about fish without implying water; nor can we talk about the sky without implying the earth. Likeness has no meaning apart from difference. The universe is a systematic whole of interrelated qualities (positive and nega-tive). Every actual thing involves a coexistence of contrary elements. Consequently to know (or comprehend) anything is equivalent to being conscious of it as a unified group of contrarieties. The truth about any thing or any idea involves the truth of contrast and oppo-sition. Thus that which existed a moment ago (thesis) contained its opposition (antithesis), and has now resulted in a compromise or union (synthesis).

Here then is the famous Hegelian formula that impressed itself so indelibly on the mind of Marx—thesis, antithesis and synthesis. All the wide reading he had done suddenly took on meaning. His-tory was no longer a tranquil growth but a working through oppo-sition—a triadic movement which is the law of all development. History was no longer a mass of happenings but a unity emerging amidst opposing diversities. So profoundly had Marx been in-fluenced by this dialectical way of looking at things that his son-in-law Lafargue once remarked that "he never saw a thing-by-itself, out of touch with its setting; but contemplated it as a part of a complicated and mobile world of things. His aim was to expand all the life of this world of things in its manifold and incessantly vary-ing action and reaction."

4

Granted that all life and all history are shot through and through with this threefold movement of thesis, antithesis and synthesis, the next question that arises is: What causes this movement?

Hegel answered by saying that it is the work of the Absolute—that is, God or Mind or Cosmic Spirit—which is marching on through time. The march of the absolute is, at bottom, a spiritual process that ceaselessly realizes itself in successive steps from the lowest forms to the highest. To Hegel, God was the absolute mind, for whom the whole organized system of things exists. God is the unitary spirit, and the whole creation lives in His own concrete differences of nature, of men and of things.

Hegel spoke and wrote a great deal about the absolute in language eminently inhuman. Essentially he was a philosopher and philosophers very often mix wisdom with obscurantism, so that side by side with their flashes of illumination there are to be found all too frequently the dark aspects of things incomprehensible. So it was with Hegel. For that reason young Marx did not hesitate to take from Hegel what he thought important and discard the irrelevant.

The Hegelian dialectic is what Marx considered important; the Hegelian absolute is what he considered irrelevant. When Marx came to answer the question: What causes the triadic movement? he bluntly stated it wasn't the absolute—far from it! Economic causes, not the march of the absolute, said Marx, account for the movements of history. Marx discovered that the economic factor is the fundamental factor in human history. He did not say, as many people erroneously believe, that it is the *only* factor. Because the Marxian theory maintains that economic forces are primary, it is frequently called "the materialistic interpretation of history."

But it would be a grave mistake to say that the Marxian theory is materialistic in the sense in which people ordinarily use that word. It is true, on the one hand, that Marx rejected Hegel's absolute; but it is also true (and this is what many wholly forget or ignore) that Marx also rejected the passive materialism of Feuerbach and the "vulgar" materialism of Buchner, Vogt and Moleschott.

Ludwig Feuerbach (1804-1872) was a German philosopher who also greatly influenced Karl Marx. Like Marx, Feuerbach accepted the Hegelian dialectic (thesis, antithesis and synthesis); also like Marx, Feuerbach rejected Hegel's idea of the march of the absolute. Feuerbach was an out and out materialist. Whereas Hegel made the universe arise out of pure reason, out of the logical absolute idea, developing through the dialectical process, Feuerbach claimed that nature (not God) comes first, and nature is at bottom matter. Feuerbach argued that God did not make man, but that man made God, and that man fundamentally is nothing more than the product of the mechanical forces of nature. Instead of seeing in the Hegelian dialectic the march of the absolute, Feuerbach saw nothing else but the march of material forces.

Feuerbach's materialism was of the most mechanical kind in which man came to be regarded as nothing more than a machine— a creature of his own appetite. So thoroughgoing was the materialism of Feuerbach with its denial of the role of mind, that his statement *Der Mensch ist was er isst* (man is what he eats) summed up in one sentence the nature of this mechanical generalization.

But to Marx man was more than a machine. To explain the whole of society on the basis of "man is what he eats" is contrary to facts, for man is in possession of consciousness and his consciousness is determined by a highly complex set of historico-economic situations. To claim that man is the result solely of environment overlooks the fact that environment itself can be changed by man. "The materialistic doctrine," Marx said in one of his critical notes on Feuerbach, "that men are products of conditions and education, different men therefore products of other conditions, and a different kind of education, forgets that circumstances may be altered by man and that the educator has himself to be educated."

Unfortunately for Hegel he was intoxicated with philosophical idealism; unfortunately for Feuerbach he was intoxicated with philosophical materialism. Marx early in his career grasped the inconsistency, the incompleteness and the lopsidedness of both. It seemed to him that Feuerbach's attempt to take Hegel's absolute idea and relabel it "matter" solved nothing. Both views contained a blunt disregard of economic and industrial facts. Both views were far more inaccurate than the followers of Hegel and Feuerbach were prepared to realize.

5

Certainly man is more than a machine. Marx knew it—he was in love! He was secretly engaged to Jenny, the daughter of Baron von Westphalen. His first year at the University of Berlin did not give him much happiness, for he was tossed about by spiritual and mental unrest. Not only was he far away from his beloved Jenny, but in those formative years Marx was also a poet sensitive to all the delicate nuances of beauty and romance. To those who are acquainted with the seemingly sober and unemotional pattern of his later career it may strike a somewhat strange note to recall that the first published work of the author of the theory of the economic interpretation of history was a lyric poem! "Everything was centered on poetry," he said of his early student days in Berlin, "as if I were bewitched by some unearthly power." Romantic rather than classical literature made the strongest appeal to him at this particular time, when he was working night and day studying philosophy, jurisprudence, history, geography and countless other things.

Against the wishes of her family and friends Marx claimed Jenny. Not all the study, discussion and intellectual adventure of these student days could reduce or minimize his romantic attachment. Under duress the engagement was temporarily broken. Relatives of the Westphalen family did not like the idea of a Prussian nobleman's daughter marrying a Jew. Even though Karl Marx had been baptized when he was only six years old, still it was remembered that practically every one of Marx's male forebears, both on his father's and mother's side, had been rabbis.

In 1841 young Marx received his degree of Doctor of Philosophy. Together with an instructor and friend, Bruno Bauer, he sought a position as lecturer at the University of Bonn. But he did not get the appointment. He was about to marry Jenny when the lectureship was refused him, and he suddenly realized that he had yet to find a career. Here the forces of economic necessity played their part in directing the young man's destiny to its goal. He turned to journalism for his livelihood, joining the staff of the *Rheinische Zeitung,* a radical paper published in Cologne. But the paper did not last very long. Early in 1843 the government sup-

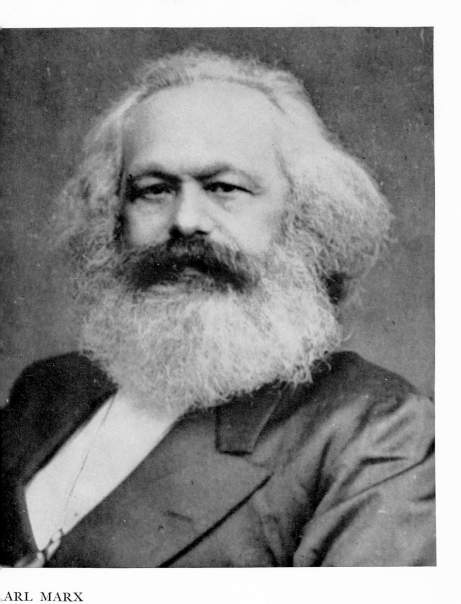

ARL MARX

pressed it. Nevertheless Marx was in love—and that the government could not suppress. So in the summer of this year he married Jenny and a few months later moved to Paris.

6

Long before he came to Paris he had felt the great need of knowing more about French political and economic thought. Not that French thinking was anything new to him, but there was always in him the restless quest for more accurate knowledge and a deeper understanding.

From his early childhood years Marx had been familiar with French ways, for he was brought up in close sympathy with his father's ideas (Marx's father was a lawyer and a disciple of the eighteenth century philosophers). In a study of the theory of economic interpretation no one ought ever to underestimate the powerful influence of the French materialistic philosophers upon Marx —men like Diderot, Helvetius, d'Alembert, Holbach. These men were the forerunners of the French Revolution, ruthless critics of church and state. Moreover, they always looked to the material facts, not to metaphysical abstractions, for the explanation of the nature of man and of society.

Already in his youth Marx had felt this powerful intellectual current. As a child he was familiar with Diderot and Voltaire. And now that he was grown up and actually living on French soil, he felt within himself something strangely akin to those august thinkers who were unwilling to believe anything on authority. From them he learned how to investigate facts with patience, how to insist on the value of positive knowledge, and how to attain to a comprehensiveness which would confer upon him the power of generalization. Like these men young Marx began to exhibit an encyclopedic learning: a mind like a vast ocean lapping many shores.

Marx was now twenty-five years old. When he arrived in the French capital with his bride, the socialist movement was at its zenith. But the socialism of that day was not the socialism of Marx. So great has been the impression left by Marx upon socialist thought that one hardly ever hears about the socialism of Owen, Saint-Simon and Fourier, whose theories he wiped out by his projection of the economic interpretation of history.

No man in the world had studied with such avidity the works of the French socialists as Karl Marx. For that reason no one was better prepared to analyze them and point out their defects. The fundamental fault in all the socialists he had read was their unscientific approach. Instead of attempting to seek out the origins and sources of capitalism and in this way come to realize the essential nature of the system they were fighting, they wasted their time and that of their readers in painting fanciful utopias where all the difficulties of capitalism would be eliminated by a beneficent government of workers. The fallacy of utopianism was easily grasped by Marx. What these socialists needed was a sound appreciation of the economic realities underlying human existence. What was to be done was also clear to Marx: to discard utopias and to apply the vigor of dialectical analysis of past history to present politics as well as to future societies. It was useless to play with hopes and fears and ideas. There was the stern reality of economic law to be faced.

7

In Paris he associated with both German and French writers. There was the poet Heinrich Heine, the publicist Arnold Ruge, the socialist Pierre Joseph Proudhon. He was intimate with them all. Heine's poetry made an especial appeal to Marx. Long years after the poet's death when Marx was living in exile in London, he loved to quote the incorrigible nonconformist Heine, "that queer fowl, a poet," as Marx once put it.

Marx in Paris was a busy young man reading, studying, meeting people. The summer and autumn of 1843 were given over to intensive intellectual work. He reread the histories of France, Germany and the United States, seeking for those economic factors that would bear out his own interpretation of history. The writings of Machiavelli, Rousseau, Montesquieu and Ricardo were likewise given the keenest kind of sifting and analysis. Out of all this vast reading there developed in his mind additionally strong confirmation of his early views touching the relation of history to economics.

History, Marx came to believe, must be scientifically studied without resort to mystical conceptions such as Hegel's absolute idea. To separate history from natural science and industry was like separating the soul from the body and "finding the birthplace of history, not in the gross material production of earth, but in the misty cloud formation of heaven."

Thus it was abundantly plain to him that economic phenomena determine all other historical facts and make it possible to explain the vast complex of human affairs. In this matter it is clear that absolute and irrefutable proof is hardly possible. In the physical sciences a great many phenomena repeat themselves, with a sufficient uniformity as to details and time intervals to be stated, for practical purposes, in the form of "laws." In the social sciences, at best only a high degree of probability seems attainable. Therefore that theory works best which explains most satisfactorily the body of facts under examination, so that the high degree of probability is secured by the convergence toward one conclusion of a number of facts so great that any other explanation becomes absurd.

Taking certain ideas of Hegel as a point of departure, Marx was able to demonstrate the whole nexus of relations that exists between the superstructure of society and its material basis. He unraveled the connection between economics and politics, between economics and culture, between economics and the course of history. For the first time history was set up on its real foundation, not as a narrative of war and peace, of royal genealogies, of unrelated dates, but as a record of man's vital existence through the ages. Instead of being a romantic tale it now became the study of the great mass of mankind, how it lived and struggled and moved forward.

The lamentable disregard for the economic aspects which characterized the thinking of the philosophers and historians of the past was completely checked by Marx. With profound insight and determined scholarship he marshaled his arguments in such a way that he was able to construct a moving dynamic theory of history. Moreover, by that theory he was able to point out how one stage of society grew into another in a steady transition. The new society did not wait impatiently off stage while the old took its final bows. It grew up within the old, and when it had attained full maturity, the shell of outmoded laws, political institutions and culture fell from it.

The more Marx delved into history the more he realized the

importance of economic production. Production determined the spirit of whatever age he studied. The social, political, religious and intellectual life of a people is built upon it and around it. Because it is the basic element in the struggle for existence, it conditions and develops the consciousness of men. Marx set the horse before the cart for the first time with his statement: "It is not the consciousness of mankind that determines its existence, but on the contrary its social existence determines its consciousness."

This was the keynote, sounded now for the first time, of the theory of economic interpretation of history. Before we proceed further with Marx and see how he elaborated his conception, it is worthwhile to consider previous theories of history, to see just how weighty was the tradition that this obscure German journalist, unaware where he would get enough money to support himself and his wife through the winter, now set out to overturn.

8

As long as language has existed men have employed it to record their doings. But history is more than the sum total of all of man's records about himself. It is a phase of the universal process in which he lives and of which he is. To compile records and collect data is not sufficient; the records and the data stand in need of interpretation. History, therefore, is more than the record of history, more than the narrative of surface events.

The ancient Greeks were the initiators of genuine historical writing. Herodotus, the father of history, is still an important source book. Now Herodotus of course is full of fairy tales, but he is also full of vivid descriptions of the life and times in which he wrote. Interpretation, however, except in the shallow sense of seeking to glorify Athenian democracy, was lacking.

With Thucydides a canon of historical criticism was established: first, that it must be accurate; second, that it must be relevant to the main stream of events; third, that what we know of the past "will be useful, because, according to human probability, similar things will happen again." Polybius, perhaps a better historian in the modern sense than either Herodotus or Thucydides, established a method of scientific history, in which he insisted upon a knowledge of geography and topography, and a philosophical attitude.

All these Greek writers, and the Romans who followed them,
failed to understand the underlying economic and social causes
of historical events and movements. Polybius in his limited way
perceived an impersonal, latent basis, but it seemed to him ethical
rather than economic, while both Thucydides and Herodotus emphasized the influence of personalities and dramatic effects.

With the fall of the Roman Empire and the growth of Christianity as the principal power of Western civilization, history soon
lost even the meager scientific basis it possessed, as the Fathers of
the Church proceeded to convert it to their own theological purposes. The first of their desires was to establish a reputable past
for Christianity: to do this it was necessary to take certain aspects
of Jewish history, hitherto assigned to an insignificant position in
historical writing, and elevate them to the rank of the major movement in civilization, finally fulfilling its destiny in producing the
Church. Then they laid hold of the miracles and legends surrounding the personality of Jesus, his disciples and the saints, and wove
them into a mighty transcendental drama. In doing this they had
to minimize and discredit all pagan history. Accordingly they
painted all non-Christian history as a horrible nightmare of war,
pestilence, crime, misery and godlessness. St. Augustine for example
saw only two kingdoms on earth: the kingdom of Satan and the
kingdom of God. Everything pertaining to the Church was of God
and therefore good, whereas all else was of Satan and consequently
wicked.

This theological interpretation, with its idea of divine interposi-
tion and direction through miracles, was a consistent attempt to
give coherency to the stream of events. As such it made a powerful
appeal to the medieval mind. For fifteen hundred years it remained
the supreme and "revealed" interpretation of history.

With the dawn of the Renaissance and the Humanist movements
in the arts and sciences, this theological manner of viewing history
could not long continue. Even in the medieval period just before
the Renaissance there were historians who sought to get back to
the calm and careful amassing of data that had been the custom
before the Church Fathers began to write their manuscripts. Most
notable of these was Otto Freising, who wrote world history with
less of a supernatural bias, although there was not yet that recog-

R

nition of underlying causes which the more advanced Greek and Roman writers had attained. Beside Freising, there was the Arab Ibn Khaldun, who was one of the first to insist upon a development in history and to conceive of it as a process of origin and growth.

With the coming of the modern era men like Flavius Blondus, Machiavelli, Guicciardini discarded the Church's clumsy attempts and proceeded to pick up the thread where the Greeks and Romans had been cut off. With Machiavelli a particularly new and important addition was made: the recognition of cause and effect in the political evolution of the city of Florence. Unfortunately, the value of this point of view was not immediately perceived. The idea of causation in the study of history was too far removed from the rut created by the medieval Church. Slowly and by very gradual degrees, however, it began making some headway. Voltaire, Vico, Turgot, Condorcet and others were able to emancipate themselves from theological restrictions. In his *Age of Louis XIV*, Voltaire sought to describe the totality of French civilization in terms of the "folk-soul" or the "genius of a people," which he considered the main determining factor in history. Vico, the Italian, wrote in terms of a theory of cycles. Turgot and Condorcet laid stress on the principles of continuity and causality.

Brilliant and courageous as were these newer writings, they still missed the main point; none had yet got to the fundamentals of historical causes. In Montesquieu we find an advance over all predecessors. This Frenchman sought to analyze Voltaire's "spirit of a people" in terms of topography, geography, climate. He insisted that the institutions of a society were worthwhile only insofar as they were adapted to the spirit of that society. This point of view was a tremendous leap forward and gave ample promise for the future. (It must always be borne in mind that Marx was saturated with the French philosophers and that the indistinct glimmerings of their thought reached its effulgence through him.)

With the nineteenth century began the creation of the philosophical superstructure that was to reach its peak in Hegel. The principal exponents of this philosophical idealism applied to history the Hegelian *Weltgeist* (World Spirit), which to them culminated in German *Kultur*. History to Hegel was (as we have already seen) a dialectical movement full of wide swings now to the right and now

to the left, in which people are little more than instruments in the
hands of God, the Absolute, expressing itself through the *Zeitgeist,*
the Spirit of the Age.

Quite different from this point of view is the conception of history found in the writings of Michelet, Froude, and Thomas Carlyle
—all contemporaries of Marx. In the works of these men there is
not only a profound contempt for the economic basis of daily life,
but an insistence on the role of the hero, the great man, the individual leader, the striking personality. In this highly subjective view
of history, with its unconcern with other than the immediate environment, we can see clearly the background of the opposing historical schools against which Marx hurled his challenge—the economic interpretation of history. No historian but Marx could have
written in that day that "in changing the modes of production
mankind changes all its social relations, the hand mill creates a
society with the feudal lord, a steam mill a society with the industrial capitalist." Why? Because Karl Marx was the first to grasp the
essential difference between the "techniques" of production and the
"modes" of production. By *techniques* he meant the inventions, the
machines, the skills, the organization of factories whereby men produce the goods they need. By *modes* he meant the social and property relations which determine the ownership and control of these
means as well as their distribution. When the techniques of production undergo great development, the older social and property
relations frequently become inadequate and act more and more as
a barrier to the continuing progress of society. This lag creates an
intolerable situation. To permit the techniques (the means) of production to develop further, and thereby to serve more adequately
the needs of man, it becomes necessary to overthrow the older social
and property relations and establish new ones. This is what Marx
meant by a revolution.

Thus the clash between the techniques of production and the
modes of production is the fundamental fact that Marx demonstrated to historians who had been ignoring it for centuries.

9

Marx was in Paris only a short while when he undertook, jointly
with Arnold Ruge, the publication of a periodical called the

Deutsch-Französische Jahrbücher (Franco-German Yearbooks). Unfortunately the adventure began and ended with the first number. It was not long after this that Marx and Ruge became intellectually estranged. In August, 1844, under the title *Marginal Notes*, Marx published in a Paris magazine a lengthy polemic against Ruge, defending socialism and revolution and taking the part of the German proletariat.

Unlike Darwin, Marx was a fighter—a thinker and a fighter rolled into one. "Before all else, Marx was a revolutionist," declared Friedrich Engels, when he spoke the last words that closed the theorist's career at Highgate Cemetery in London. "Few men ever fought with so much passion." These words that Engels uttered so touchingly in 1883 were true of Marx in September, 1844, when Engels came to Paris to join hands and heart with Karl and Jenny.

Fortunately for Marx there was Engels. Never did a theorist need a friend and helper more. To be sure, they had a great deal in common. Both men were born in the Rhine province of Prussia —Marx at Treves in 1818, Engels at Barmen in 1820. For centuries this district had witnessed the intermingling of the forces of French and German civilization: here they fought and trafficked, producing a blended culture of a rich and active type.

Marx and Engels first met in Cologne in 1842. It was a brief meeting for Engels was on his way to England to represent his father's business. The firm owned a cotton mill near Manchester.

In 1844 Engels came to Paris to see Marx with the very definite purpose of aligning himself with the economic theorist. Engels had already contributed an article to the first and only issue of the *Deutsch-Französische Jahrbücher*. It was this article entitled *Outlines for a Criticism of Political Economy* that marked the beginning of a lifelong friendship. The two men had found a close correspondence between their conceptions of history and society. Strangely enough Engels, while apart from Marx, hit upon the idea of economic interpretation. Like Wallace in the case of Darwin, Engels was first to admit that Marx's discovery was wholly independent and that the Marxian explanation was "scientific."

Until he had met Karl Marx and was converted, Friedrich Engels was an utopian socialist. During an active business career he managed to find abundant opportunity to think about economic problems. Because of their complexity he was eagerly seeking a more satisfactory approach when Marx expounded his views. Straightway Engels became the first Marxian disciple, second only to Marx in insight, comprehension and self-sacrifice.

10

Under the stimulus of Engels, Marx began to formulate his ideas more and more clearly, and to cast about for something upon which to sharpen his teeth. He soon found it in his one time friend Bruno Bauer.

Bauer, typical of the young Hegelians, had failed to heed Marx's call for a reorganization of the dialectical heritage of Hegel on a more realistic basis. Bauer persisted in maintaining the mystical doctrine that ideas and great men are the only sources of historical movements. Marx, of course, used the Hegelian formula of thesis, antithesis and synthesis, but he substituted a naturalistic principle (which he identified with the economic factors of existence) for the Hegelian notion of the absolute idea. In other words, Marx called for a dialectic of economic conditions and development.

Now it so happened that Bauer and his brother Edgar had founded a new paper in which they attacked the Marxian tendency in Hegelianism. Marx, with the assistance of Engels, hastened to reply in a book which made its appearance under the sarcastic title *Die Heilige Familie* (The Holy Family).

For us the book is exceedingly valuable not so much because of its bitter polemic but because we find in its pages the first clear statement of the theory of the economic interpretation. "Do these gentlemen think that they can understand the first word of history," asks Marx, "as long as they exclude the relations of man to nature, natural science and industry? . . . Do they believe that they can actually comprehend any epoch without grasping the industry of the period, the immediate methods of production in actual life?" He ridicules the airy philosophers who refuse to see that the birthplace of history is not in the clouds of heaven but in the gross material production of the earth on which they stand. Change in human society does not originate from the metaphysical idea, the Hegelian *Weltgeist*, or any such speculative notion, but from the material conditions of life. For this reason the economic foundation, Marx argued, was the *Unterbau* (basis) of society which has always determined the *Oberbau* (superstructure) of art, religion and science.

11

As he advanced further in economic history Marx attacked the older socialists in the person of Pierre Joseph Proudhon (1809-1865). The French capital at this period literally swarmed with social theorists. There were anarchists, socialists, communists, Weitlingists, Proudhonists, syndicalists, Cabetians, Fourierists, Owenites—all agreeing in their condemnation of the old system, but bitterly opposing one another in their conceptions of how that system should be changed. To Marx it was clear that the diversity of views was due to each man's "opinion." Now, the true definition of opinion is ignorance of facts, for where there are *facts* there is no need of opinion. Furthermore, who is to decide between opinions and declare this right and that wrong? Marx asked men to set aside their opinions and get down to the basic facts of the interrelationship of economics and history.

Just as Darwin found it necessary to set aside the biblical doctrine of special creation in order to study nature scientifically, so too did Marx have to set aside all utopian doctrines in order to study the phenomena of society. Both Darwin and Marx dealt with vast and intricate phenomena. Both had to demolish current doctrines. Both accomplished the demolition of time-honored fallacies through the irresistible impact of facts. Unlike Darwin, Marx did not experiment, for the position of an economist is different from that of a biologist.

Against all the dreamers, all the utopians, all the sentimentalists, Karl Marx turned the battering-ram of science. Of what value are the many idealistic schemes to create a better human society when they are based upon no sound understanding of the causes for the evils which men desire to overcome? Why carelessly spin out of thin air farfetched notions of a perfect state? Are not social conditions bound up with productive power? Then why dream of changing things without first understanding the nature of productive power? Anybody can dream, said Marx, and so the philosophers give us all kinds of schemes, but the essential thing is to possess such accurate knowledge of the facts of the inner mechanism of history that society can be changed because of those facts. It was this inner mechanism that the utopians lacked; they had no dialectical approach (Marx undertook to teach dialectics to Proudhon!); no method of social analysis; in a word they were unscientific.

Furthermore, to these utopians socialism was in no way bound with space and time. They thought that it could be established at any time, at any place, without any reference whatsoever to the stage of economic development. It was only necessary—they naïvely believed—that men should come as quickly as possible to the conscious realization of what is good for them and, behold! the present system of society could be changed. Thus the utopians based their arguments upon an appeal to human nature to right *all* wrong.

To Marx, this entire point of view was utterly unscientific. Socialism, as a mere scheme calculated to improve the material conditions of society, had to be rejected as utopian. History had taught him that social systems cannot be changed at will. No magic spells or incantations can metamorphose the world. He had discovered that social systems are but a reflex of their economic foundation and therefore cannot be changed except as there has been a change in the economic foundation. For this reason Marx called for the economic interpretation, emphasizing the fact that economic interests, which are behind human behavior as well as human thinking, are rooted in the modes of production and exchange. "In the social production which men carry on they enter into definite relations that are indispensable and independent of their will; these relations of production correspond to a definite stage of development of their material powers of production."

Production, in other words, is the foundation of history; with a change in the foundation a corresponding change in the entire superstructure will follow. No system of society, declared Marx, can be established whenever and wherever we have a notion of establishing it. "No social order ever disappears before all the productive forces, for which there is room in it, have been developed; and new higher relations of production never appear before the material conditions of their existence have matured in the womb of the old society." Simply put, economic interpretation led Marx to the position that a better system of society can take the place of a wrong system only at a certain definite time, when certain conditions exist and when society has reached a certain degree of economic evolution. This Marxian point of view implies, of course, the dialectical approach to society. For this reason the task of the social scientist is not one of inventing a perfect system but of examining the "historico-economic succession of events" which produces struggle (antithesis) and of discovering the material facts destined to serve as a means of ending the conflict (synthesis). The future state cannot be manufactured by any world reformer.

12

In the thick of all these intellectual labors Marx together with Engel was busy waging fierce war on the Prussian government and taking a very active part in the seething life of the revolutionary groups of Paris. The Prussian government complained to France that the attacks upon its dignity were increasing in coarseness and impudence. At first the French government was reluctant to do anything in the matter, but was finally persuaded by Alexander von Humboldt to take steps against Marx, Ruge, Bakunin and others. On the eleventh day of January, 1845, Marx was expelled from Paris. He crossed over into Belgium and settled down in Brussels where he lived until 1848.

Marx in Brussels was no different from Marx in Paris, the same astonishing thinker and revolutionist. He had been in Brussels only a short time when he received a book from Proudhon entitled *The Philosophy of Poverty*. "I await the lash of your criticism," wrote the author to Marx.

He got it.

In refutation Marx wrote not on the philosophy of poverty but on the *Poverty of Philosophy*. It was an unforgettable and stinging rebuke which created a sensation and added much to Marx's reputation.

Proudhon's ideals were those of a peasant socialism, a primitive division of society into small communities without any strong central authority. Casting aside industrialism as an unmitigated evil, he sought to return to the days when the land, not machinery, was the source of livelihood. He recognized dimly what Marx himself was soon to demonstrate brilliantly: that labor was the source of value and that capital without labor was valueless. Proudhon knew from his superficial study of Hegelian dialectic (conducted in Paris under Marx's aegis) that wealth and poverty, capitalist and proletariat, were concomitant and necessary to each other in the present system; but this was as far as his analysis penetrated.

For all its looseness of reasoning and recklessness of conclusions Proudhon's book met with a great popular reception. So great, in fact, was the attention it received that any answer to it was bound to be widely read.

Proudhon's essential error, which Marx exposed, was the concept of eternal, unchanging economic categories: the mistake of assuming that the economic and social forces in 1847 were those of all time. With devastating clearness Marx showed that Proudhon had no historical sense, apparently no realization of the march, shift and evolution of historical institutions. If he had, he would have known that the relations in which the forces of production manifest themselves are not eternal laws but correspond to definite changes in man and his productive forces. The principles, ideas and categories of a society are shaped conformably with the social relations flowing from production. The conception of private property, for example, changes in each historical epoch in a series of entirely different social relations. Money itself is not a definite fixed thing but a social relation, a reflex of a form of production which had rendered obsolete the system of exchanges of goods between individuals. And as for machinery it is "not any more of an economic category than is the ox that pulls the plow; it is a productive force." Social life at any given time, therefore, is the product of economic evolution. Suppose, by way of illustration, that a glass contains a liquid or powder. While the glass does not determine the nature of the liquid or powder, it does determine its shape. So does economic evolution determine the social, political and spiritual life of man.

Furthermore, argued Marx, it is ridiculous to think that all one need do to reform the world is to remove the evil elements from society and leave only the "good." Each society is the product of its internal clashes, its inherent oppositions; the proletariat can only exist as a proletariat as long as there are capitalists to exploit it. What the proletariat should do is this: not seek to eliminate the capitalists alone, but to eliminate itself as proletariat; in other words, to establish a classless society in which exploitation of one class by another would not exist.

13

The theory of economic interpretation had at last been placed before the world. But there was still work to be done. The next step was to form the organization that would carry the banner of this new theory to the workers, spread the new gospel, promote the now clearly anticipated social revolution. A more definite relation between the abstract theory and the concrete immediate realities of the political situation had to be established. This Marx and Engels now proceeded to accomplish.

Europe had been for several years in a state of ferment. In England the trade union movement was making great headway, and the Chartist agitation was in full force. In Germany the workingmen in large numbers were becoming socialists of one kind or another. Democratic agitation against the reactionary monarchy frothed and bubbled in a series of upheavals. The Parisian proletariat was also beginning to realize its own class consciousness. Marx felt himself in the midst of an era of revolution and sought an opportuniy to co-ordinate the proletariat in a drive to overthrow capitalism and establish the Communist society.

Since 1836 the refugees from German political persecution had been organized in Paris under the name of the League of the Just, and branches had been formed in the principal European cities. In the Brussels chapter Marx soon began to dominate the scene; with Engels he conducted extensive propaganda for the organization throughout Europe. At the first Congress, held in London in 1847, they managed to gain partial control and effect the transformation of the League of the Just, which hitherto had had no definite policy, into the Communist League with a Marxian viewpoint. To establish this policy definitely Marx and Engels hastened to the business of drafting a manifesto which should declare the aims and policies of the League.

The result was the *Communist Manifesto* (the document which has guided socialist and communist doctrine for more than seventy-five years), stamping the Communist League as the representative organization of the now clearly defined revolutionary proletariat.

Almost immediately after the writing of the *Manifesto,* the February revolution of 1848 broke out in Paris. Marx went there at the invitation of the Provisional Government after Belgium had deemed it advisable to expel him from Brussels. In March revolution flared in Germany, and Marx hurried to take part in it. All Europe was seething. In the excitement of immediate political events the *Manifesto* gained only a brief, if approving, perusal by the workingmen of Europe. For in June came the bloody suppression by Cavaignac of the proletarian uprising in Paris, and the establishment of the rule of the bourgeoisie more firmly than ever. At the same time in Germany the counterrevolution began to gain headway, and reaction set in once more. Uprisings continued all over Europe, to which Marx lent his encouragement and support. But the bolt was shot; the bourgeoisie was firmly in the saddle. Marx, who had recognized the first revolts as bourgeois movements and had regarded them as necessary steps to the proletarian revolution, now realized that his zeal had led him to hope for more than actuality permitted. Because of the prevailing economic distress, he hoped for a renewal of proletarian discontent and revolutionary sentiment, but now an accident stepped in to help save the day for capitalism. Gold was discovered in California! The resulting betterment in economic conditions all over the world caused a revival that dashed Marx's hopes to the ground. By the summer of 1850 he was advocating the liquidation of the revolution and the disbanding of the Communist League, for its economic basis for existing was gone. Thus the force of hard economic reality brought the zealot Marx back to the calm consideration of his revolutionary program, which in the mad hope for immediate realization he had neglected to apply as carefully and conscientiously as he himself had urged it be applied.

But the *Communist Manifesto* remained the challenge of the labor movement. And it is still the *Manifesto* that, in its brief pages, represents the succinct outline of Marxian teaching based upon the theory of the economic interpretation of history.

14

The *Manifesto* states that "the history of all hitherto existing society is the history of class struggles," and what, asked Marx, is the nature of the conflict on which the historical process depends? He answers this question by saying that it is a conflict of class based on the possession of the means of economic production.

Let us see how he works it out.

In every age there have been a ruling and a serving class, an upper and a lower crust. In every age this distinction has been imposed and determined by the current means of production. In every age a bitter struggle has been waged between oppressor and oppressed, between rich and poor, between the possessors and the non-possessors. And that struggle continues even now and cannot cease until all classes are abolished and all antagonisms resolved.

Marx traced the development of the modern bourgeoisie from the time it broke the shell of feudalism and began to spread itself through the towns and villages of the Middle Ages. From the medieval serfs had sprung the chartered burghers of the earliest towns; from these burgesses the elements of the bourgeoisie had arisen. The discovery of America, the expansion of world-wide markets, opened up new ground for the rising merchant and manufacturing class. Manufacturing had begun because the old guild system of production by the hands of artisans was incapable of meeting the greatly increased demand for goods. The markets kept ever growing, and manufacture by hand mills no longer sufficed; so machinery was introduced to increase and speed up production.

Out of the growth of the bourgeoisie there emerged for the first time the "world" market with its international commerce and tremendous means of communication. And as the bourgeoisie advanced economically, it advanced politically: feudal lords, medieval communes, city-republics—all these forms were rendered obsolete as the bourgeoisie gradually forced its way from the status of a taxable "third estate" to that of supremacy. The creation of modern capitalist society is a direct reflex of the interests of the middle class.

But more than that, the bourgeoisie in its progress revolutionized all the old values of medieval life—the chivalry, culture, ideology, beauty and even the religious motives. It substituted for the old order the point of view of the merchant, a money relationship in every department of life.

Along with the rise of the bourgeoisie there grew up a proletarian class. The bourgeoisie, necessarily, could not endure without a proletariat to give it labor power sufficient to meet the ever-expanding need for products, commodities, markets. In so doing, the emphasis had been shifted from the country to the town. The great city, teeming with proletarians, was the modern political center. Centralization was constantly going on, concentrating property more and more in a few hands, expropriating more and more those who had been left behind in the race for markets and trade.

Now, if the above picture of economic change can be clearly seen, the next step, according to Marx, is to understand it dialectically. How? The thesis, antithesis, and synthesis is as follows. The bourgeoisie or capital-owning class has established a monopoly of the means of production. In so doing it has called into existence its antithesis, a capital-less laboring class of the proletariat. The conflict between bourgeoisie and proletariat, between capital and labor, will finally resolve the antithesis and produce the synthesis, a classless society.

In calling upon the proletarians of the world to unite Marx felt that it was the task of the *Communist Manifesto* to awaken revolutionary class consciousness, to have ready a program of action when it finally awakens, and to lead the way to the new society wherein the dictatorship of the proletariat would gradually emerge into a classless society. From this point Marx went on to outline his own proposals over against the proposals of other groups which made their appeal to the working class—such groups as the French socialists and the followers of Robert Owen. These he classified as reformers, bourgeois liberals, and utopians. Once more he outlined the failings of their doctrines, as he had already done in his case against Proudhon.

Thus when he was not yet thirty Marx had achieved almost enough of a career for any man; but, of course, he had no thought of retiring and letting others work out the principles he had given to the world. He continued his work, plunged in the very heart of the revolutionary movement.

During the German revolution he had established the *Neue Rheinische Zeitung* which in its short existence carried some of his most brilliant articles. He called on the citizens to offer armed resistance to attempts at tax collections by the reactionary Brandenburg ministry. Arrested and tried at Cologne, he was acquitted after making a brilliant speech in his own defense. Uprisings in Dresden and the Rhine Province, led by Bakunin, evoked his hearty support. With their collapse came his abrupt expulsion from Prussia and the suppression of the *Neue Rheinische Zeitung*. He issued a final edition, printed in red ink, and went to Paris. But before going to Paris, Marx, feeling morally responsible for the debts contracted, pawned all he had. His wife assisted him in giving up precious heirlooms, silver and furniture. It would have been easy to leave without paying, but Marx would not. With all his hatred of the institution of private property he had a vivid sense of honor.

In Paris, Marx witnessed the second uprising which was suppressed in July, 1849, when Louis Bonaparte gained the throne. Once more he was told to get out, and he hastened to seek refuge in London. A few days later he was followed by his family. Here he remained, except for short intervals, for the remainder of his life.

15

When Marx finally settled down in London in 1849 he had enjoyed the distinction of being expelled from three European countries and of having seen three of his journalistic ventures collapse.

Now began a period of great hardship. Money was constantly scarce in spite of a legacy Jenny received from her mother. Even periodic help coming from the loyal Engels, who sent the Marxes all he could spare from his income as a clerk, was hardly enough. In 1851 Marx managed to get work writing weekly articles for Horace Greeley's New York *Tribune,* which was much interested in the liberal-radical movements in Europe. But at a sovereign an article he hardly managed to pay his rent and postage, while piece after piece of apparel and furniture found its way to the pawnbroker.

To make matters worse, illness began to plague him, what with a liver disorder and other ailments aggravated by his practice of working late at night, taking insufficient nourishment, and smoking vile cigars. Fortunately for Marx he was a powerfully built man with a constitution that could stand long years of maltreatment and neglect. His personal appearance was always impressive.

He was not a tall man, but he had a tremendous leonine head. Hyndman's description of him (though referring to a much later date) is, in essentials, true of him all along, "commanding forehead, great overhanging brow, fierce glittering eyes, broad sensitive nose and mobile mouth, all surrounded by a setting of untrimmed hair and beard."

Despite exile and poverty Marx felt that he had a task to complete. He had projected a theory of history that had made available a vast storehouse of hitherto unknown or disregarded facts, thereby demonstrating most vividly the impoverishment of orthodox interpretation; he had made a courageous effort to show how that theory might be applied to history; and upon the basis of that theory he essayed to outline a program for the revolutionary labor movement. Now, in exile, he wanted to write a searching and thoroughgoing criticism of capitalist economy, mark clearly the contradictions of the present system which his previous works had only shadowed, and dispose once and for all of the orthodox, apologist analyses of the bourgeois economics.

All his days and evenings were spent in the library of the British Museum reading innumerable files of newspapers, assimilating thousands of articles, making notes from books of every conceivable shade of opinion and subject. Each morning he was at the door of the Museum as it opened, and never did he leave until the attendants turned him out. He seemed to be a veritable part of the institution, this dark, heavily-bearded German with piercing black eyes, sitting at a desk with dozens of volumes piled about him. Later on he developed a circle of co-workers who came with him, and aided him in his research. While his research activities continued at the Museum, Marx did not withdraw from active participation in the labor movement. He took great interest in the British trade unionism and in the Chartists who fought so strenuously for ideals very close to his own.

In 1859, the year that saw the appearance of Darwin's *Origin of Species,* Marx published his *Introduction to the Critique of Political Economy,* in which he presented an excellent definition of his theory of economic interpretation and explained how it had led him to attempt an analysis of capitalist economy.

16

Meantime, he was constantly in the midst of polemic, politics, discussions and quarrels with friends and enemies. Marx was a fiery, not-to-be-contradicted man on most occasions, and it was only by the tremendous force of his personality and the vigor of his ideas that he retained what friends he did. He had quarreled with Bauer, Proudhon, Herwegh, Bakunin, Ruge—and each time with intense bitterness.

Now he split with Ferdinand Lassalle, who had been his colleague on the *Neue Rheinische Zeitung,* and with Karl Vogt over the question of Louis Napoleon's plan to aid Italy's unification by a treaty with Sardinia against Austria. He saw in it a scheme to further Napoleon's own aims and denounced it as such, attacking Lassalle and Karl Vogt bitterly for their support. Time has proved Marx right, but Lassalle never forgave, and Marx never sought forgiveness for the vehemence of the attack. Vogt lashed out at Marx, calling him slanderer and degenerate. So outraged was Marx that he prepared an entire volume in reply, *Herr Vogt,* in which he denounced his adversary as a paid agent of Napoleon. Here again Marx was vindicated, for when the French Republic eleven years later published the secret accounts of the Bonaparte government, there was the item in the secret service funds, "Vogt, received August, 1859, forty thousand francs."

It is difficult to pass any final judgment on the personality of Karl Marx. Most of his enemies and many of his friends found him harsh, severe, unpleasant; and the general impression prevailed that this was the true aspect of the man. But we have to set against these strictures the evidence of such a man as Heine, who testified to Marx's real charm. "Marx is the tenderest, gentlest man I have ever known." Marx may, as is claimed for him, have made governments tremble, but he never made his wife or children tremble. His was the happiest of family circles. To the children on the London streets, with whom he was always ready to play, he was known affectionately as "Daddy Marx."

In any just appraisal of Karl Marx there are two aspects of the man to be considered. There is on the one hand the patient, cold logician, analyzing history with the scalpel of fact and the probe of theory; there is also the impetuous, sentimental revolutionary, seizing upon tiny uprisings as the first step in an imminent world revolution that was soon to establish the dictatorship of the proletariat and the classless society.

His economic doctrines fall short of the caliber of his theory of the economic interpretation of history, because so many of his conclusions are *a priori*, wish-fulfillment ones. He was seeking evidence that capitalism was going to collapse and the working-class come to power; he grabbed at every shred that could be used to demonstrate this thesis, and now and then turned his back on important data that were not directly in line with it.

Marx had also the tendency to rationalize his earnest desire for revolution, often going to amusing extremes in a childish enthusiasm. He once came home full of this enthusiasm: he had seen, in an exhibition on Regent Street, the model of an electric locomotive. This symbol of the rapid advance of the industrial revolution he interpreted in terms of his own hopes as meaning that the economic basis for the political revolution was rapidly nearing completion. Like a child he talked for days of the impending revolution, until his ordinary good sense reasserted itself and he regained his logical perspective.

One aspect of this wish-fulfillment trait may be found in his literary style. His inversion of Proudhon's title *The Philosophy of Poverty* to the *Poverty of Philosophy* is a prominent example. He constantly sought brilliant rhetorical effects by the use of this device of inversion, such as, "The weapon of criticism cannot replace the criticism of weapons," "Luther shattered faith in authority, because he restored the authority of faith," "Philosophy cannot be realized without the abolition of the proletariat; the proletariat cannot abolish itself without realizing philosophy." Now, while this technique demonstrates the dialectic basis of thought, Marx realized its dangers—a too facile phrasing and grouping of apparent antitheses. In his later work Marx got away from this habit, but it is an example of a tendency to lose, sometimes, the fine edge of his logic in a blasting thunderous rhetoric.

S

17

A stroke of bad luck met him in 1861. With the outbreak of the Civil War in America he lost his small income from the New York *Tribune*.

As far as the Civil War itself was concerned, although he was fully aware that it represented a clash between opposing groups in the ruling class, he nevertheless was heartily in favor of the Northern cause. Quite apart from his philosophical and historical convictions, he was sufficiently imbued with the pure love of freedom to be thoroughly opposed to the institution of chattel slavery. What is more, he was instrumental in aiding the Northern cause by more than mere tacit approval. When the Gladstone ministry in Great Britain was playing with the idea of recognizing the Southern Confederacy and granting it large credits, it was Marx who helped organize the great demonstration of the British working class that compelled Gladstone to change his mind.

He was beginning to assume more and more importance in the trade union movement of England; and when the second International Exhibition was held in London in 1862, he helped to bring together the visiting workingmen from France and other countries, and the idea of forming an international organization was discussed.

Marx worked feverishly for this goal. In September, 1864, he had the pleasure of attending, as the representative of German labor, the meeting at which was formed the International Workingmen's Association—the first International. It was not from the start a Marxian organization; from 1865 to 1867 the followers of Proudhon officially dominated it. In the meantime Marx disseminated his views and finally gained power. This the Marxists held until the adherents of Bakunin, now a thoroughgoing anarchist, forced an entrance into the organization and in a few years split it from head to foot and caused its collapse.

During its career the International was the medium through which the theory of the economic interpretation of history was publicized. Even the followers of Bakunin and Proudhon, although opposed to Marx's program and antagonized by the aggressiveness of his personality, were completely convinced of his main thesis—

the economic basis. The theory had become a definite part of the heritage of knowledge.

Meanwhile his work on his greatest book had been going forward. By the end of January, 1867, the copying of the first volume of *Das Kapital* was completed; Marx planned a trip to Germany to arrange for its publication.

18

With the publication of the first volume of *Das Kapital* the great economic theorist produced his crowning work. He never was able to finish editing and collating the tremendous mass of material collected for the second and third volumes; Engels did this for him after his death. But the first volume was enough: it needed no New Testament to bring this work rapidly to its present position as the Bible of the working-class.

The chief characteristic of capitalism, says Marx, is the discrepancy between the value that labor produces and the value that it receives in return in the form of wages. This discrepancy, which Marx called surplus value (it may be recognized under many names: unearned increment, interest, profits, return of investment, etc.) is what the capitalist takes for himself, as the reward for his "contribution" to the process of production. Marx asserted that since all value was created by labor—he took this as an axiom— what the capitalist reserved was stolen goods; and the only thing that allowed him to make good his theft was, of course, the fact that he controlled the state and that his class was the ruling class.

Marx's searching analyses of capitalism and his prediction as to the course it would take have been proved astonishingly accurate by a multitude of facts since his death. The recurrent crises he predicted have come again and again, always with increasing severity. The mad scramble of the expanding bourgeois class for new markets has been amply demonstrated by events in China, Africa, South and Central America.

When the second edition of *Das Kapital* was published in 1873, Marx sent a copy to Darwin, who responded:

DEAR SIR:

I thank you for the honor which you have done me by sending me your great work on Capital; and I heartily wish that I were more worthy to receive it, by understanding more of the deep and important subject of political economy. Though our studies have been so different, I believe that we both earnestly desire the extension of knowledge; and this, in the long run, is sure to add to the happiness of mankind. I remain, dear Sir,

Yours faithfully,

CHARLES DARWIN.

Toward the end of his life poverty released its grip somewhat, and Marx was able to indulge himself in one of the prerogatives of age—mellowness. His circle of friends had widened, and with his wife and children and friends he became a tenderer and less bitter person.

But it was not all primroses and honey, Marx's old age. There was the split-up of the International by the destructive tactics of Bakunin. There were constant arguments with his friends on questions of doctrine, Marx trying to adhere to the straight line pointed out by his theory, never tolerating the utopian withdrawals and petty-bourgeois modifications that liberals and opponents sought to introduce. By an uncompromising belligerency for his ideas Marx, however, set a bad example to his disciples who sought to emulate him with arrogance and almost dogmatic assurance. Notwithstanding all this, he was a man who beneath a sometimes rough exterior hid a boundless love for all who labor and are heavy-laden.

His illness grew increasingly difficult to bear; terrible headaches clouded his working hours. But he remained active, interested, always fighting for his revolution. He added Russian to his already wide mastery of languages and launched into a study of rural conditions in that country. He saw another uprising of the proletariat crushed in France in 1870, when the Paris Commune, after seven weeks of brilliant efforts to establish a workers' state, fell before the assault of reaction. Another hope was shattered. Marx, however, never lost his courage and his faith. To his last moment he was fighting for his ideas. In a life of ostracism, exile, and grinding poverty he refused all compromise.

One of his younger colleagues once said to him, "I marvel, comrade, that you who have struggled so long can be so patient." Marx replied, "When you have been impatient as long as I, you will not marvel at my patience."

He suffered a tremendous shock when in December of 1881 his wife, the companion of his vast career of trials and hardships, was taken from him. Engels said, when he heard the news, "Marx is dead, too."

It was true. The shock was more than he could bear, and when a year later his eldest daughter died suddenly, grief overwhelmed his powerful physique and he collapsed.

All his old ailments beset him now with new force; he returned from his daughter's funeral to die. The doctors however hoped to keep him alive, and he himself thought once more that he would be able after all to finish *Das Kapital*. But it was not to be.

On the afternoon of March 14, 1883, Friedrich Engels hastened to the Marx home at 45 Maitland Park Road, Haverstock Hill. He had received an urgent summons from the family. Marx had had a heart attack, and it was feared that he might die at any moment. Engels ran upstairs to the study. There was Marx seated in an armchair; he seemed to be asleep, but when Engels reached the chair Karl Marx was dead.

11. Pasteur . . . THEORY OF DISEASE

WHEN Christopher Columbus had returned from his voyages and the Spanish Empire was glorying in the unexpected enlargement of its dominions, something else that apparently had been found in the New World was impressing itself upon the attention of the early sixteenth century. A new disease, fierce and virulent, had made its initial appearance in Europe. Syphilis had flung down its gauntlet in challenge to the medical science of the day.

Syphilis is caused by a tiny unseen organism which enters the human body where it reproduces in great numbers, often destroying as it goes. The information about syphilis which is common knowledge of today, was unknown to the most eminent doctors of the fifteenth century when the disease (which apparently was brought back from the West Indies by some of the companions of Columbus) made its first appearance in Europe to the consternation of civilization.

2

Whether or not syphilis was introduced from America or had existed previously in Europe, it now began to attract attention. Girolamo Fracastorius, a celebrated physician of Verona, interested himself in this new disease. It was he who composed a famous medical poem around the character of a shepherd whom he called *Syphilis*. The poem first appeared in 1530, and although Fracastorius said the legend was written in his lighter moments, it brought him more fame than all his scientific writings. In the poem we are told the story of Syphilis the shepherd who, for an act of impiety, was struck with the disease. However, in his scientific study of syphilis (then called the French pox) Fracastorius set forth rational views of infection that were truly remarkable for that far-off age. He came very near expressing the modern conception of bacterial infections. Upon examination it must be said that Fracastorius' views bear a superficial resemblance to Pasteur's germ theory.

There exist, Fracastorius asserted, tiny seeds of infection, *seminaria contagionum*. These can be transmitted from one person to another—either by direct or indirect contact—through articles of clothing or furniture touched in common, or at a distance, by means of the wind. Thus diseases spread in the population as a whole, because of these essential seeds that cause infection and are capable of indefinite multiplication.

Fracastorius also described the affinity that particular seeds have for particular kinds of people, or particular species of animals, or a particular sex. Some men could walk unharmed through a pestilence that was destroying a community about them. There is even an affinity for certain parts of the body: one kind of infectious particle or seed attacked only the lungs, another kind laid waste only the kidneys.

He not only described these things but permitted himself certain speculations about them. There can be no doubt that had he possessed a microscope he would have made tremendous strides toward establishing an adequate germ theory. (The microscope unfortunately did not come into use until a hundred years later.) For the age in which it appeared Fracastorius' book was a remarkable document, but it failed to overthrow current beliefs. Medicine continued to plow its way along the bottom of the rut of tradition, clinging to remnants of witchcraft, spells, medieval superstitions.

Besides syphilis, Fracastorius was interested in all infectious diseases; and in those day, when medicine made no distinction between the contagious kind of ailment and any other, to have recognized the fact of infection was in itself a great advance. He described contagion as a sort of putrefaction caused by particles not perceived by our senses. He recognized the contagiousness of measles, tuberculosis, smallpox, rabies and above all syphilis. The dread plague which at one time forced the Pope to consecrate the river Rhone, so that the multitudes of dead could be thrown into it without delay; the medieval epidemics of "dancing mania" which ravaged entire countries; the weird scourge of leprosy that had been known and abhored since Bible times—all these Fracastorius studied and classified and sought to trace to their origins.

In 1546 he published a remarkable *Treatise on Contagion* which is a fascinating series of bold hypotheses and speculations. It is also a magnificent example of the elementary awakening of creative thinking in medicine.

Fracastorius did not arrive at his ideas of infection by pure guesswork; he had carefully observed the diseases of which he wrote. No physician of the age worked harder through the epidemics and plagues. With a vast clinical experience and one of the largest practices in Italy he even found time to attempt some crude experiments to test his hypotheses. In the annals of science Fracastorius is assigned a singularly important place as the first person to draw a parallel between the processes of contagion and the fermentation of wine—a luminous juxtaposition!

Centuries later Pasteur spread the co-ordinating wings of his genius over these same processes and found the way to his theory.

3

While the other sciences were moving forward on all fronts, medicine lagged behind, groping in the dark against unknown enemies. Physicians did not fully understand what they were fighting when they undertook to free a patient of disease: they could note symptoms, take pulses and temperatures, but their prescriptions were compounded of guesswork, hearsay and tradition. A glaring example of the profound ignorance was the doctrine of "laudable pus." This view upheld the notion that pus was a necessary and beneficial accompaniment in a wound of any kind. So general was the belief that pus aided healing that it survived well up into the end of the nineteenth century!

Surgeons today make every effort to avoid the formation of pus, knowing it to be the herald of infection and blood poisoning. But these fourteenth, fifteenth, sixteenth, seventeenth century surgeons invented one method after another to bring about suppuration, not understanding that the means they used to cause pus to appear were at the same time the means of dooming the patient to almost certain death. Only a few men opposed the idea of laudable pus. Henri de Mondeville (1260-1320), one of them, wrote trenchantly: "Many more surgeons know how to cause suppuration than to heal a wound." He and a few others pleaded for cleanliness in surgery. The only result was a storm of abuse and ridicule.

Medieval doctors were completely at a loss in battling plagues, those fearful, devastating pestilences which swept over Europe, leaving an awful trail of corpses and misery. Nearly everybody attributed them to the influences of the stars, to the appearance of comets, to droughts, to inundations, to Jews who poisoned the wells, to crop failures. Sometimes medical authorities came closer to the truth when, for example, they supposed that mice or swarms of insects might have something to do with it. But they never thought to follow out the hints Fracastorius had dropped.

In the seventeenth century there were two men who seemed to foreshadow to a certain degree the insight into the nature of disease that Louis Pasteur was to bring. These two were widely differing personalities: Thomas Sydenham of London, clinician, an observer of disease, master of the healing arts, a man of single-mindedness of purpose; and Athanasius Kircher of Fulda, optician, musician, physician, Orientalist, mathematician, creator of hypotheses and gifted with many intuitions in wide-ranging fields of knowledge.

The Englishman Sydenham (1624-1689), whose motto was "Experience, not reason, is what teaches," was a fanatical enemy of every theory. Yet he wrote in a hopeful spirit about the future of medicine. In a day when doctors were reluctant to admit any limitation to their healing arts this "English Hippocrates" stressed the inadequacy of current knowledge. One of the hopes voiced by Sydenham was that for each and every disease there might be developed a specific remedy as absolutely effective as quinine was known to be for malaria. This too was opposed to the general trend of thought, which in those days was serene in the vague belief that somewhere there existed one perfect panacea, that would instantly heal each human ill, from insanity to boils.

Sydenham, studying the nature of contagion, which he clearly recognized in his investigation of the plague when it struck London, knew that not only delicate persons were subject to contagion, but that a strong man who went into an infected area might surely sicken in a day or two. He felt that disease was caused by "infectious particles," which are taken in with the very air we breathe. He hoped that some day the nature of these particles would be ascertained. Nor was he wrong in this long-range expectation. History has shown that Syndenham belonged to that elect company whose hopes are slowly absorbed in the impersonal life of the times that follow them.

The case of Athanasius Kircher (1602-1680) was different. Here was a professor of philosophy who loved to speculate. From some mountain top of his own creation he was forever peering into the vast unknown with new and quickened perceptions. In addition to his achievements in mathematics and oriental languages he will always be remembered as the first investigator to use the microscope in an attempt to discover the causes of disease. By a flash of imaginative genius, the expression of long-continued processes of thinking, he hit upon the nature of contagion. It was more than a guess: it was bold penetration, the work of an alert speculative mind in quest of an explanation.

An hypothesis is the presumption of the existence of the general state of affairs lying at the back of certain phenomena. A good hypothesis will eventually allow conclusions to be drawn; and if the hypothesis be correct the new conclusions will be confirmed and these in turn will give added confirmation to the truth of the hypothesis. The fact that fevers are catching, that epidemics spread, that infection could remain attached to particles of clothing, all gave support to the view that the actual cause was something alive.

Kircher did not hesitate to announce, and he was the first to do so clearly, that the infectious particles were *living*. (Fracastorius had hesitated to call them living.) To be sure, this was "opinion," but it was scientific. Now a scientific opinion is one which there is some reason to believe true; on the other hand an unscientific opinion is one which is held for some reason other than its probable truth.

Of course it is obvious that a supposition is by no means the same thing as the discovery of a fact. When Leverrier declared that an eighth planet, Neptune, existed outside Uranus, but had never been seen by man, or when Mendeleeff prophesied the existence of three undiscovered chemical elements, these were for the moment only suppositions which were not proved facts until afterwards. The same is true of Kircher who rightly assumed that tiny living particles were the cause of disease. What was more, he investigated anthrax, bubonic plague, and other scourges. With the aid of his microscope he claimed to see in the blood of victims the micro-organisms that caused disease and he described some of these plague germs. That of course was his mistake; for we know from his description that all he saw were the red corpuscles of the blood.

4

After Sydenham's and Kircher's work medical science continued to struggle valiantly with its problems. Despite slow progress the necessary foundations were being laid for the great era of Pasteur—the era that led to intoxicating victory. Everywhere men were ferreting out the secrets of the human body, informing themselves about its working, learning its construction, studying the relation of function to structure. A clearer acquaintance with disease and its manifestations was growing. Furthermore, the more intelligent among physicians, although they still lacked a comprehensive theory, had been able to work out certain cures and certain preventive measures which had long baffled their predecessors.

For example, the idea of cleanliness in operations was gaining strength. Many medieval surgeons had advocated the use of boiling oil in a wound to prevent gangrene and septicemia. More and more opponents to the doctrine of "laudable pus" were coming forward. In the particular infection of childbirth fever, which carried off thousands of mothers annually, a few men were insisting upon cleanliness and sanitation as the only means to cut down this enormous mortality.

As the nineteenth century opened medical science was still confronted by the enigma: What caused disease? To be sure, doctors possessed a certain bowing acquaintance with disease; they could in most cases trace its course and often predict its outcome; sometimes they could even prevent its spread by isolating those who had contracted it. But they did not know how to treat it, because they did not know its nature.

5

A ray of hope leading towards the ultimate solution of the mystery of infectious disease came in the person of Max Joseph von Pettenkofer who, like Pasteur, was a man of irrepressible genius in chemistry and a profound theorist.

Pettenkofer, who lived from 1818 to 1901, had one of the mos
colorful careers in medicine. He is justly regarded as the founde
of modern hygiene. Unlike the Englishman Sydenham, who was a
enemy of all theories, Pettenkofer was constantly at work framin
hypotheses, not as an idle exercise of the imagination but definitel
as an outgrowth of creative practical affairs. It is said that the peop)
of Munich often called his physiological institute "The Hypothesi
Palace."

It must be understood that Pettenkofer did not actually foun
hygiene; he had his predecessors. But after he delivered his *Lecture*
on Hygiene in 1865 at Munich he unquestionably raised this branc
of knowledge to the rank of first magnitude. No scientist befor
him had ever possessed his grasp of the subject; no scientist befor
him ever approached his passionate insistence on cleanliness. Kin
Maximilian under whose patronage he worked spent thousands c
florins out of his private funds to promote Pettenkofer's exper
ments.

Oftentimes in reading the lives of these scientists-theorists on
is amazed at such immense intellectual ability, ceaseless observz
tion and vast encyclopedic learning. Pettenkofer, like Pasteur, wz
interested in human welfare. "A man of pure science," he onc
wrote, "always concerns himself first with truth." He must ask hin
self: "What is left from my experiences and from the results c
my thinking that will serve to rejoice the hearts and lighten th
sufferings of those with whom we are together so short a time her
on earth? As a man the savant is bound to think of this, and he
either a weakling or a monster if he thinks or acts otherwise."

The work on hygiene was stimulated by the cholera epidem
that struck Germany in the summer of 1854. Thousands of peop)
were gathered in Munich to witness the formal opening of th
General Exhibition of Industries in the famous Glass Palace. O
July 15, 1854, the kings of Prussia and Saxony were there to len
their presence to the glittering occasion. No sooner had the grez
fair opened than the dread cry "Cholera!" was heard. People ra
like rats at the continuous ringing of the death bells. Death stalke
in Munich.

The Pettenkofer household did not escape the epidemic. H
faithful cook died and one of his daughters almost succumbe

Pettenkofer himself fell ill but quickly recovered. "These experiences naturally came very close to me and prompted me to investigate the ways of cholera."

After much painstaking work there appeared in 1855 a preliminary report which was followed two years later by a more complete statement. These reports contained Pettenkofer's views known as the "soil" or "nidus" theory. "The origin of cholera," declares this theory, "is due essentially to (a) the germ or ferment, which in itself causes no cholera in the human organism, (b) a material or soil which receives the first factor and as a result thereof passes into a fermentation or budding, from which (c) a local miasma arises, which can cause cholera when it is not left to develop in that place and is breathed in by men at a certain degree of concentration. In other words, the sick man furnishes the soil for the harmless germ, the germ utilizes the soil as a ferment to develop the miasma, and this under certain conditions generates the cholera."

Every theory is a forward thrust into the unknown. When Pettenkofer first announced his views (a linking of the contagious and miasmatic hypotheses) it must be remembered that bacteriology was in its infancy. In the light of the great gains made later by Koch and Pasteur a large part of Pettenkofer's doctrine turned out to be wrong. Nevertheless it paved the way for victory for it stressed the production of disease by the fermenting process of decaying matter.

Merely to read the above classical statement of Pettenkofer's theory may not in itself be a particularly thrilling experience. But it must be remembered that Pettenkofer *lived* his theory. In a very true sense it is a statement of his being, of his entire personality, of his daily thought, practice and capacity for self-sacrifice. Doctor Axel Munthe in the preface to the American edition of his memorable *Story of San Michele* speaks scathingly of those who rapsodize about death from a comfortable distance but actually grow pale when the grim Deliverer approaches. Was not Leopardi, the greatest poet of Italy, who longed for death in exquisite rhymes, the first to fly in abject terror from cholera-stricken Naples? Did not the great Montaigne, whose calm meditations on death are enough to make him immortal, bolt like a rabbit when the pest broke out in Bordeaux?

Not so Pettenkofer. On October 7, 1892, he undertook a rare and moving act of defiance in answer to his colleagues who challenged his theory. On that day he swallowed a culture of cholera bacilli sent to him by Professor Gaffsky from pest-ridden Hamburg. It is estimated that he took into his body several millions of the dangerous germs just to demonstrate that not every infection generates illness. "Even if I had been deceiving myself and the experiment had been dangerous," he wrote in explanation, "I would have looked death in the face calmly."

Pettenkofer's demonstration was an heroic act. It proved that bacteria alone are by no means enough to explain the facts of an epidemic. Pettenkofer was right, but (and this is often the tragedy of the theorist) on a mistaken hypothesis!

6

It was Louis Pasteur, a "mere chemist," who finally established the true theory of contagious and infectious diseases. It may have been because he was a chemist, and consequently free from the conservatism and complacency of the medical profession, that he was able to do it. In all events, his accomplishment remains one of the enduring victories in the "conquest-march" of the human intellect.

Louis Pasteur was born in 1822 in a small village in eastern France. His father, a hardworking tanner, struggled industriously to be able to give his son the education he himself had never had, envisioning for him a future as a professor, a savant, or a great writer.

But the young man did not impress his teachers in the preparatory schools. Although he was careful, he was considered too slow and plodding. Quite often their patience was tried by his constant insistence on understanding a proposition thoroughly before going ahead to more advanced stages; too often he irritated and confused them with questions. Although his examinations for the degree in chemistry were considered somewhat "mediocre," the influence of J. B. Dumas, one of the leading chemists of the day, whose lectures at the Sorbonne Pasteur attended, led him to a gripping interest in this science. Perhaps more important than Dumas' influence was the practical consideration that this seemed to be a promising profession to enter. At any rate, Pasteur became a chemist and proceeded to apply to this field the earnestness, the self-discipline and perseverance that his early education had implanted in him.

He continued to be slow-moving and methodical; he continued to ask pointed questions; and he continued to refuse to take things at face value. In the chemistry class, for instance, the details of obtaining the substance phosphorus was merely told the students. (It was too expensive a process to be demonstrated in the laboratory.) But Pasteur, always testing, always inquisitive, bought some bones, took them to his rooms and burnt them, pulverized the ash, treated it chemically, and was then able to show his fellow students and his teachers a phial containing sixty grams of phosphorus obtained by his own unaided efforts.

No sooner did he receive his doctor's degree than he turned his attention to a problem that was puzzling many chemists. Now he was to give a clear demonstration of that remarkable penetrating effort that became so characteristic of his long and illustrious career. He began by making a profound study of crystalline forms and their connection with the rotation of polarized light. There were two acids which had been found to be present in the fermentation of grapes—tartaric and racemic acids. The crystals formed from these two substances looked alike, they had the same chemical properties and the same constituents. There was in fact only one way they might be distinguished: tartaric acid crystals were optically active— that is, they changed the direction of polarized light—while racemic acid crystals were optically inactive, or neutral. This difference was a complete enigma to such successful chemists as Mitscherlich and Biot.

Pasteur carefully studied the crystals of tartaric acid under the microscope. He found that they were hemihedral in shape; that their facets or tiny faces were all inclined towards the right; and that they reflected the beam of light to the right. But what about the crystals of racemic acid? Here he found the same hemihedral shape; however, some of the facets of the crystals were inclined to the right and others to the left. Understanding burst upon him. Racemic acid crystals were made up of two other tartrates, both optically active; but one turned the polarized light to the right, and the other turned it to the *left*. When the two were present together they neutralized one another and it was therefore that racemic acid crystals were optically inactive. This was a great discovery for a young chemist of twenty-six to have made; the thrill of it was magnificent beyond all imagination.

He checked his results hurriedly, and then took them to the great Biot, who was enthusiastic. "My boy," the old savant said with emotion, "I have so loved science all my life, that this touches my very heart." From that moment Biot became Pasteur's mentor and protector. Through his efforts the young scientist was elected to the post of assistant professor of chemistry at Strasbourg.

7

Strasbourg. Love!

Marie Laurent was the daughter of the rector of the university. Pasteur met her in January, 1849, when he first arrived; in May they were married. Pasteur wrote to his friend Chappuis: "I believe that I shall be very happy. Every quality I could wish for in a wife, I find in her." For many years she was to bear him children and hold his meals hot while he stayed hours overtime in his laboratory. She listened patiently to his excited descriptions of grand vistas that he saw opening before him in this or that experiment; and she shared the pain and suffering that accompanied seemingly endless trials. Marie Laurent Pasteur was made of the same endurance that characterized Emma Wedgwood Darwin and Jenne von Westphalen Marx. Extraordinary women of intellectual titans.

When Sir Isaac Newton was asked how he had discovered the law of gravitation he answered, according to Voltaire: "By thinking about it ceaselessly." Pasteur was the ceaseless, indefatigable thinker: ideas led into each other, played tag in his mind. A new and overpowering thought was beginning to make itself felt. He was still involved in his tartarates, when the idea occurred to him that all life was made up of dissymmetry, since these crystals formed from organic material were dissymmetrical. He felt himself on the verge of piercing the mystery of the cosmic order. But he maintained self-control, realizing that suspended judgment is the greatest triumph of intellectual discipline. Before broadcasting these ideas in the guise of "philosophy," he felt constrained to put them to the test of experiment. They collapsed utterly. His first step into the realm of theory was a failure. Yet there remained with him the discipline of the experience itself which perhaps can best be described in words which Thomas Huxley once used with memorable severity: "The assertion that outstrips the evidence is not only a blunder but a crime."

Still one idea had clung to him: the resemblance between the phenomena of crystals and the phenomena of life. And soon an experiment encouraged him to go farther along this path. He introduced a certain type of mildew into racemic acid, causing it to ferment. Soon he saw that only a portion of the acid (the dextro-racemic) was decomposed by the ferment; apparently it fed solely upon the right-handed molecules. The other portion (laevo-racemic) was left intact. Thus he succeeded in establishing a connection between this particular dissymmetry of crystals and the vital process of fermentation.

Nobody had ever thought how closely related these processes were. The theoretical mind, however, has a way of making things which at first appear diverse hang together. An impending overturn of age-old beliefs was soon to take place by reason of the discovery of this connection between the world of crystals and the world of micro-organisms. Pasteur knew only too well that it would be a long-drawn-out battle to prove that fermentation was caused by living organisms and that decay and putrefaction differed only from fermentation in that other organisms were at work on other kinds of nutritive material. The world, of course, now knows that fermentation is a vital process made possible by the action of living organisms.

The great German chemist of that generation, Justus Liebig, regarded the phenomenon of fermentation as merely a process set in motion by the decomposing of the dead yeast cells whose bursting molecules accelerated the decomposition of the fermentable matter. When Pasteur announced living yeast at work as a cause of fermentation and of the existence of a special lactic yeast which caused another kind of fermentation, the great Liebig could do no more than ridicule these views. Liebig claimed that "the changes designated by the terms fermentation, decay and putrefaction are chemical transformations." The only difference Liebig could see between fermentation and putrefaction was that in the case of

T

fermentation the gases evolved are without odor while in putrefaction the gases emitted are of a disagreeable smell—that is, putrid.

To thwart Liebig and finally drive him beaten from the field was no easy task. Pasteur had behind him the solid scientific work of Schwann in Germany and Cagniard-Latour in France. Both men, using crude microscopes, nevertheless had seen that yeast is made up of little globules that can reproduce themselves. With these assured facts in mind Pasteur proceeded to separate single living yeast plants under his own microscope and then to grow pure cultures from the organisms thus separated. Living yeast now acquired a new champion.

When Pasteur had won his victory he made a special journey to Liebig's home to shake the hand of his German colleague and assure him that the fight had been waged only in the interests of truth. But the gesture was in vain. Apparently Liebig could not match the younger man's magnanimity; it is said that he met Pasteur very formally in a black frock coat and would not admit defeat.

We have already seen that the idea of fermentation had been for some time bound up with that of contagious disease. Pasteur recognized the connection afresh when he made the inevitable comparison between the micro-organisms that seemed to cause fermentation and the tiny transmissible micro-organisms that had been vaguely associated with it ever since Fracastorius toyed with the idea of infection. The subject of fermentation took on such transcendent importance in his mind that he wrote to his friend Chappuis: "I am pursuing as best I can these studies on fermentation which are of great interest, connected as they are with the impenetrable mystery of life and death."

In 1854, at the age of thirty-two, when Pettenkofer and Munich were in the throes of cholera, Pasteur became professor and dean of the newly created faculty of sciences at the University of Lille. It seemed as if those who gave him this appointment had read the future, for he encountered at Lille a direct stimulus to the line of thinking that was slowly unwinding before him. Lille was a manufacturing city, and not least among its products was wine. Shortly the new dean was called upon to make his contribution to the commercial prosperity of the region.

One of Pasteur's pupils had spoken to his father enthusiastically of the professor's lectures on fermentation; and the father, a manufacturer of alcohol from beetroot juice, decided to go to the new dean with a difficulty that had arisen in his business. His alcohol had turned sour, as had that of many of his competitors that year. He brought samples to Pasteur to examine.

Here was a direct challenge to the young theorist. Here was a clear-cut need to perform experiments to test those basic ideas on fermentation as a vital process. Pasteur examined under the microscope the globules of fermentation, and noticed that under normal conditions they were round; but when the alcohol soured in lactic fermentation they became long.

Pasteur filtered the long globules and established the fact that they were the sole and specific ferment which caused lactic fermentation. He showed also that this ferment would produce the same product, lactic acid, no matter what the fermentable material: grape juice, milk or beetroot juice. He found that either alcohol or lactic acid might be produced at will from a solution of sugar and certain other materials, depending on the introduction into the solution of the ferment of yeast or of lactic acid.

Within a short time after these experiments, Pasteur solved almost all the fermentation difficulties of the wine industry. He showed that each disease of wine, which spoils its taste, was due to a specific ferment, a specific micro-organism, and he conclusively demonstrated this to the wine manufacturers in a series of incontrovertible experiments. Sour wines, "ropy" wines, bitter wines, flat wines—all these were due to the presence of a foreign ferment which overcame the yeast and spoiled the wine. And for each of these diseases the ferment was specific and invariable.

To protect wines from this deterioration, Pasteur suggested heating them to about 60° centigrade, when the normal fermentation had been completed. This would kill all the foreign organisms and protect the wine permanently. Instantaneous success was achieved with this method by manufacturers. This was the first process called *pasteurization*. Not hesitating to show their gratitude, the manufacturers heaped honors upon Pasteur, medals, ribbons, and speeches of appreciation. Further approbation and additional recognition came from the vinegar makers, to whom Pasteur next showed how to protect their product from butyric fermentation, another specific disease, caused by a specific micro-organism.

8

But if the manufacturers to whom millions of francs were saved by Pasteur's methods were convinced and grateful, the many scientists whose pet theories had been overthrown were not. They girded up their loins, sought for flaws in the long list of Pasteur's achievements, and hurried to perform experiments of their own to disprove his. For it was one thing to describe bacteria and explain what they did—quite another to explain whence they came. Chief of the objections raised against the germ theory was the doctrine of spontaneous generation (the origin of life out of nothing), that ancient fallacy which even to this day is not altogether dead.

Until the seventeenth century no one seriously questioned this belief in the spontaneous origin of life. We have already seen in the chapter on Darwin how the Italian scientist, Francesco Redi, blasted this doctrine when he showed that meat covered with a fine gauze would not develop maggots (because the flies laid their eggs on the gauze instead of the meat). In spite of Redi's irrefutable demonstration the idea of spontaneous generation was widespread. Toward the middle of the next century it found a vigorous champion in Needham, an English clergyman, who claimed to have produced living microbes from putrescible matter by heating it and burying the vases beneath hot cinders. Voltaire ridiculed Needham, finding ammunition for his attacks in the experiments of Spallanzani. This able Italian thinker declared that Needham had not sufficiently heated his vases, or that they had been porous enough to admit micro-organisms. To refute Needham, Spallanzani sealed his own vases hermetically in boiling water for an hour. Under such conditions he found that absolutely no micro-organisms whatsoever were generated (because all germs originally present had been killed by heat—sterilized!). When confronted with Spallanzani's experiment the adherents of Needham merely claimed that Spallanzani had destroyed the creative power of the air inside the vases by "torture," that in consequence his experiments were inconclusive. And there the matter rested for nearly a century!

It was revived in 1858 by Henri Pouchet, director of the Museum of Natural History at Rouen, who sent a note to the Academy of Sciences at Paris asserting the truth of spontaneous generation, and declaring that he was prepared to prove it by vigorous experiment. Pouchet's assertion was, of course, a direct challenge to Pasteur's theory which he called a ridiculous fiction. If fermentation could come about spontaneously, then micro-organisms might arise in spite of pasteurization; moreover, one could not control their spread from person to person in causing disease.

An intense struggle now began between the adherents of Pouchet with their doctrine of spontaneous generation and Pasteur who was out to convince the world that life as we know it never originates spontaneously, that minute organisms—bacteria, germs, microbes— are far more active agents in this world than had ever been guessed; that breadmaking, cheese making, tobacco curing, tanning, are carried out by germ action. It was supposed that meat putrefied and decayed of its own accord and that it somehow produced the bacteria in the process. But as a matter of fact, Pasteur claimed that the real explanation was just the other way round: that meat would not putrefy of itself but that it was made to decay by bacteria which had got into it.

In the midst of the furore of debate Pasteur went about testing his case by rigorous experiments. First he drew air through a filter of cotton wool and found it black with dusts which under the microscope were seen to be tiny plants or bacteria. He took these subvisible organisms and planted them in solutions, where they developed and produced various sorts of fermentation. Next, he devised an experiment that was conclusive: he took two flasks, one with a long curved neck, the other with an ordinary open top, and filled them both with previously boiled putrescible material. The solution in the ordinary open flask soon began to ferment, while that in the other (to which everything in the air except the dusts could penetrate) remained intact. Pasteur triumphantly exclaimed: "Never will the doctrine of spontaneous generation recover from the blow dealt it by this simple experiment." And indeed it was a telling blow. Pouchet soon came back with new objections. If the air is the carrier of these thousands of different kinds of germs, it would be so thick with them that one could not see, or else there must be some zones with more, some with less germs, which appeared to him and to his followers ridiculous.

Pasteur followed up this advantage. He replied that indeed there are regions varying in the number of germs they bear in the atmosphere. While Pouchet ridiculed such an idea, Pasteur proceeded to prove it by another simple and conclusive experiment. He took sterile putrescible material, filled hundreds of phials with it, sealing each with a flame to kill all dusts that might possibly enter. Then he opened these phials in various parts of the country, each just long enough to let it fill with air, and then sealed them again. Just as he expected, many of the phials which had been opened in quiet, dustless cellars, on mountains, in country fields, did not ferment at all, while those he had opened in city streets, in gardens, in homes, showed well-advanced stages of fermentation after a short time.

The presence of living particles at various heights in the atmosphere is of practical interest to mankind. Since Pasteur's day scientists have built up a remarkable body of knowledge on the amount of living and organic matter inhabiting the vast aerial ocean that envelops our earth. In recent years, aided by aircraft, they have been able to advance his original ideas. Pasteur studied the living contents of the air up to a height of only a few thousand feet; he conceived the idea, though he never executed it, of making spore-hunting trips in a balloon. Today, "stratosphere" expeditions include in their equipment apparatus for sampling the air and its contents at levels far beyond anything that Pasteur thought possible. The upper limit beyond which no organic matter of any kind is present has not yet been found.

In spite of Pouchet's continued opposition, which took the form of badly carried out experiments, Pasteur decided to turn his attention to other things. For himself, free from prejudices and preconceived ideas, the question of spontaneous generation was settled. It was strengthened by John Tyndall's demonstration that flasks of sterilized material remained uncontaminated. Pasteur reported his results to the Academy, and gave a hint of his plans for further work. "What would be most desirable would be to push these studies far enough to prepare the road for a serious research into the origin of various diseases."

His destiny was becoming clearer with each succeeding discovery. The idea had been growing in his mind that his work was bringing him slowly to the study of the human pathology; and indeed, everything he did seemed to point in no other direction. In 1863 he told Louis Philippe that his ambition was to arrive "at the knowledge of the causes of contagious and putrid diseases." And when he published his views on beer (he had investigated breweries in England and France and finally come to conclusions similar to those he had reached in his studies on wine), he called attention to the unmistakable connection between the diseases produced in beer by micro-organisms and those infectious diseases which cause suffering in animals and man.

9

Now he was ready to attack the idea of disease. Again destiny seemed to point the way. His old teacher Dumas asked him to investigate a scourge that had devastated the silkworm industry of France. This disorder was called "pebrine," after the word pebre (pepper), and was characterized by the appearance of little black and brown spots on the bodies of the diseased worms. These spots looked like pepper grains. Pebrine had begun to wreak disaster upon the French silk industry in 1849; by 1861 the revenue had sunk from one hundred and thirty to eight million francs. All sorts of foolish remedies were tried in a frantic effort to save the business. The diseased worms were dusted and fumigated now with ashes, charcoal, sulphur, then with chlorine and coal tar. Some people sprinkled the mulberry leaves with mustard meal, soot, quinine powders, rum or absinthe. It was all in vain, the plague could not be stopped.

In answer to Dumas' request Pasteur began to study the disease for he wished to substitute facts for phantoms. Naturally he came to his task better equipped than any previous investigator. He had a theory! Like Arion, the ancient poet and musician of Lesbos, Pasteur held a magic instrument in his hands. Because there is something truly magical about a great theory, the parallel from mythology is not without its inspiration. Arion, when robbed and thrown into the sea by Corinthian sailors during a voyage, is said to have called to his aid by the sweetness of his tones a dolphin, which took him on its back and carried him to land. In an old picture which the great medieval anatomist Vesalius prized one sees the bard, his instrument in his hand, just reaching the island of rescue. Around the sketch are the words, *"Invia virtuti nulla est via"*—"For the man of courage, no way is closed."

Fortified in his belief that infectious diseases and fermentations were the result of germs, Pasteur began his research with the point of view that a specific micro-organism was responsible for the silkworm blight. That was in 1865. By the end of the year he firmly believed he had established the fact that the tiny oval corpuscles found on the bodies of the silkworms were the cause of pebrine, and rashly guaranteed that if the silkgrowers would segregate the healthy silkworm eggs (that is, those free from the corpuscles) the silkworms would all develop normally. Confident he had solved the problem, he returned to Paris to prepare his results and await the final proof that he was right.

In 1867 he went back to the silk district and found a truly dreadful state of affairs. Almost all his apparently healthy silkworm eggs had hatched unhealthy worms. What was more, it seemed that not even his belief that the corpuscles were the cause of the disease was justified, for there were none to be found on these sick worms. He faced the prospect of a great loss of prestige and a severe setback to his theory.

But he did not throw up his hands in despair. He went back to his laboratory—the laudable example of a man who could change his mind with scrupulous honesty if he thought the evidence warranted it. With the aid of his microscope he examined the stomachs of this particular batch of diseased worms: he could see no corpuscles. But there were other things—hadn't he seen something like them before? Actually he found a different micro-organism than those of the familiar pebrine. Unquestionably here was the answer—*"Il y a deux maladies,"* he exclaimed. "There are two diseases!" These newly discovered micro-organisms were similar to the bacteria he had come across in his studies of butyric fermentation. They were anaerobic, too—that is, they could not exist in the presence of oxygen. So there *were* two diseases: pebrine and flacherie.

The strain of keeping up the fight against spontaneous generation, in analyzing and finding a preventive for the silkworm diseases together with plans for new experiments and new fields of investigation, was more than he could carry. In October, 1868, a high cerebral tension was brought about, and he was stricken by an attack of paralysis. For several weeks he was not expected to live. Work on the laboratory which he had persuaded the Emperor to build for scientific research was suspended. Fortunately for the world Pasteur regained his health. He returned to the silkworm region to continue his campaign against pebrine and flacherie. Shortly he conquered both diseases and the silkworm industry was saved.

Again the germ theory triumphed—and again it was expressed in understandable terms of francs and sous. Pasteur took a quantity of healthy seeds to an abandoned silk property of the Emperor's where pebrine and flacherie had ruined the industry. In the very first year, by employing his own scientific methods, Pasteur was able to pour an unexpected income of 22,000 francs into the imperial coffers.

10

A great theory is a deep well of truth—not all the water in it can be drawn up in one bucket. We have already seen how much knowledge in support of the germ theory Pasteur was able to lift out of the problems of fermentation, the controversy over spontaneous generation, and the conquest of the silkworm blight. More information was yet to come; this time out of that chamber of horrors, the Franco-Prussian War of 1870.

Medically speaking the Germans were much better prepared than the French. Before entering upon the first attack they had carefully built a behind-the-lines hospital system which they expected would cut down their mortality from the scourge of gangrene, septicaemia, erysipelas and other forms of blood poisoning. Every preventative known to official science of that day was provided for. Their chief surgeons, Stromeyer and Nussbaum, succeeded in many of their objectives but they failed miserably in one: they performed seventy amputations through the knee without a single success. And of course the French Army, totally unprepared in affairs of this kind, was in a much worse condition. Out of thirteen thousand amputations—legs, fingers, toes, arms—ten thousand patients died. No commentary on inadequate medical methods could be more telling than this.

Yet practically all this horrible mortality might have been prevented. There was a young English surgeon, Joseph Lister, who had published at the beginning of the Franco-Prussian hostilities a description of his new method of antiseptic surgery and its applicability to the war. If Lister's advice had been heeded, perhaps nine-tenths of those who perished might have been saved. Indeed, after the close of the war, Nussbaum sent an assistant to Edinburgh to learn the Listerian method. With the knowledge brought back the German surgeon was able to reduce gangrene mortality in his hospital from eighty percent to nothing.

Joseph Lister was thirty-seven years old when in 1865 he had read Pasteur's paper on lactic fermentation. For several years previous to this he had emphasized the need of cleanliness in healing wounds: it was his opinion that cleaning the wound itself was sufficient to prevent infection. Pasteur's revelation that the air was full of bacteria had shown him the serious limitation of his technique. To clean the wound was not enough; everything that came in contact with it must also be disinfected and freed from bacteria. So Lister devised the Listerian method of antisepsis. This meant that the hands of the surgeon and his assistants, all instruments and sponges, and all dressings must be sterilized with carbolic acid. Lister even went so far as to keep a spray of carbolic constantly about the point of an operation to purify the air. With hospital infection thus understood, millions of lives no longer needed to be sacrificed.

In 1874, almost at the outset of his own campaign against disease, Pasteur received a letter from Lister. The note described the antiseptic method and related its success. To Pasteur, who just one year before had been elected to the Academy of Medicine, this unexpected message was a source of great encouragement. Now he could face the doctors of the Academy who were his colleagues, but who nevertheless resented the intrusion of a chemist into their esoteric circle and considered the germ theory little more than the vaporings of an upstart.

So utterly reactionary were the views of official medicine that even in the face of Lister's triumphs with the antiseptic method, not to speak of Pasteur's victory over the silkworm diseases, the physicians were still unwilling to give the new theories a tolerant hearing.

Typical of the opposition was a speech by Doctor Chassaignac, a prominent surgeon, who at the first meeting after Pasteur's admission to the Academy of Medicine bitterly denounced Doctor Davaine, who had speculated on the connection between the disease of anthrax and the bacteria he had found in the blood of animals who had died of it. Chassaignac, while Pasteur listened, attacked Davaine and ridiculed the entire germ theory, calling it "laboratory surgery, which has destroyed very many animals and saved very few human beings."

Several other members of the Academy spoke, most of them expressing their opinion that hospital miasma (a vague term used to denote all hospital epidemic infections) was due to faulty ventilation of wards and that bacteria were the result and not the cause of disease. Then the president called on the new member to give his opinions on the matter.

Pasteur, the "mere chemist," rose and stood before that hardheaded group of doctors, some openly sneering, others regarding him with amused tolerance. With emphasis and vigor he spoke for the germ theory of disease, deplored the shortsightedness of those who could not see its truth, reasserted his observation that the correlation between certain diseases and certain micro-organisms was absolutely indisputable. He told those complacent doctors that they themselves often carried the dread hospital infections from one patient to another, and that if they wanted to avoid contagion they must take care to disinfect their instruments and hands.

Of course they were not pleased to hear these things—especially the older men. A group of young men, however, undergraduates in medicine, listened. Turning to these students Pasteur said: "Young men, you who sit on these benches, and who are perhaps the hope of the medical future of the country, do not come here to seek the excitment of polemics, but come and learn method."

11

Davaine, as we have seen, had speculated on the connection between anthrax, that horrible disease to which cattle and even men fell victim, and the tiny rodlike bacteria he had seen in the blood of those dead of the disease. Pasteur was not content merely to speculate. He threw himself with earnestness into the study of anthrax which was literally ruining the cattle industry. In some flocks twenty sheep or more died out of every hundred.

Davaine had inoculated rabbits with the anthrax blood and they had accordingly died of the disease, showing in their blood the same bacteria he had noticed in the original specimens. But two other investigators had performed the same experiment, and had found no such bacteria in their rabbits after death. Davaine claimed that they had inoculated diseases other than anthrax.

From Germany came the report of Robert Koch, who, working alone in a small country village, had managed to cultivate the bacilli of anthrax in a pure culture. These pure cultures, when inoculated into animals, produced the disease as expected, each case showing the bacteria. This seemed to clinch the case for the germ theory. However, there came the announcement by the scientist Paul Bert that when he had inoculated anthrax blood, in which the bacilli had previously been killed by compressed oxygen, nevertheless he had been able to produce anthrax in his animals—that is, the bacilli were present. How explain that?

It was Koch who discovered the reason for Paul Bert's failure to kill the anthrax bacteria. Studying the development of this germ, Koch observed the formation of spores, tiny rounded bodies with thick protective walls which could undergo great changes of temperature and of environment without dying. Like the seeds of plants they could revive and grow. Obviously the anthrax spores had withstood Bert's compressed oxygen and had upon inoculation grown and produced the disease. The spore was to blame!

Pasteur tried to convince his colleagues at the Academy that this was the true explanation. Nothing seems to us, removed in time, more absurd than the opposition which persisted in blocking his path. Among his adversaries there was a professor of medicine, Doctor Colin, who seems to have possessed a positive genius for contradiction. It is hard to account for Colin's attitude other than on the score of jealousy, stubbornness or stupidity. Throughout the entire period during which Pasteur was solving the problem presented by anthrax Colin argued, bullied, contradicted every step of Pasteur's advance.

LOUIS PASTEUR

After an engraving by Champollion, 1897

Courtesy of Dr. Samuel A. Brown

And now that he had established the bacillus as the sole cause of the disease, how was he to cure it? This appeared to be an insoluble problem; so Pasteur decided to take the easier way and tried to see what could be done by means of prevention. He learned that cattle which had died of anthrax were buried all together, and that cattlemen had not taken the trouble to choose a spot where healthy sheep could not graze. Pasteur inspected the ground over one of these graves and found it alive with anthrax spores! This then was the mode of transmission. Healthy animals would come and eat the grass growing over these graves and take in the spores which would produce the disease. This being the case, prevention appeared simple: merely be careful to bury the animals in barren ground, where no grazing would be permitted.

But this complicated and inconvenient process was rendered unnecessary by a tremendous discovery that Pasteur stumbled upon. He had been working to discover the micro-organism that causes chicken cholera, the disease that swept the feathered inhabitants of the barnyard exactly as the Black Plague swept the great cities. He had already succeeded both in isolating it and growing it in successive cultures just as he had done with the anthrax bacillus. Coming back to his laboratory, after some weeks' absence, he found several old cultures of the cholera germ and tried inoculating it into some hens. As he expected, they had a slight attack and then recovered (the culture having been weakened by its long exposure to oxygen). Next he tried to inoculate these same hens with ordinary virulent cultures; he then dismissed them from his mind, thinking they would be dead the next day. Imagine his surprise and tremendous interest when he found them the next day and the following day and many days thereafter in perfect health.

He had rediscovered vaccination!

12

Almost a hundred years before Pasteur made this rediscovery a young Englishman, Edward Jenner, had found out in 1798 that if the disease of cows known as cowpox were inoculated into humans, they were thenceforth free from smallpox. After discovering this interesting fact Jenner was at a loss to understand just why vaccination gave immunity. Pasteur, however, on rediscovering the same phenomenon understood that a slight attack of the disease conferred immunity—that is, he could produce a weak or attenuated serum (culture) of a germ and that inoculation with this serum would make the animal immune to the more virulent form of the microbe. Jenner had found a fact but it took Pasteur to discover its underlying scientific principle: namely, if a living being were already stricken with a virulent germ disease, inoculation with the attenuated culture of the germ would afford resistance to the disease and in a large percentage of cases effect a cure. From this understanding has come protection for human beings against innumerable maladies.

Pasteur now hastened to test the value of this new discovery in the case of anthrax. He met a little difficulty here; it was not so simple to weaken these bacilli as it was those of chicken cholera, because spores formed so quickly. But he found that the spores did not form at a temperature of 42° centigrade. By keeping his cultures at this temperature, he found that he was able to attenuate them to any degree he wished. This done, he proceeded to test the value of his protective vaccine upon laboratory animals. It worked to perfection. With tremendous enthusiasm he announced the discovery on February 28, 1881.

Overnight the whole country became interested in this work. His opponents, however, still ridiculed him. "The microbe alone is pure," said one leering critic, "and Pasteur is its prophet." Of the many who expressed doubt and distrust, Rossignol, an editor of the *Veterinary Press,* was the most outspoken. He called for a public trial directly challenging Pasteur and his anthrax vaccine. He doubted that Pasteur would consent.

Against the advice of friends who feared the risk of a public trial Pasteur accepted, announcing at the same time a complete and ambitious program of vaccination that would definitely prove his case. At the farm of Pouilly le Fort, where the trials were to be held, fifty sheep were to undergo experimentation. Twenty-five were to be vaccinated; twenty-five others would not be vaccinated. These fifty would then be inoculated with virulent cultures. "The twenty-five vaccinated sheep will survive," declared Pasteur, "the twenty-five unvaccinated will all perish."

On May 5, 1881, the day of the first trials, a great crowd of veterinaries, physicians, cattlemen, farmers, apothecaries and savants was present to witness the first vaccinations. At the last moment two goats were substituted for two of the not-to-be-vaccinated sheep, and an ox for one of the to-be-vaccinated sheep. Assisted by his three associates, Chamberland, Roux and Thuillier, Pasteur injected his vaccine into the right thighs of the chosen animals. The ox and goats were marked on the right horn, and the sheep on the ear, to distinguish them from their unvaccinated comrades. The company then adjourned to the large hall of the farm, where Pasteur lectured on his researches. Interest was aroused but skepticism was still rampant. On May 17 a second inoculation of the vaccinated sheep was made, with a stronger virus. The day for the inoculation of the virulent, deadly culture into both groups of sheep was set for May 31.

Doctor Colin was still muttering against Pasteur, unprepared to yield an inch in his immovable attitude. On his way to the final trial, he took pains to caution a friend against the germ theory and its propounder. He instructed his friend to shake the phials of virus just before they were to be injected, because Pasteur was planning to trick them by inoculating the unvaccinated group with culture taken from the bottom of the phial, where the bacteria had settled, while the vaccinated group would be inoculated with the innocuous surface layer. His friend promised to comply with these instructions.

On May 31 Pasteur was cool and confident. When Colin's friend asked to shake the phials, Pasteur assented; when asked that a larger dose be given than had been planned, he willingly complied. Another veterinary asked that the injections be made alternately between the two groups. To this and all other requests Pasteur and his assistants agreed; they shot their vaccines into the fifty animals with firmness and assurance, and then asked that everyone return June 2 to see the results.

Pasteur's amazing confidence profoundly impressed the spectators; his opponents began to wonder whether after all they had not been wrong to sneer. Frankly, they were disturbed by such an exhibition of cool assurance.

Pasteur returned to Paris to await the fateful day. Had he not been overrash, he asked himself, in rushing madly into a public test of his vaccine before he had taken time to perfect it? Perhaps the introduction of the oxen and the goats might spoil his success; he had never tried his vaccine upon these animals. Or perhaps Chamberland, Roux and Thuillier, to whom he had entrusted the business of seeing that the right cultures were used in the right cases, had made a mistake? He tormented himself with these questions and found it difficult to concentrate on the new work he was undertaking in his laboratory, the investigation of hydrophobia. If he failed in this, his scientific prestige would be tremendously damaged. He knew only too well how opponents magnify one's failures and forget the successes.

On June 2 Pasteur arrived a little late. He noticed that some boys in the streets looked at him curiously as he hurried to the barn where the experiment had been conducted. Did they already know that a horrible disappointment awaited him? He hurried as fast as his paralyzed body would allow.

When he entered the barn, his fears were instantly dispelled; a loud shout of applause greeted him. He looked about eagerly. Everything was as he had predicted. Twenty-two of the unvaccinated sheep were already dead, their carcasses distended, blood oozing from their mouths. The other animals were in the last stages of anthrax, gasping for breath, trembling in every limb, wheezing piteously through their gory mouths.

The vaccinated animals were all in perfect health.

Colin was not present.

13

The experiment at Pouilly le Fort was the top of the hill for Pasteur; from that time on success was assured. A new school of scientists, open-minded enough to take advantage of his trail-blazing, gladly joined in paying homage to the man who had grown with his theory and had used it for the benefit of mankind.

In 1882, Pasteur was elected to the French Academy, the highest honor of his country. Alexandre Dumas, the novelist, expressed the feeling of France when he called on Pasteur and thanked him "for consenting to become one of us."

Upon his admission to the French Academy the debate over spontaneous generation was revived. In the Academy of Medicine, too, the old die-hards were still upholding the ancient fallacy. They continued to feel that much in medicine was endangered by the views of Pasteur. After all, for centuries all contagion of the flesh was charged to spontaneous generation within the body just as bread fermentation was credited to spontaneous power within the wheat kernel. Their leader, Doctor Pidoux, maintained that "disease is in us, of us, by us," and refused to concede that even smallpox was contagious and inoculable, in spite of the fact that successful vaccination had been going on since Jenner's discovery. Koch had discovered the bacillus of tuberculosis, establishing that micro-organism as the sole responsibility for the dread white plague. And still these stubborn men of medicine refused to see; they preferred the old-fashioned belief in the spontaneity of disease. They insisted a malady sprang up of itself, spontaneously generated, compelled by no outside agency. A body became ill because it was so constituted, not because of anything such as infection.

Pasteur was visibly disgusted with their intolerance and obstinacy. He made fewer and fewer visits to the meetings of the Academy of Medicine, giving more time to the Academy of Sciences. Besides, he was on the track of his last great discovery, the final and completing step necessary to establish the germ theory as vital and important truth. He was attacking the problem of hydrophobia.

Hydrophobia is a disease contracted by infection from the bite of a dog suffering from rabies. The disease, if unchecked, is almost invariably fatal. For centuries people knew only one way to help the victim of a mad dog's bite and that was to cauterize the wound at once: a redhot iron seared its way into the tortured flesh. This done, the unfortunate person could do nothing but wait. Perhaps the disease had been checked by the cauterization. If it had, there was occasion for rejoicing. But if it had not—and often it failed—there was nothing to do. The virus multiplied itself in the blood stream of its victim, while he went about his daily tasks, a doomed man. Then one day—it might be two or three weeks, it might be four months—the virus would reach the spinal cord, it would eat its way to the base of the brain, and the horrible symptoms of hydrophobia would show themselves—frothing at the mouth, raving, delirium, fierce thirst, until at last death released the sufferer.

When Pasteur began his investigation of hydrophobia all he

U

had was his theory. He suspected a microbe, but of its course and behavior he had no notion.

On October 26, 1885, he read to the Academy of Sciences "A Method of Preventing Rabies After a Bite." The greatest fruit of the germ theory now belonged to all humanity.

Nor was the world backward about taking advantage of it. Patients began to arrive from every part of the country to undergo his treatments. The workers at the laboratory were constantly busy preparing cultures and giving inoculations. Physicians came to study the new therapy for hydrophobia.

Recognition, full and unmitigated, was now his. A subscription was opened to establish the Pasteur Institute in Paris. Two and a half million francs were subscribed. Work began at once. The architect refused to take a fee; the builders themselves would accept only expenses. On November 14, 1888, the Institute was opened.

It is doubtful whether in the whole history of mankind a scientist and a theorist had ever before been honored with such spontaneous good will. It is indeed doubtful whether any man in any station ever received such an outpouring of appreciation and high regard. Even the medical profession, which had been so resentful that a "mere chemist" should show it how to do its job, offered its homage. The antiseptic method came to be adopted by surgeons everywhere; hospital mortality now shrank from fifty to five per hundred. Maternity hospitals, benefiting by his recommendations in regard to sanitation and infection, greatly reduced their death rate. In the face of such incontrovertible evidences even the old antagonists who had attempted to obscure his reputation could no longer withhold tribute.

All in all it was a grand triumph of personal faith—of methods, character, perseverance. His life had been indeed a singularly outstanding series of logical and consistent discoveries whose principal lines of attack merged one into another. Who would ever have thought that the germ theory would get its start as a result of tartaric acid experiments, that this would lead into discoveries in the field of fermentation and that out of this would come the controversy over spontaneous generation; that the settlement of this knotty problem would open the gate for victory over animal diseases which in turn would supply the key to the mystery of those contagious woes which have tormented the flesh of man? At the celebration of Pasteur's seventieth birthday Joseph Lister journeyed from England to tell him: "You have lifted the veil which had covered infectious diseases during the centuries; you have discovered and demonstrated their microbial nature."

It not only demanded unparalleled toil to do this, but it took a strong inner faith in one's self to withstand scorn. Yes, all his life he had been a man of faith: to be sure not the kind of faith that willingly believes in spite of evidence, but the faith that pursues truth in scorn of consequence.

The French Government, which in 1874 had awarded him a recompense in the form of an annuity of 12,000 francs, now raised that sum to 25,000 francs, which was to revert to his widow and then to his children. The gratitude of the world poured in upon him. What a difference between Galileo with his telescope and Pasteur with the microscope: it took fully two hundred years for the Italian scientist's ideas to be vindicated. In his own lifetime Pasteur fought a winning battle. He was a well-satisfied man.

But his time was nearly up; his health was bad; he could no longer undertake new experiments. Yet he knew that the net results of his discoveries would swell into the greatest benefit ever conferred by one man upon his fellows; that they would lead to remarkable antitoxins, widespread immunity, as well as to unforeseen triumphs of surgery. Actually, more than forty contagious diseases are today curable as a direct result of the methods he discovered. Pasteur lived to see his pupils Pierre Roux and Alexandre Yersin conquer diphtheria by means of antitoxin. He had the satisfaction of knowing that younger scientists all over the world were applying his theory and conquering new fields with it.

On October 23, 1894, a paralysis attack sent him to his bed; there he remained to the end of the year. In January he regained a little strength. Roux had arranged all his old instruments, test tubes, cultures, in a little museum, and the sick man was taken to see them. For the last time he gazed upon his laboratory, the scene of a lifetime of work. Then they took him back to bed.

Toward the fall of 1895 his strength began to go from him. Late in September he had another stroke, and for twenty-four hours remained almost entirely paralyzed.

On Saturday afternoon, September 28, 1895, Louis Pasteur died peacefully.

12. Freud . . . THEORY OF THE MIND

IN 1884 there was a young assistant physician at the General Hospital in Vienna who was studying anaesthetic properties of the drug cocaine. He wrote a preliminary report on it, and made the note that it benumbed the tongue and palate after a solution had been swallowed. He added the suggestion, "We may presume that this anesthetizing action of cocaine could be utilized in various ways."

Before the young physician, Sigmund Freud, could continue his investigation along this line, he had an opportunity to visit his fiancée, whom he had not seen for two years. So he put aside his research for the time being.

His report, however, was read by Koller, a young Viennese student, who told a friend, "I gather from what Freud writes that it may be possible to anesthetize the eye with a solution of cocaine." These two young men went ahead with experiments, and later in the year the Ophthalmological Congress at Heidelberg listened to a paper by Koller upon the new use of the drug. In one bold stroke Koller achieved for himself a position in medicine's hall of fame —he had solved one of surgery's most vexing problems.

If Sigmund Freud had not neglected the opportunity that Koller grasped, perhaps he would never have gone on to make the inconceivably greater discoveries of psychoanalysis. But it is useless to speculate on what might have been. What actually happened we all know: Freud changed his intellectual domicile; he moved into another field to revolutionize human thought, and to bring to light an important theory touching the mysteries of the human mind.

Freud was twenty-eight years old when Koller made the discovery which he himself might have achieved. Born of Jewish parents in what is now Czechoslovakia, he had been brought to Vienna at the age of four. In this center of European culture Freud grew up and was educated. Here too he first experienced that antagonism against the Jew which early forced him to be self-reliant, independent, and unconcerned with the opinions of others.

At the Gymnasium, where he excelled so conspicuously that he was rarely required to take an examination, young Freud managed to stand at the top of his class for a period of seven years. He was an uncommon student, sensitive to the vast ranges of knowledge and already giving evidence of a deep and acute power of analysis. At first his career had been a matter for doubt. But he was interested in life and human beings. Medicine seemed to be an obvious course of study for such a young man.

The theories of Darwin were creating at that time a great stir in Europe. To young Freud they brought both inspiration and enthusiasm. He began to share the hope that man's knowledge of the natural world, already so greatly expanded by Darwin, might be still further advanced in new and unexplored fields. He felt that he himself would like to be an instrument in these discoveries.

What finally led him to study medicine was an essay by Goethe which had been read aloud at a lecture just before he left school. In this essay Goethe rhapsodized about nature, describing her tremendous variety, her infinite abundance, and her consummate mysteries. Young Freud was deeply moved. The poet had spoken to his heart. There now seemed to be only one path that he could take in order to approach closer to these profound beauties, only one path compatible with his economic circumstances. Then and there he decided to study medicine.

But the choice made in a moment of enthusiasm did not prove all he hoped for. In the first place, he encountered at the University of Vienna a strong current of anti-Semitism which deeply disturbed him; then there was the orthodox medical teaching, cut and dried, heavy with the weight of superstitions and points of view accumulated over the centuries. Would all this prove an effective barrier to his eagerness in penetrating the secrets of nature?

Apart from psychology, the various medical sciences had little or no attraction for him, and the entrance to even this tremendously interesting field was cluttered up with futile theories and prejudices that obscured the pathways. He began to realize that his talents were peculiar ones, and his limitations stringent. He seemed unable to fit in anywhere, and his enthusiasm dropped for a while—nothing appeared to him either worthy of, or capable of improvement by, his attention. As a result his medical studies languished, and it was not until 1881 that he took his degree.

In the meantime he had found at least temporary contentment in experimental work in the physiological laboratory of Ernst Brücke. Here he began to delve into the mysterious workings of the nervous system, spending long hours dissecting the nerves of rare fishes and acquiring a firm grip on the physical basis of nervous phenomena.

But his theoretical pursuits were far from earning him a livelihood. Brücke advised him to leave the laboratory and seek the more remunerative work of interne in the General Hospital. There he retained his passion for research, and he was able to transfer his attentions from the nervous apparatus of fishes to that of human beings. Consequently in 1883 he became an active worker in the Institute of Cerebral Anatomy while continuing his employment as a junior physician at the General Hospital. It was now apparent that he was drawing closer to his own real interests: he was laying the groundwork in physical research into the constitution of the nervous system for the nonphysical (psychical) theory he was one day to elaborate.

Now more than ever he plunged deeper into the study of nervous diseases, especially organic ones that sprang from injuries and malformations and constitutional failings of the physical bases of the mind. But here again he met with discouragement. There was virtually no treatment for such diseases; one was forced to be one's own teacher. Psychiatry, the division of medicine treating nervous disorders, enjoyed little prestige at that time, although throughout Europe there was growing an awakening realization of the necessity for closer and more scientific study of the mind, both in its normal and abnormal manifestations.

Freud achieved in 1885 the distinction of being appointed lecturer in neuropathology and, with Brücke's recommendation, received a traveling fellowship of considerable value whereby he might go to other countries to ground himself better in the material with which his lectures were to concern themselves.

It was with this fellowship that the door was opened to Freud to make the first great step in the intellectual adventure of the theory that was to be his life's work.

2

In Paris (where he elected to pursue his studies under the fellowship) the medical savant Jean Martin Charcot was working on hysteria in his clinic at the College of the Sorbonne. His success and novel experimental methods had spread his fame all over Europe, for Charcot's study of hysteria had been conducted largely with the aid of hypnotism, through which he had found himself capable of producing paralyses and local symptoms in patients by mere suggestion.

Hysteria is nowadays universally recognized as a psychic disorder; but before Charcot had demonstrated this, there were all manner of opinions of its origin, ranging from the "bad blood" idea to the "devils" Christ cast out of the woman as described in the New Testament. It usually manifested itself by paralysis, semi-trances, cataleptic attitudes, and similar random and apparently inexplicable symptoms.

Charcot claimed, and demonstrated with his experiments in hypnosis, that hysteria was not a product of the tissues of the body but of the mind: a condition imposed upon the body by the mind. He went no farther than this; he was content, for the rest, to catalogue what he considered the major stages of hysterical attacks (a division since his time discarded, since there is no regularity in hysteria) and to prove that these attacks were genuine disorders, not malingering or shamming.

To Charcot's clinic came Freud, with his mind beginning to expand to the possibilities of the study of the neuroses as distinguished from the purely physical nervous disorders with which he had hitherto busied himself. His skill in the diagnosis of organic nervous disorders had become remarkable, and had gained him some reputation. He himself felt, however, that this skill was utterly useless in dealing with the vast field of neurosis—that disorder of the mind that is solely of the mind and without apparent reflex in the body. In Charcot's clinic he hoped to find this deeper understanding.

He did not find it; but something more important happened.

Studying under Charcot the numerous cases of hysteria that came to the clinic, Freud perceived that, in those cases where the symptoms consisted of paralysis and loss of feeling in localized regions of the body, these regions were bounded not by the actual anatomical boundaries, but by those supposed to be the boundaries in popular belief. Thus a patient complaining of an oppression and anesthesia in the heart would have this numbness not in the actual cardiac region known to doctors, but in the place erroneously supposed to be occupied by the heart in the common conception. This obviously was a clue to the psychic origin of the disorder.

Freud told of his observation to Charcot, who agreed with him, but was obviously not interested in penetrating any farther into the psychology of the neuroses. Charcot was circumscribed by the physical and anatomical fundamentals of his education; he could summon neither interest nor belief in anything beyond or outside of these. Freud realized that if there was anything to be learned it was for himself alone to investigate.

Once, in Freud's presence, Charcot threw out a hint of something for which Freud's mind was not yet ripe. At that time it was merely a small suggestion; years later it was to recur to him with special significance. It came about in this way. In describing to another physician the case of a neurotic couple, the wife an invalid and the husband impotent, Charcot had suggested that in such cases it was always sexuality that was at the root of the disorder. Freud, hearing him, wondered idly: "If he thinks so, why doesn't he ever say so?" But Charcot, following the French medical tradition, shunned the idea of sexuality as a cause of disease. To the bold and untrammeled mind of Freud this kind of restraint seemed contrary to the best interests of science. Had he then known more about his theory-to-be, he would not have allowed the hint to be dropped. But Freud was only in the making in those days and the incident was soon forgotten.

But if Charcot drew back from going along with Freud on this newer road, he nevertheless gave the young man by his own example a fine code of patience, restraint and imagination that was to aid him considerably in achieving the outlook and equipment of a theorist. Charcot, as Freud himself has pointed out, was a seer, a man who looked at things over and over again, intensifying his impression of them, until suddenly understanding would come to him. He possessed also the capacity for grouping his observations in a well-knit system so that order emerged from chaos. All this was excellent training for Freud.

From the autumn of 1885 to the summer of 1886, Freud studied at Charcot's. On his way back to Vienna he stopped at Berlin and worked for a few months in the children's clinic of Max Kassowitz, where he made extensive observations of the mental and nervous disorders of childhood. On his return to Vienna in the fall he married the girl who had been waiting for him. This new responsibility, added to an ever-pressing economic necessity, settled him down to the job of making a living and a career as a practicing physician.

3

It was his duty to report on what he had learned abroad to the Society of Medicine in Vienna. In all good faith he prepared to do so. He told them of Charcot's proofs that certain physical manifestations of hysteria are not necessarily physical in origin, but may be mental, since they could be induced by a mental influence, namely hypnosis. Charcot's experiments with hypnosis showed that it was possible by suggestion to produce an hysterical symptom in the male quite as intense as in the female. Freud told them all this in clear and scientific language. And they laughed and scoffed at him.

Of course, it must be understood that in those early days in Vienna, psychology, which is now the science of *mind*, was almost identical with the science of the *brain* and the nerves. That is, the human mind was looked upon as a machine and consequently all discussion turned upon such things as the structure of the lobes and the divisions of the brain. In those days to know the mind meant an understanding of the physical side, a study of the nerves in their various outbranchings and ramifications. It necessarily followed from this that the physician's duty was to treat the various ailments of the mind only by material or chemical means.

In view of these beliefs it was only natural that his Viennese colleagues should smile in disdain when Freud said that Charcot had definitely proved that certain physical manifestations of hysteria are not necessarily physical in origin but may be mental. It was only natural too that they should laugh outright when he went on to say that many physical diseases are the product of thought.

It was Freud's first direct encounter with the reactionary forces of orthodox medicine. For a while it stunned him; but when he recovered it filled him with the self-same disgust that overwhelmed Pasteur when his germ theory had been laughed out of court. Freud heard one doctor dismiss the story of male hysterics with the remark: "But how can there be male hysterics? *Hysteron* means the uterus" —thus placidly retreating to the stage of medical knowledge current in Greece some three thousand years before!

After the meeting a number of physicians went up to Freud and urged him to forget these fantastic fairy tales he had been deceived into believing. He was a young, earnest medical man; there was no reason for him to go in for this sort of nonsense. He had a career to make.

In the middle of his protestations that every word of his report had been true and verifiable, Freud quickly realized the futility of his arguing. These men would not believe; they did not mean to believe. Within him there began to crystallize a strong contempt for orthodox opinion that stood him in great stead many times in the next few decades.

He did not give up. He sought out cases of male hysteria in the clinics of Vienna, and after much opposition on the part of the physicians in charge, who did not want him to study their patients, he managed to bring one to the Medical Society for demonstration. This time he could not be laughed down; but, though the doctors applauded, they straightway dismissed the matter from their minds. Freud, however, had been marked with the stamp of the heterodox, the radical. He was excluded from the Institute of Cerebral Anatomy.

4

Not all the medical men of Vienna turned their backs on Freud. Besides those who were merely forbearing there were a few who realized that this young man had an active, penetrating mind, was a cool observer and a sharp reasoner. Most important of these to Freud was the well-established family physician, Doctor Josef Breuer.

Breuer had been Freud's good friend before he went to Paris, and had told him of his own experiences in the treatment of neurotics and hysterics. There had been one case in particular that had seemed to give a clue to the mystery of the origin of hysteria; and now that he had definitely turned his mind in this new direction, Freud began to study this case afresh.

The patient had been a girl suffering from hysteria. Her symptoms were temporary but recurrent paralyses, disorders of speech, sleepwalking tendencies. Breuer had used hypnosis and had asked her for her reminiscences, seeking to get deeper into the origins of the trouble. Each of her symptoms, he learned, had a point of beginning, a place where it had first appeared. As soon as he had traced the symptom back to this point by hypnotic questions, it had vanished. In this way he was able to eliminate most of her trouble.

This seemed to be getting somewhere. Breuer called the process catharsis, or the cleaning out of disorder. He believed that the cure was effected by suggestion, which served to bring back to a normal path the energy which had been diverted into a symptom. Freud was enthusiastic. He began to use Breuer's technique on his own patients, and the two men worked together in their effort to arrive at a clearer understanding of these mysteries.

Freud had found himself almost helpless as far as treating nervous cases was concerned; Breuer's method, however, seemed to open up a vista of possibilities. The therapy of the day in neurotic disorders consisted in electric treatments, which Freud realized were virtually worthless, since their efficacy, if any, was due to suggestion by the physician. There was also the water cure, which poor Darwin had been subjected to, but Freud saw he could neither make a living nor benefit his patients by sending them out of town to a hydropathic establishment after one consultation. It was thus that catharsis turned out to be a welcome new method.

Breuer had let his discovery go for several years after the first case. Freud wondered why. He also wondered why Breuer had never told him the ultimate outcome of the case—whether the patient had been permanently and completely cured or whether she had relapsed after a while, as had happened with earlier attempts at hypnotic treatment. But he did not pause overlong in wonder. He began intensive work with Breuer in the new method, and was rewarded with remarkable results. They decided to write a book.

Before its publication Freud left Vienna again for a visit to France. This time he went to Nancy where the neurologist Bernheim was doing remarkable things, so it was said, with hypnotism. Freud, whose hypnotic abilities were by no means perfect, thought that this was a good opportunity to perfect them, and besides it was a splendid chance to gather new material to supplement the mass of observations and half-drawn conclusions stirring in his mind.

5

In Nancy he witnessed interesting things. Bernheim believed that all the virtue of hypnotism rested in suggestion, and with this point of view he had made some remarkable cures and some even more notable experiments.

There was one experiment in particular that impressed Freud greatly, shedding as it did a new light upon the mass of material slowly taking form in his own mind. Bernheim would tell a man in an hypnotic state to perform some trivial act—open an umbrella, for instance—after he awakened, that is, about five minutes later. The subject would awaken, would act normally for a short period, and then would inevitably go to the umbrella and open it.

This, although interesting, was nothing new. What was astounding was that, when the subject was questioned as to why he had opened the umbrella, he was embarrassed, evaded the question. Nor was it because he was consciously ashamed of his reason for doing so: he had thoroughly submerged the origin of his act, and could not answer the question.

Bernheim went farther. Without resorting to hypnosis, he would bring the origin of the act back into the subject's mind. With suggestion, reiterated persuasion, the subject would be induced gradually to recall all the incidents of the hypnotic trance. The embarrassment was thereby removed and the necessity for evasiveness eliminated.

Freud pondered a great deal on this and other experiments of Bernheim. They seemed to tie themselves up with the experiences he had had with Breuer, when forgotten origins of symptoms had been brought to the foreground of the mind by the method of catharsis under hypnotism. There seemed to be a mental mechan-

SIGMUND FREUD

Courtesy of Edward L. Bernays

ism that existed to repress certain ideas; and from his experience
Freud knew that these ideas were usually unpleasant ones. Nor
was this repression a conscious thing; it would have had no value
if it had been. It seemed to be an automatic, *unconscious* process
that kept from the patient's awareness unpleasant or shocking
associations.

But Bernheim's technique did not fulfill its promise. A highly
gifted neurotic patient, whom Freud had brought with him from
Vienna, was subjected to Bernheim's concededly superior hypnotic
powers. Freud, who had been able to aid her only temporarily
through hypnosis, had supposed that the difficulty lay in his own
inability to bring about a profound enough hypnotic trance. So
Bernheim tried to do something for the woman. He failed; and
frankly admitted to Freud that his success had been only with hospital patients and not with private cases.*

Freud returned to Vienna, still without a theory but in a high
state of enthusiasm. A beginning was now being made. He had
the doctrine of repression: that the hysterical symptom originated
in an unpleasant sensation or experience or impulse, which, having
been repressed, released its energy through the devious path of the
symptom. But this was only a beginning; a vast field of investigation and exploration stretched out in front of him.

He plunged into the construction of a theory with three principles firmly entrenched in his mind.

It appeared to him that the first of these principles must be
determinism, because the symptoms he dealt with were not meaningless. They were not random or haphazard. They had a definite
cause and a definite reason for appearing as they did. This impression of determinism Freud had borne with him since hearing
Goethe's essay on nature while still in school: nothing in nature
is the result of chance, everything has its law.

His second principle he had derived directly from his experiences with patients. The sought-after origin of the symptom was
not on the surface—that is, it was not conscious. It operated in a
hidden part of the mind: the unconscious. With this definite divi-

* This phenomenon is probably due to the general tendency that makes hospital and ward patients more suggestible and submissive to the physicians than
private patients.

sion of the mind into an unconscious and a conscious, Freud was only indexing everyday observation; but what an uproar it raised! The philosophers and old-fashioned psychologists could not concede that there was any more to the mind than what was immediately at hand. How could there be an "unconscious mental"? they asked. Did not mental mean conscious? With such quibbling Freud could waste no time. The facts were there for all to see: the evidence of a single hypnotic experiment alone sufficed to convince that there was something beneath the surface—something that required unnatural means to come to the surface.

Freud's final premise was the most significant of the three. This also had been taught him by the cases he had studied; repression was necessitated by unpleasantness, associated in some way with the repressed material. This unpleasantness might be merely a result of a shock suffered in an experience, which caused that experience to be forgotten—that is, hidden in the unconscious—or might be the accompaniment of strong conflicting emotions within the patient, such as sexual love for a person too closely related for legal or moral gratification of the impulse.

With these three concepts in mind—determinism, the unconscious, and the avoidance of the unpleasant in conscious life—Freud now set out to solve the mysteries of human mentality.

6

In 1895 Freud and Breuer published their results in the *Studien Ueber Hysterie*. They called the attention of the medical world to phenomena which had never before been properly interpreted or understood. They gave case histories from their own practice, illustrating the phenomena of conversion, by which an emotional experience was changed into a physical manifestation, such as a symptom, which had no conscious or apparent relation to the exciting cause. "The hysterical symptoms are built up at the cost of the repressed emotions." They gave in the *Studien* the method of catharsis, and cited case after case in which this new technique had been proved successful.

They presented to the world of medicine a definitely worthwhile method for treating a disease that up to that time had been completely obscure, and the world of medicine ignored them. What notices the book did receive were for the most part derogatory, but at least the book reviewers recognized the existence of this new interpretation. The majority of the medical profession, however, turned its back in scorn.

There was a deeper reason for this antagonistic attitude by organized medicine than merely its conventional conservatism. There was something in the *Studien* that gave a hint of a revolution to come, a revolution that was to shake many time-honored puritanical notions and overturn cherished moralistic values. Even Breuer had drawn back from recognizing in the study of hysteria the factor that Freud realized must be recognized, the fundamental source of every case of neurosis that had come before him: the inevitable drive of sex.

To be sure, there was comparatively little emphasis laid on it. Freud had not yet penetrated deeply enough into the mystery to have encountered the bogey in all its intensity. Breuer, fourteen years the elder and a family physician, with the prejudices and opinions of his time, had deprecated even the discussion of sexuality that managed to get into the *Studien*. Nevertheless the beginnings were there.

Against the potentiality of this threat all the powers of darkness and prudery began to arm themselves. For the ban upon the discussion of sexual matters was deep-rooted. The subject was taboo virtually everywhere, in schoolroom, in the home, in the lecture hall—for the most part even in the doctor's consultation room. It was not so much a conscious conspiracy of silence against what we today flippantly refer to as the "facts of life"; it was a deep-set, all-pervading taboo that governed the minds and souls of every stratum of society.

Here and there a few bold spirits had started a battle for enlightenment. Havelock Ellis was just beginning to issue his *Studies in the Psychology of Sex,* exhaustive researches and compilations of all material contributing to the knowledge of the many sides of this vast subject. Krafft-Ebing in Germany had published, for medical men only, his *Psychopathia Sexualis,* relating the history of thousands of cases of abnormal and diseased sexuality. Edward Carpenter was then offering his *Love's Coming of Age* to publisher after publisher who refused to print it. Except for these and a few other bold pioneers the darkness of ignorance was complete.

To relieve the stygian blackness of this situation there came Sigmund Freud whose mind, through some quirk of inheritance or environment, had managed to escape the widespread prejudices and taboos against sex. Neither expecting nor wanting to find any one source more than another, he had studied the cases of thousands of neurotics, and had evolved a method by which those sources might be brought to the surface. Now that this method was in full operation, even while the *Studien Ueber Hysterie* was coming from the press, Freud was encountering more and more clearly defined evidences that at the core of each of the traced symptoms was nothing but a reaction of one kind or another against sexuality.

7

Freud did not start with a preconceived idea that sex was all-important. Although his mind was far and away more receptive and clear-thinking than those of other investigators, he had at first accepted the current tendency to ignore sexual factors in neurosis. He felt at first that he would be insulting his patients by assuming such factors. But against his will, as it were, he found these factors continually forced upon him.

He published a paper on anxiety neurosis before he published the *Studien*. Anxiety neurosis was a special kind of nervous disorder, characterized by phobias and apparently inexplicable fears. He applied his technique to his patients in order to get at the origin of the symptoms, and in each case the patient finally revealed a gross abuse of the sexual function. Masturbation, *coitus interruptus, coitus reservatus,* these were the sort of abuses that almost invariably were present in cases of anxiety neurosis. When the patient ceased the practice and returned to a normal sex life, the symptoms vanished. What else could Freud conclude? The sexual function was at the base of the disorder.

In his discussion of hysteria and the neuroses of defense, where an hysterical symptom of one kind or another was adopted as a means of escape from an unbearable idea, in each case he found that the unbearable idea was connected with sexual experiences and sexual sensations. There were such cases as that of the girl who suddenly became an hysteric when her sister died. Treatment by hypnosis disclosed that the trouble had arisen at the deathbed, when the thought had suddenly flashed across her mind that now her brother-in-law was free to marry her. Shocked by having, even for a moment, entertained such an idea, she had developed the hysteria as a defense. When their origins had been brought to the surface by catharsis, the symptoms disappeared.

Everywhere that Freud came across a neurosis of the sort he had been studying, he encountered sooner or later the factor of sex. He was cautious about generalizing. In his paper on the defense neuroses he merely stated that "such unbearable ideas develop in women chiefly in connection with sexual factors. . . . In all the cases I have analyzed it has been in the sexual life that a painful effect had originated. . . . I merely . . . state that hitherto I have not discovered any other origin of it."

When he later thought the matter out, he could see clearly why neuroses sprang from sexual causes. Was it not in precisely this sphere that ignorance and suppression were most pronounced? Were not sexual impulses more than any others denied free expression? What was more natural than that that part of nature which came into direct conflict with civilization should be the region whence disorders arose?

He thought that it would be comparatively easy to persuade his medical colleagues of this. They must certainly in their own practice have encountered the sexual factor time and again. Certainly they would be eager to hear the conclusions of a man working in a field where the sexual factor was the chief motif. Freud decided to forget his former rebuffs at the hands of organized medicine and present these latest conclusions to the world.

Once more he was rudely disappointed. These men did not want to hear any data concerned with sexuality. They received him coldly, called him an extremist and faddist. An atmosphere of disapproval settled upon the medical meetings when Freud read his papers. Even the doctors who had previously patted him on the back were no longer so tolerant. They denounced him as obscene, perverted, lewd. One detractor openly boasted before a group of his colleagues that he employed Freud's method of going to the origin of a symptom, but stopped immediately and silenced the

x

patient as soon as he or she began to talk of things sexual. This was the last straw. Such speciousness in argument made Freud realize that he must accept the status of an outcast; that he belonged to those who have "disturbed the sleep of the world."

Convinced that he had struck out upon his road alone, he set himself with renewed zeal to the task of unraveling the mysteries of mind as an independent investigator. He threw to the winds every fear and drove single-mindedly towards his goal. His material existence, which had so often dictated his choice of a course of action, now became a secondary consideration. He lost many patients because he asked them questions about their sexual life. They were shocked, irritated, shaken; and they decided to consult a less blunt and less outspoken doctor. His friends, except for a very few, faded away; a "vacuum formed about his person."

8

But what conquests of the mysteries had he not already accomplished on his own initiative! He had first of all laid bare the fact of repression—that the unpleasant in life, the unbearable emotionally, is repressed into the unconscious, while the energy attached to it finds its equivalent expression in a neurotic symptom. He had seen, also, that these repressions were apparently invariably attached to the sexual life of the patients.

He had learned also, by consolidating the discovery of Breuer with the teachings of Charcot and adding the interpretation he himself had made, that when the disturbing, repressed emotion was given a chance at expression (by the mere fact of its narration to the doctor) this simple expedient was sufficient to discharge the energy and correspondingly relieve the symptom.

From these facts he had progressed to other deductions, each an inevitable step in the elucidation of that theory of the mind towards which he strove. Since the repression was eliminated (with the elimination of consciousness by the means of hypnosis), it must follow that the repressing agent was a part of the conscious. He adopted what he called the "topographical method of approach," and sought to work out a chart which should be an index—purely hypothetical of course—to the various agents and factors of the mind. By this means of approach he represented the consciousness as dominated by the *ego,* which holds in check and represses the impulses arising in the unconscious. These impulses are chiefly those of the *libido,* a term Freud took from the Latin to denote the whole sum of energy connected with the sexual instinct. As years passed, he was to find the topographical approach more and more convenient in elaborating his conceptions.*

The goal of the treatment was, then, to release the energy inherent in the symptom and the repression by bringing the repressed material to the surface. In other words, it was to strengthen the ego, and let it recognize the sources of its own discomforts and disorders, so that it might make a reasoned, intelligent, *conscious* disposition of them. This, Freud felt, was all that the doctor could do; the point was now to find out how best this end might be served.

He was fast finding that his old methods were inadequate. For one thing, they restricted him to the treatment of hysteria and its allied forms of disorder. Hypnosis had other drawbacks. It often afforded only temporary relief. It did not seem to penetrate deeply enough into the unconscious. It was, besides, dangerous, for persons hypnotized too often had a tendency to acquire a mental lassitude and general predisposition that made them susceptible to the slightest suggestion on the part of the physician, even when they were in a normal waking state.

From another point of view, hypnotic methods definitely limited the analyst in his effort to discover the mechanisms that caused the disorder. By eliminating consciousness, it eliminated the repressing forces, so that these forces could not be observed. He was cutting himself off, by the use of hypnosis, from one of the most potentially fruitful sources of observation. It was by observing the conscious struggling against the repressed impulses that important facts could be learned concerning the nature both of the impulses and of the conscious.

There was also to be considered the fact that he himself had never become a very successful hypnotist, and this failing might be the case with many men otherwise capable and acute.

Freud, therefore, was considering seriously the abandonment of

* In the concepts of ego, superego, and id Freud completed his "topography of the mind."

hypnotism and the cathartic method, when one day an incident occurred which precipitated his decision. A female patient whom he had had under hypnotic treatment for some time suddenly threw her arms about his neck on awakening from a trance, and a most embarrassing situation might have arisen, if the unexpected entrance of a servant had not cleared the air. Freud wanted no more such incidents, which he had absolutely no way of foreseeing from the information he gathered in the hypnotic treatment. By tacit agreement hypnosis was no longer employed, and he was forced to resort to a new expedient.

He recalled that Bernheim had been able to employ suggestion by encouraging a subject to recall the forgotten incidents of his hypnotic trance. With a little prodding and a show of firm insistence, he had managed to reconstruct in the patient's conscious mind the image of the occurrences of the trance. Obviously, the patient really "knew" these occurrences; it was merely that some automatism of his mind suppressed them.

Freud's own neurotic patients must also "know" the origin of their symptoms; the point was then to find a way to bring them to know it consciously. For this purpose he began to use Bernheim's method of insisting on the subject's remembering, sometimes laying his hand on his forehead. It worked well; the forgotten origins returned at first gradually and then suddenly flooded the patient's mind with vivid recollection.

The method had certain defects: it was too easy to suggest something to the patient that a repressive ego would eagerly adopt as a substitute for the truth. It involved a great strain on both physician and patient. But it was the best available; and Freud employed it for some time.

With the abandonment of hypnosis and the Breuer methods of achieving catharsis, Freud changed the name of his technique. He devised for it the title psychoanalysis.

9

Freud's discovery, in continued research, of sexuality and libido in children was something the world was unprepared to receive in view of a semireligious belief in the absolute innocence of childhood. From time immemorial people had regarded childhood as a period apart from the rest of life, a period free from the so-called sordid processes of sex and desire. That there should exist in "the sweet purity of childhood" any clear resemblances to grown-up desires and to grown-up sex urges was something utterly unthinkable—and shocking!

As a matter of fact, Freud himself was reluctant to believe it. For he too was reared in the same age-old tradition. Inevitably, however, he was led by the analysis of hundreds of sexually disturbed people to find the origin of the disturbances in this new, this revolutionary concept of infantile sexuality. The Sphinx of Sex, yielding to the cool advance of his analytic genius, had revealed another of her aspects to him: he was coming closer and closer to the final mysteries.

He knew that his idea of libido must be expanded to include this new region, hitherto undreamed of. Sexuality could no longer be confined to the narrow field of adult desires and their fulfillment. Children were sexual, he could see that from the childhood reminiscences his patients poured out. But they were not sexual in the same way as adults. The objects of their desires were different. Their impulses were vague and amorphous. More important, their repressive mechanisms were unformed, and the taboos and disgusts and morality of grown people could not affect them. Here was a new type of sexuality which needed to be analyzed and understood before he could hope to comprehend the mind in all its phases.

But something came up at the very outset of his new research that sidetracked him, threatened to bring all his analysis to an impasse and almost wrecked the theory he had so laboriously worked out. He had never had occasion to discard the views of Charcot, that hysteria originated in a violent experience which damaged psychic equilibrium. When his patients, therefore, began telling him of childhood reminiscences of violent sexual happenings, he was at first inclined to believe them. Undoubtedly it was true that in some cases the direct cause of the neurosis was a forcible seduction of the patient in early childhood by an older person. Freud did not question the authenticity, therefore, of the stories of seduction and abuse of the passive bodies of children which his patients told him in great detail. But when many such cases began to accumulate in his notebook he began to wonder.

There was one young woman in particular whose father Freud knew as a man of the most irreproachable honor. Carrying his analysis to the stage where reminiscences of her early childhood had been reached, Freud was amazed when the patient confided to him that at the age of six her father had seduced her. Freud felt it could not be true. Yet he had obtained this confidence along paths of analysis that he had carefully tested, carefully thought out and established. Could it be that he had been working along totally false grounds? Had he made an initial error that had invalidated all his later findings? Such doubts assailed him, but careful recapitulation failed to show any such error.

There was only one possibility. The story told by the patient was not a lie, he could be sure of this; but it was fictitious and imaginary—in short, an hysterical phantasy. Was it therefore to be discarded as unimportant? Here Freud's fundamental principle of determinism entered the picture. If the patient had conceived such phantasies, it must have been with an unconscious motive. There must have been a purpose in creating these detailed images of imaginary happenings. This purpose, if uncovered, would be sure to yield clues and implications to expand his knowledge of mentality. "If hysterics trace back their symptoms to fictitious traumas," Freud reasoned, "this newer fact signifies that they create such scenes in fantasy, and psychical reality must be taken into account alongside actual reality."

What did the sexual life of the child consist of? Obviously its desires were not those of the adult. Rather they were directed toward random objects, toward the individual himself, toward his surroundings, toward his parents. The fantasies conjured up by the patients were obviously elevations to an adult level of sexual activities considered disgraceful or insignificant or inglorious. Whereupon Freud, realizing this, set about learning from his patients—and, later, by observing the activities of children—just how infantile sexuality manifested itself.

He found confirmation of his premise that the sexual function existed from the very beginning of the individual's life. The distinction that had to be made, however, was that at first the infantile mind did not distinguish this impulse from any other vital function. Eating, drinking, playing, excreting, and other physiological processes all served as modes of expressing the libido that stirred within the child. The genitals, through which the adult satisfied his sexuality, were undeveloped in the child, had not yet become the center of erotic activity. But the libido was nevertheless present, just as was the desire to eat and drink, and consequently it found its expression through the available and already developed channels of physiological life.

The libido did not always develop smoothly and normally. Childhood was filled with situations, experiences, and maladjustments which tended to make one of these early components unduly strong, or to give a premature gratification to the instinct before its proper and normal outlet had been provided. Such a mishap often caused a *fixation* of the instinct at the point where it occurred; so that the individual was frequently inhibited from progressing further than this infantile or pre-puberty stage in his sexual life.

And here Freud came upon another astonishing fact, the promulgation of which brought down upon his head more anathema than any preceding part of his theory.

10

The next foundation stone of the psychoanalytic structure was the Oedipus complex.

After the auto-erotic stage of early sexual desire had been passed, Freud found that the libido began to look outside for its love objects. While still in the early days of infancy, when the pregenital stages were still predominant, the child began to center its love objects in the person of one or the other of the two nearest individuals—the parents.

Boys turned their desires and their love toward the person of their mothers; girls developed the same emotional relation toward their fathers. To be sure, this was nothing particularly new or unfamiliar: the phenomenon of boys romanticizing about their mothers and girls about their fathers had been observed many times before.

But no investigator had ever sought to draw from this situation the implications and interpretations that lay behind it. Freud found that the love of a boy for his mother did not stop at that. He was not content with loving the mother. The boy (Freud realized from the tales his patients told him) developed hostile wishes against his father, was jealous of the man who preceded him in the loved one's affections, sought to take the father's place.

These two components—love of the mother and antagonism to the father—Freud found sooner or later in every case of a male neurotic that he analyzed, and an analogous situation with the female. He quickly realized that this was the fundamental structure of one of mankind's great myths—the Oedipus story of the man who unwittingly (unconsciously) killed his father and married his mother. And the myth held true to what psychoanalytic research had disclosed. Oedipus, when he became conscious of his offense against morality and his violation of society's taboos against incest, had gone mad (become neurotic), had torn out his eyes and fled from the land.

Impressed by the vividness with which the old Greek story followed his own investigations, Freud called his newest discovery the Oedipus complex.

Now he had a clue to the fantasies of sexual assault that his patients had invented: they had gone through childhood accumulating the Oedipus complex. The adult woman presented the analyst with a picture, not of the inglorious actuality of the past, but of her own fulfilled wishes, in which her desire to assume her mother's role toward her father had been achieved. Fantasies, then, were wish-fulfillments—desires become actuality. The unconscious, battered and checked by the repressions of the outer world acting through the ego, invented a shadow world of its own, in which its desires were completed and its love gratified.

There were other kinds of fantasies besides these that were brought out in the analytic treatment, and there were other aspects of fantasies that now demanded his attention.

11

His patients were continually telling him their dreams.

He did not ask for them, but when a stage of analysis had been reached where the repressive mechanism had been to some degree eliminated, the patient began to relate the dreams he experienced, as if intuitively he knew that these were further clues to the intricate mysteries of his mind. Freud soon came himself to realize that in the dream he might find an able assistant in his analysis.

It now appeared evident that in sleep, when the rigid bonds placed upon the unconscious by the ego were relaxed, the desires and yearnings of the patient came closer to expression and sought in the fantasy-creating ability of the brain the outlet that in waking life was closed to it.

Dreams, which had long been considered by science as nothing more than the distorted reflexes of indigestion and similar insignificant physical manifestations, Freud discovered had a meaning. The ancients had thought the gods sent dreams in order to predict the future; in medieval times the function of interpreting dreams had been relegated to witches. At any rate, dreams were considered idle nonsense and any suggestion that they had meaning was regarded as a foolish superstition. But now Freud realized the dream *had* meaning, as much meaning as he had found in those hitherto despised neurotic symptoms. More tenaciously than ever, he clung to his original principle: that everything in nature has its function and its law. It was once more vindicated as he unraveled the age-old mystery of dreaming.

He realized at the outset that the apparent content of the dream was not the fundamental thing. These fantastic, disconnected and distorted images that swirled through the sleep of his patients were merely translations of desires and ideas hidden as deeply in the unconscious as the origins of any ordinary neurotic symptom. The surface manifestations of dreams were *symbols* of, that is substitutes for, basic ideas. In sleep just as in waking there was a repressive mechanism operating to twist and distort and render unrecognizable the unpleasant truth that lay at the bottom of mentality.

All that he learned bore out his main, original idea—everything in psychic life had a meaning. The apparently irrelevant hysterical symptom, the so-called perversions, considered generally to be random choices dictated by chance heredity, now possessed definite significance. The wild and incoherent ramblings of the dream—the evasions employed to forget important parts of the dream—all these phenomena had purpose.

He interested himself for a time in the phenomena of that ordinary, everyday, *normal* process known as forgetting. Why did people forget? Because the thing was unimportant? Sometimes, no doubt. But there were plenty of cases in his own experience when important things had been forgotten—things that should be remembered. Why was this?

He examined several instances of this type of forgetting. His expectations were rewarded—here again no casual chance was operating in the mental process. In each case of forgetting the thing forgotten was mentally associated with something unpleasant—an experience, or a distasteful personality. A lover forgot a rendezvous, not because of the pressure of business, as he told his mistress, and convinced himself, but because he was tired of her, wished to be rid of her—and his unconscious carried out his hidden wish by causing him to forget.

Freud went farther, and examined other phenomena of everyday life. Blunders of speech and action, long considered random events, he learned were actually no such thing. The little slips of the tongue that people made, remarks that startled and amused their listeners, the errors that crept into print, absurd errors that seemed to be purely unfortunate mistakes, even the mistakes of action, in which one acted as if in an hypnotic trance, and carried out a mandate not consciously dictated—all these Freud found to have definite and traceable origins. They were lapses of the ego, the supervisory agent of the mind—which was caught off guard long enough to allow a hint of the unconscious desires to slip through to the outside world, or else caused an error to be substituted for the thing actually intended—which was found to have some unpleasant connotation or other.

12

On the original issue of sexuality, Freud was entirely alone. He fought the battles for his theory unaided. Completely by himself he built it up, developed its potentialities, tested and examined the huge mass of material it made available. The independence of thought initiated in him in his university days, when anti-Semitism had cut him off from the good things of the spirit, had been intensified by his experiences since that time. He was at times bitter, and at times discouraged, but these depressed interludes became fewer as the knowledge grew in him that he had really discovered tremendous things and had achieved a marvelous theory. For a while he adopted an attitude of resignation, for it seemed that the ostracism he had been subjected to was having its effect and the theory of psychoanalysis was not destined to come to light. In these moods he felt the assurance that some time after his death a new investigator would explore these same mysterious pathways, would encounter his work, and be aided by it.

But he kept on working.

He published his theories of the dream in 1900. The book fell almost completely flat. It was not that it lacked point: it had too much! Hardly a review appeared in the technical journals, usually so eager to notice any new material. Oddly enough the same medical profession that professed to ignore Freud's work now began to go out of its way to refute it. Here and there books were being written which attempted to elucidate fallacies in Freud's ideas: the same ideas which they refused to notice in their journals. Despite opposition, what Freud stood for was becoming known, albeit in a vague and distorted fashion. To be sure, few took the trouble to read his books and examine his arguments. One man wrote an entire volume against Freud's dream theory. Later he confessed to Freud that he had never read *The Interpretation of Dreams;* he had been told at a leading clinic that it was not worthwhile.

On the heels of his theories of the dream, Freud issued a book setting forth his discoveries in the field of everyday errors and forgetting. He called it the *Psycho-Pathology of Everyday Life.* This work attracted some attention, and later proved instrumental in bringing to psychoanalysis a great deal of popularity.

In 1905 the theories of sexuality were given to the world in coherent and complete form. Now Freud began to arouse open opposition. The denunciations that had before been scathing but made behind closed doors, so to speak, were now issued in public. The skirmish period was over. With the appearance in open view of the Oedipus complex, the theory of infantile sexuality and the whole doctrine of sexuality as the root of neuroses, war was declared upon Freud. All manner of malediction and polemic poured down upon him. He was denounced as a degenerate, a pervert, a fool, a sensationalist—terms that will remind the reader of the opposition to Copernicus, to Darwin, to Pasteur.

Although he was still the center of the mounting storm of anathemas, sneers and criticisms his lone fight was over. For more than ten years he had borne the brunt by himself; but in 1902 a group of younger men began to gather to his standard. He had gradually achieved a new circle of friends to replace those who had fled horror-stricken from his contaminated person. Most of these new friends were colleagues. They sent him patients, called him in consultations, and tried to create a wider public for his books. Several of them submitted themselves to his treatment; and one in particular showed his gratitude by forming a sort of unofficial group of young men for the express purpose of learning, practicing and spreading the knowledge of psychoanalysis.

This group began to meet regularly at Freud's house. Every Wednesday evening they would gather to discuss matters psychoanalytic, relate their own experiences and the histories of their patients. Freud presided, a paper would be read, and everyone present was expected to participate in the discussion. This was the nucleus of the Viennese Psychoanalytic Society. Among its members were Alfred Adler, Wilhelm Stekel, Otto Rank and Isidor Sadger.

Gradually the circle enlarged its influence. The Freudian doctrines began to spread wider and wider in the medical consciousness. Slowly the conquest of Vienna advanced, and as it spread it made significant headway in other countries. Each step was bitterly contested by the orthodox—as was to be expected. In all the history of psychoanalysis no country was more vehement against it than Freud's own Austria. The ugliest weapons were used in an effort to turn the tide. Opprobrium, vileness and cruel slander were hurled at the apostles. An iron ring of disapproval seemed to have been formed about the young science.

But in 1906 the scene suddenly shifted. Psychoanalysis had been gaining ground, unnoticed by even its adherents. From Switzerland came news of a great victory for the theory.

13

When Darwin received the now famous letter from Alfred Russel Wallace on that memorable June day in 1858, he could not have been more profoundly stirred than Freud was when a letter arrived from Eugen Bleuler, the great Swiss clinician. In the case of Darwin, Wallace had written to ask corroboration; in the case of Freud it was somewhat different. Bleuler wrote to the Viennese theorist to inform him that psychoanalysis was being studied assiduously in Switzerland and that the Burgholzli Clinic in Zürich was making good use of it. To one who had battled so long against such heavy odds here was encouragement of the first magnitude. Later it was to be greatly heightened when, in January, 1907, the Zürich Clinic sent its representative Doctor Eitington to Vienna to learn the Freudian methods at first hand.

Out of this experience there sprang up a voluminous correspondence between Freud and his Swiss converts. Particularly valuable were the efforts of Carl Gustave Jung, at that time assistant physician at Burgholzli, who arranged the first Psychoanalytic Congress in Salzburg. Representatives from Geneva, London and the United States were present. Of course the Viennese and Zürich groups were outstanding. Besides the beneficial discussions the meeting will long be remembered for having established the first *Jahrbuch* (Journal) for psychoanalytic studies by Freud and Bleuler, and edited by Jung.

Now that psychoanalysis had achieved the merited status of an international science, Freud, working with Jung, proceeded to carry the battle farther. In the autumn of 1909 the two went to the United States to lecture on psychoanalysis at Worcester Polytechnic Institute. Unfortunately, the overenthusiasm of the Americans did psychoanalysis more harm than good. No one felt it more keenly than Freud; he was disappointed in his American trip.

He returned to Vienna at once to continue his research and battle.

Meanwhile Freudian ideas were being advanced all over the world. In 1911 Havelock Ellis was able to write that the theories of the Viennese physician were being championed in Austria, Switzerland, the United States, Great Britain, India, Canada and Australia. Branches of the Association were formed in Zürich, Berlin, Vienna, Munich, Budapest and London. The American Psychoanalytic Association was founded in 1911 by A. A. Brill.

Psychoanalysis, no longer the exclusive work of Freud, found other men, other investigators, to check and add to the findings that had led Freud to his theory. The doctrine took on the definite aspect of a co-operative movement. The field was so broad that Freud had necessarily left a large part of it untouched. His disciples began to investigate these virgin areas.

But Freud remained the spearhead of the advance. Now that his victory had been assured he had no thought of resting on his laurels. He had attracted to himself a large number of disciples whom he respected and admired, but he was not content to sit back and let them take up the burden of carrying forward the science he had created. The battle had, at any rate, by no means been completely won; and then there were wide possibilities of further argument, proof and detail. So he turned his attention to the elaboration of some of the ideas that in the first rush of driving toward the main goal he had treated only sketchily.

One of these details was the libido theory. Libido he had defined as the energy attached to the sexual instincts, but he had been forced several times to modify and expand this idea. Infantile sexuality had caused him to reinterpret libido in terms not necessarily of adult desire, but also of all the broad and far-reaching range of feeling and emotional manifestations grouped under the names of love, friendship, affection and romance. He saw that human beings possessed a peculiar quality of *sublimation,* by which they were able to discharge a portion of their libido-energy in other modes than the sexual. The energy of the athlete, of the businessman, of the social worker, of the artist was now seen as translated libido.

A more direct explanation of sublimation Freud obtained from a new insight he gained into infantile sexuality. Before the formation of the Oedipus complex, before the individual was sufficiently aware of himself even to differentiate between parents, there was a stage where the libido was contained in the ego. This stage Freud called narcissism, from the Greek myth of the youth Narcissus who fell in love with his own image in a pool. This narcissistic state, Freud recognized, never completely vanishes throughout the individual's life but persists in various manifestations.

14

In less than a generation the Freudian theory has swept across the world. Barely thirty years old, psychoanalysis has proved fruitful in application to education, medicine, anthopology, philology, philosophy, biology, mythology, history, religion, aesthetics, sociology, law and many subdivisions of scientific research. It has affected every branch of literature, especially leaving its deep impress upon biography and the drama.

On May 6, 1936, the world celebrated the eightieth birthday of Sigmund Freud. Despite the difficulty of evaluating the work of a contemporary the leading scientific journals generously acknowledged the universal influence of his views. From obscurity he has slowly arisen into recognition and fame. The city of Vienna made him an honorary citizen and in 1935 he was elected an honorary member of the Royal Medical Society of England. It is frankly admitted that "no other man has contributed a greater stimulus toward study and understanding of psychologic phenomena." In its birthday editorial the *Journal of the American Medical Association* used these words: "The position of Freud as a great leader is secure. Great epochs in medicine are defined by great leaders. As we associate Vesalius with anatomy, Harvey with physiology, Virchow with pathology and Pasteur with bacteriology, we shall come to consider Sigmund Freud as the founder of a new trend of thought in psychiatry—an investigator with a 'profound insight into the workings of primitive mentality.' "

Psychoanalysis has done more than make new material available in science, art and literature. By providing a new approach to mental phenomena it has fashioned a new outlook on the world.

For one thing Freud demonstrated and made inescapable the concept that everything in nature has a meaning. He went so far as to make even the tiny blunders of man's speech, the insignificant gestures of his hands, the fantastic forms of his dreams take on importance and value. He removed the mark of triviality from everyday life, infusing our common living with significance and pointedness.

Literature and the criticism of literature have been immeasurably enriched by Freudian views. It is almost superfluous to cite such far-flung examples as the *Ulysses* of James Joyce, the *Remembrance of Things Past* of Marcel Proust, the novels of Arthur Schnitzler, the dramas of Eugene O'Neill, the poetry of Robinson Jeffers, the criticism of Ludwig Lewisohn, *The Magic Mountain* of Thomas Mann, all of which owe much of their orientation and a ponderable part of their actual material either to Freud directly or to the general pervasion of the intellectual atmosphere with the essence of Freudian teaching.

Significant too is the fact that Freud demonstrated that the normal mind is subject to the same laws and the same mechanisms as the abnormal, the difference being that the neurotic breaks down under the same strain that the normal ego is able to conquer and adjust. To the charge made against him that he attempts to prove that everything normal is pathological, Freud can answer that he has on the other hand demonstrated that the pathological is itself normal.

To sum up in one paragraph his contribution to the technique of understanding human nature, it must be pointed out that Sigmund Freud completely changed the science of psychology, the science which before him was a dry and dreary cataloguing of misunderstood and useless facts. He found psychology mechanical and by his genius made it functional; he found it automatic and transformed it into the dynamic. Freud made his work, originally only a laboratory technique, a guide to human life, behavior and the pursuit of happiness. For all this he has been called the Columbus of the mind!

15

But the Freudian system has not come into the world without severe attacks. One of the main issues is, of course, Freud's explanation of the role of sexuality. It is not to be denied that he has received much of the blame for the rashness and inaccuracies of his disciples. It was not until his latest book was published that many reviewers became aware that he had never asserted that all dreams had a sexual basis. It was a generalization by his disciples for which he was made to assume responsibility. That he does stress sexuality far beyond any of his predecessors is, however, undeniable: it was natural, Freud pointed out, for the disorders of neurosis to arise from the sexual instincts, because this was precisely the area that was repressed. There was no inhibition upon the other natural functions of the body. It was certainly to be expected that the emotion denied full expression would be the source of any trouble that arose.

The Freudian tendency towards looseness in definition has been discussed by Havelock Ellis. Terms like narcissism, auto-erotism, Oedipus complex, Ellis has pointed out, are frequently used in Freudian literature with varying connotations, although in Freud's own writings every modification in the meaning of a word has been explained before adoption.

In order better to deal with material it has always been necessary to group it and to interpret it, however tentatively, before one can hope to attain any comprehensive survey. For this purpose one resorts to the working hypothesis—the temporary makeshift explanation that brings a semblance of order into the chaos. This hypothesis may be later discarded—it is of course important that the man forming it keep it flexible to admit new evidence. For the time being it serves as a framework. Such "working hypotheses" are to be found in many of Freud's concepts—such as the ego, the id, the preconscious, and the various suggestions he has thrown out in the fields of religion and literature.

Oftentimes the critics of Freud have been slow to understand this idea of temporary hypothesis. To advance the dogmatic rule that in science no generalization may be made until it can be demonstrated and established in every detail is admittedly too harsh. If Copernicus had heeded this dogma, he could never have elaborated his theory; certainly Hutton, Malthus, Marx and others would have been lost in a morass of confusing and contradictory data. It is necessary to make assumptions. The ability to make them and the genius for bringing them as close as possible to the actuality are marks of the theorizing mind.

13. Chamberlin . . THEORY OF THE ORIGIN OF OUR PLANET

SPECULATIONS concerning the origin of the earth have long held the attention of mankind. The first theory to attempt a scientific view of how our planet came into being was expounded in 1754 by Immanuel Kant, the German philosopher. Logically, of course, this chapter should begin with him. But because the ghosts of dead beliefs sway man far more than the things which can be seen and measured, it is necessary to understand first those long centuries of prescientific thought when people zealously believed in the so-called "creation legends."

In geology, as in everything else, present conceptions are the results of long periods of growth.

2

Perhaps the oldest of the hypotheses formed to explain the origin of the earth was the cosmogony of Hesiod in the eighth century B.C. This early thinker was among the first of those alert and curious Greeks who sought to explain things. The mark of the theorist is that he thinks cosmically—he contemplates the universe as a whole. This Hesiod did. He conceived the earth as originating in primeval chaos, giving birth to the heavens, the mountains, and the oceans, which in turn gave birth to the gods. All these ideas Hesiod set down in his *Theogony,* a poem of grand scope displaying the early manifestations of the theorizing mind. Hesiod had a passion for co-ordination: he took the legends of the gods and their offspring and made an attempt to work them into an understandable system for the men of his day.

3

Oriental literature has preserved for us many fanciful cosmogonies. It is not difficult to imagine how myths and fables sprang up, stories which appealed to the peoples of those far off days because they were intermingled with ideas of religion.

One of the very old Vedic hymns (Rigveda X:90) declares that God formed the world from the different members of the body of a giant. Rather widespread was the belief that at the beginning of all things there was chaos—a primeval era when matter was dark, formless, and void. Out of this primeval matter it was thought that the Deity fashioned a kind of vast world-egg over which He was naïvely pictured in a brooding mood. At Elephantine in Egypt it was believed that the Deity formed this egg from the mud of the Nile. In the fullness of time this colossal world-egg hatched—that is, there was a cleft in the middle making it possible for the upper and concave half to rise and form the heavens, leaving the lower for the earth. Frequently in these old cosmogonies creation is ascribed to sexual congress.

A popular idea in vogue throughout the antique world was the belief that God created the visible universe with His hands and fingers. It was altogether natural for man in the childhood of his thinking to imagine the Deity an enlarged human being and so by analogy man did not hesitate to look upon the whole of creation as "the work of His fingers." As a potter molds his clay God was pictured as having shaped all things and then launched forth the rolling planets into space.

As time went on and man progressed in his thinking the "hands and fingers" theory of creation was considered too gross. A nobler view was evolved. No longer was creation to be thought the product of God's fingers—it was now ascribed to His voice: "And God *said*, Let there be light: and there was light."

The Hebrews were not the only people of antiquity who made this interesting transition from the crude idea of creation by fingers to the more impressive idea of creation by voice. Egyptian literature records a similar advance.

4

With the rise of Christianity the creation legends of the Hebrew scriptures became a part of the thinking of medieval times. Despite the fact that the Bible was accepted as a divine revelation of final and indisputable truth theologians argued across the centuries over "creation" theories. Gregory of Nyssa and Augustine advocated a more spiritual understanding but they were loudly shouted down. So firmly did the notion of creation by fingers grip the minds of

Europe that in sculptures, mosaics and stained glass windows medieval men represented God working with His hands creating and shaping the world. In the cathedral of Upsala one may still see the legend of creation carved in stone above the tomb of Linnaeus, the famous Swedish naturalist of the eighteenth century. Here, in a broad succession of scenes, God is represented in the form of a human being achieving the various acts of creation by sheer physical exertion.

Closely allied with this biblical theory of creation by fingers is the story of fossils. As was shown in the chapter on Hutton people believed that fossils were evidences of Noah and the Flood. Others, however, held the view that fossils were imperfect models which God had discarded. The Swiss naturalist, Bertrand, suggested that fossil plants and animals had been placed in the rocks "directly by the Creator, with the design of displaying thereby the harmony of His work and the agreement of the productions of the sea with those of the land."

5

The controversy over creation by fingers and voice was no less heated than the one dealing with the time element. Did God create the world in six days or did he do it instantaneously? In the opening chapter of the book of Genesis the statement is very clear that creation involved six days, but the record chapter knows nothing of this six-day operation. It deliberately speaks of "the day" in which "the Lord God made the earth and the heavens." Here indeed was a sore dilemma fixed between these two contradictory accounts lying next to each other within the same book. Which account were theologians to believe?

Long and bitter were the quarrels on this question. Finally a reconciliation was arrived at in which the two divergent accounts were declared in harmony with each other—that is, it came to be believed that in some mysterious manner God created the universe in six days and at the same time brought it into existence instantaneously. In its most classical dress this reconciliation was pronounced by St. Thomas Aquinas who eased the puzzling difficulties by saying that God created the substance of all things in a moment yet it took Him a full six days to arrange, shape, separate and polish up His creation.

With the development of learning men began to question the foundations of "revealed" statements. Just as the Ptolemaic theory was overthrown by Copernicus, so thinking men in increasing numbers could no longer be bound by or permanently satisfied with the brief and mouth-closing utterance "God created." They demanded to know how. What agencies were employed in creation? What was the succession of events? Out of these demands have come some of the most majestic thoughts that have entered the mind of man. To understand them, even in part, is "to render an intelligent being more intelligent."

6

Modern men had to build a scaffolding of thought to enable science to reach the skies: this knowledge was not achieved by leaping there at one bound. It took stupendous daring coupled with unparalleled resourcefulness and incredible perseverance to achieve results. For it must always be remembered that progress did not solely depend upon the discovery of new facts; it was highly conditioned by the intellectual climate of those days best illustrated by that medieval picture which shows a ship turning back at Gibraltar into the Mediterranean, with the inscription NE PLUS ULTRA—"Go no farther!"

Simply to write about this gigantic task of explaining the origin of the earth, as a part of the solar system, has a tendency to belittle the effort because we must state the result and omit the description of many fruitless quests, false hopes and blind alleys. Again and again men of science had to be capable of rising Phoenixlike anew from the ashes of their mistakes. The reason we study their theories is purely humanistic. Being men we are interested in other men, and especially in such men as have helped us to fulfill our highest destiny.

We begin our modern story with René Descartes (1596-1650), that acute and original French philosophical genius who divorced himself from traditional ways of thinking and based his system upon science. Descartes is important in the history of theory since he gave the necessary impetus to the scientific method by his insistence upon the subjection of every opinion to critical examination. He pointed the way to truth by stressing the importance of *doubt*.

Just because people have said so and so and believed such and such for centuries does not mean that these beliefs are truths. Not every thought that comes from books, tradition, authority, or the Church is to be accepted. In fact, declared Descartes, none is to be accepted except upon rigid examination.

No wonder Descartes' views were disliked. He began his philosophy not upon the virtues of faith but on doubt. Nothing was to be taken for granted, everything was to be studied, sifted, analyzed and proved. Such is the meaning and significance of his remarkable treatise entitled *Discourse Touching the Method of Using One's Reason Rightly and of Seeking Scientific Truth.*

In the history of theory Descartes is important to us because he could clearly see that science had to begin with great acts of doubt even as religions begin with great acts of faith. Copernicus doubted that the sun goes around the earth; Galileo doubted that heavy bodies fall faster than light ones; Harvey doubted that the blood flows into the tissues through the veins. Had not Descartes been crippled by his morbid fear of the Church, he would have expressed himself more fully along these lines. But the time was not ripe and he had no wish to suffer at the hands of any inquisition.

Besides being a philosopher Descartes was a mathematician and a man of science. His one desire was to explain all of the world (except God) by mechanical and mathematical laws. Because he lived in an age of inquisition and heresy-hunting, Descartes had to be unusually careful not to fall into any trap. While in Holland he had already written the greater part of a treatise called *The World,* in which he upheld the Copernican theory; but on learning of Galileo's torture and condemnation, he suppressed the heretical portions of it and instead proposed the vortex theory in order to express his ideas without running counter to the Church. For this reason his theory only half reveals what he thought; nevertheless he did express a belief that the earth and the planets were originally glowing masses like the sun.

For a time after Descartes, scientific thinking halted. Little progress was made in cosmic speculations until the French scientist Buffon (1707-1788) devoted a portion of his voluminous *Natural History* (printed in 1749) to a theory of the origin of the earth.

Buffon favored the idea of solving the problem of planetary evolution by the laws of mechanics. He regarded the earth and planets as parts of the mass of the sun shaken off by the shock of a comet, whereby the "impulse of rotation and of revolution in the same general plane was communicated to them." This thought of a passing star pulling from the sun the material now in the planets and their satellites was long neglected until it was revived in 1880 by Bickerton of New Zealand and modified by the American theorist, Thomas C. Chamberlin. It is an important contribution to the understanding of the modern conception of the origin of our solar system, as will be made evident later on.

7

We now come to Immanuel Kant (1724-1804) whose name was mentioned in the opening paragraph of this chapter. We are here not so much interested in the totality of his philosophy as in the impact of his solar theory. This humble German philosopher very ably crystallized the advanced thought of his time and developed many of the ideas grouped together under the familiar name "nebular hypothesis."

In their theories and speculations men have wandered far; they have not only traversed the earth, but they have traveled among the stars, through intergalactic space, to distances so vast that the mind must perforce use symbols to understand them. Kant was of this tribe of speculative mortals who could circumnavigate the cosmos and return with a co-ordinated vision of it all.

The reason for this irrepressible quest for a united view of the universe may be found in the very nature of man himself—the only creature impatient of limitation. Plainly put, man wishes to understand the universe in origin, in space and in time; for he himself forms part of it, and it forms part of him. In the mind of Immanuel Kant this "search" reached unbelievably great proportions. Are these stellar distances enormously fantastic? Then Kant will evolve for you a theory whose magnificent inclusiveness will show a linkage between all planets and the sun.

Born of a poor and lowly family in Prussia, Kant became one of the most important philosophers and theorists of all time. Curiously enough, Kant never traveled more than thirty miles in his lifetime;

it is said he never left his native city Königsberg. Yet this little man loved to lecture on the geography and ethnology of distant lands! In those long quiet hours he spent in his study, or when he walked alone, his thoughts turned to vast speculations. Among eighteen essays and short studies published before his fortieth year eleven are discussions of a scientific nature. In several of these papers there are advanced ideas and hypotheses of profound originality.

Kant began his career as a private lecturer at the local university. At the outset he applied himself to a study of the earth; later on he switched to metaphysics. While he held the lowly post of private instructor, much about which he wrote dealt with earthquakes, wind, volcanoes, fire, planets and a host of related subjects. In 1753 he announced, at the end of one of his essays, that he was about to publish a book under the title *Cosmogony, or an Attempt to devise the Origin of the World, the Constitution of the Heavenly Bodies, and the Causes of their Motions from the Universal Laws of the Motion of Matter, according to the Theory of Newton*. The work which he announced appeared in 1775 entitled *Universal Natural History and Theory of the Heavens*.

Unfortunately, Kant's book suffered an untoward fate. Except for a brief notice in a Hamburg journal it attracted almost no attention. When it was exhumed many years after his death it showed at once that this modest philosopher belongs to that line of original thinkers who have passed over the threshold of the ordinary into the realm of the extraordinary. Here was a mind that felt and sensed the spaciousness of all things—a powerful and untiring brain. In presenting excerpts from Kant's *Universal Natural History and Theory of the Heavens* two leading American astronomers, Doctor Shapley and Doctor Howarth, use these words in appraisal of Immanuel Kant as a pioneer in the field of cosmic speculation: "He proposed many of the hypotheses which have been but recently restated or demonstrated, including the island universe interpretation of spiral nebulae, the displacement of the sun to the north of the plane of the Milky Way, and the slowing down of the earth's rotation through tidal friction arising from the moon's attraction. His most significant contribution was the speculation on the origin of the planetary system—a nebular hypothesis that preceded the better-known Laplacian theory by forty years."

Kant theorized that the material of the solar system had its origin in a vast nebula. This original nebula would look like one of the great clouds of gaseous matter which our modern telescopes reveal among the stars. As this cloud cooled and contracted, it acquired a whirling motion from west to east and formed a rotating gaseous disc which gradually condensed at the center to form the embryo sun.

Kant believed that at first the nebula was a cold mass at rest. In time it began to contract through the mutual attraction of the particles of the nebula upon each other. As the nebula began to split up into component parts (and as contraction kept going on), enough heat was thereby generated to heat the component parts white-hot. Kant made the quite arbitrary and unwarranted assumption that this process would give rise to a rotation of the whole mass. He imagined that the central part of the nebula remained the largest and in time became our flaming sun, while the matter which gathered around the other nuclei formed the planets and their attendant satellites. All the planets, Kant thought, have been or will be inhabited. Those that are farthest from the central mass (the sun) have had, in all probability, the longest period of growth. As such they ought to have a higher species of intelligent organisms.

8

In 1796 the French astronomer Laplace, evidently unaware of Kant's theory, advanced one of his own. It appeared in a book entitled *Exposition du Systeme du Monde*. This theory, though inferior in some ways to that of Kant, had points of similarity. Laplace developed his theory in detail with a mathematical precision beyond Kant's ability. At once it captured the imagination of the scientific world; under the name of the nebular hypothesis it became the classical and accepted theory of the cosmos for more than a century.

Laplace theorized that the sun began as a vast heated nebula consisting of gas which had acquired a rotary motion. He assumed the nebula to be in a state of slow rotation around an axis. As the gas gradually cooled it shrank and consequently whirled faster and faster.

Because of contraction this nebula of glowing gas became spherical in form. Rapid rotation of its equatorial belt, together with other forces, caused the parental sun to eject at various stages great rings of solar matter, leaving each ring behind as the shrinkage of the mass continued. Each abandoned equatorial ring of gas drifted from the parent sun and consolidated into a planet (a ring was assumed for each of the planets) whose orbit around the sun was the same as the ring from which it was formed, and whose rotation was also from west to east. As the blazing parent globe further contracted it ejected more rings, like the rings of Saturn, until the sun left off shrinking and no more planets were born. Excess of rotation, according to Laplace, caused the sun to break up and give birth to planets.

Laplace believed that through gravitational action each ring collected itself into a globe and that these globes, like the main mass, cooled, shrank, and rotated faster. If the ring was large enough, one or more satellites evolved with the planet. The small spheres cooled and solidified more rapidly than the larger bodies. After the last ring was formed the remaining material became the sun—that huge reservoir of heat and light, one and a quarter million times the size of the earth.

According to the Laplacian hypothesis our earth was at first hot and gaseous when it left the sun. Later it became liquid, though still very hot, like slag in a blast furnace. By a further cooling process the surface of the earth was formed, a cool crust over a hot and liquid interior. In these early eons all the water, now in the oceans and lakes, was pictured as a vast envelope of steam. Later, as the earth continued to cool, the vapor gradually condensed, forming oceans and rivers. As rivers began to flow, sands and muds were carried down to the ocean. These river products later hardened into sandstone and shale, and thereby gave birth to the first sedimentary rocks resting on the original crust.

Because of the original hot and gaseous state of the earth the early climates were naturally supposed to have been very hot and moist. Later on, we shall see what an important factor the subject of climate proved to be in arriving at a truer understanding of the earth's origin. The cardinal point of the Laplacian doctrine, the idea of a cooling and contracting globe, supported the view that the earth is constantly cooling and eventually will freeze. The latest glacial period, the only one known to the followers of Laplace, was thought to be proof of the progressive cooling of our planet. His followers who elaborated upon his ideas pointed to the moon as an illustration of what will be the ultimate end of earth. They pictured a slow refrigeration process going on which will eventually result in a frozen death for all.

9

The nebular hypothesis was in harmony with most of the facts known a century and a half ago. As a theory it seemed both ample and satisfying, for it offered a clear and easily comprehended explanation of the origin of the solar system and our planet as a part of it. Nothing captures the imagination and approval of people quite so much as simplicity of explanation. This in a measure accounts for the quick acceptance of Laplace's views. But there was also another reason. Laplace's eminence as a man of learning (he was a recognized mathematician and astronomer) conferred upon his hypothesis wide approval and prestige. Its very boldness and splendor seemed to be in keeping with his recognition as a considerable man of affairs under Napoleon.

The nebular hypothesis represented the first clear scientific formulation of the conception of cosmic evolution. It was indeed a magnificent theory worthy of the profound mind that formulated it. But the organization of the solar system is more complex than it was believed to be in Laplace's time. That his theory must now be abandoned is not to deny its far-reaching influence and the vast amount of good it did in destroying traditional biblical notions along with the fantasies of classical antiquity. In its time it was noonday glare upon the mental eyesight of those who saw only the views of the Dark Ages. And even at this late date, surprising as that may seem, there are people who have not yet got used to it.

Since the nebular hypothesis was formulated great progress has been made in the accumulation of new facts. The outer moons of Saturn and Uranus, quite unknown until long after Laplace's death, revolve in the opposite direction from that required by his theory. A more complex planetary system than Laplace could have imagined has come into view. In every branch of science much that was supposed to be true is now inadequate. Chemists, for example, supposed the weight of a chlorine atom was 35.46 units until Aston showed that chlorine atoms were a mixture of two kinds whose weights are 35 and 37. Consequently, almost all deductions from the old premise were right, but the premise itself was short of the truth.

Likewise, in replacing Newton, Einstein has shown that we can explain things better if we substitute other conceptions for those of absolute space and absolute time. Similarly, an explanation called the planetesimal theory (or *hypothesis*, for some would assign it to this lower rank) has been developed to overcome Laplace. It is a new theory, more in harmony with recent discoveries, and certainly more in accord with very important mathematically demonstrated laws. For an approach to the planetesimal theory we turn to the life and work of an American theorist, Thomas Chrowder Chamberlin, born on a farm near Mattoon, Illinois.

10

Chamberlin (1843-1928) began his scientific career when he became professor of natural science at the State Normal School in Whitewater, Wisconsin, in 1870. Here he remained two years when he was called to accept the chair of geology at Beloit.

Like James Hutton who took an immediate interest in the country around Edinburgh, this youthful professor seized the opportunity of studying the earth features in Wisconsin. Because it is a region noted for its important glacial deposits, Chamberlin immediately applied himself to the interesting problems at his front door. "I was instrumental in starting the Wisconsin Geological Survey of 1869 and subsequent years. That was where I really started in science. My field—eastern Wisconsin—was very heavily covered with glacial formations, and as a matter of necessity I had to give much attention, if not foremost attention, to glacial problems. This gave me a trend in that direction, and naturally there arose in my mind the question of the cause of so extraordinary a thing as the great ice invasions."

The climatic conditions in past ages as revealed by traces of ancient glaciers occupied much of the young professor's thinking. On the basis of the nebular hypothesis all early climates should

THOMAS CHROWDER CHAMBERLIN

After the portrait by Ralph Clarkson

Courtesy of the University of Chicago

have been hot and very moist. Yet glacial deposits had been found in pre-Cambrian rock nearly a billion years ago. Moreover, right under his own nose in Wisconsin, Chamberlin found evidences of very cold climates contrasting sharply with the climate of today. How was one to explain all this?

At this point Chamberlin began to feel the inadequacy of Laplace's views. Take such a fact as the Salt Range of India, where extensive deposits of gypsum and salt have been found in strata of the Cambrian period. Chamberlin asked himself how one could reconcile a Laplacian moist earth swaddled by a dense vaporous atmosphere from pole to pole with a great desert tract of this sort? "Even more pointedly than the epochs of aridity," he declared, "do these early epochs of glaciation seem incompatible with the view of a hot earth universally wrapped in a vaporous mantle in early times."

It must not be thought that in the formative stages of his theorizing Chamberlin immediately discarded Laplace. On the contrary, he made every effort to believe the nebular hypothesis. Only after a long drawn out intellectual battle did he finally abandon it, and then not lightly but only after innumerable attempts to twist it this way and that so that at least it could be brought up to date, in other words, modified. Exactly the same thing happened to the Ptolemaic theory. Before it was finally overthrown it had undergone a score of modifications. But it was all useless and in vain because science, in sifting out facts, spares nothing, not even sacred traditions, for science has its own sacred tradition of the open mind.

Once he became convinced that all was not right with the Laplacian view he pushed his studies more eagerly until he had at his fingers' tips a mass of evidence ranging through the entire known sweep of geological times. We find him in 1878 studying the glaciers of Switzerland, gathering additional data, and then in Greenland in 1894 when he accompanied Peary on his polar expedition. Always a man to assume responsibilities, Chamberlin now took on the added task of assistant state geologist while professor at Beloit. That was in 1873. In 1877 he was made chief. Four volumes entitled *The Geology of Wisconsin* contain the results of an exhaustive geological survey of the whole state made by him and his associates.

From Beloit, Chamberlin went to Washington, D. C., where he became head of the division of glacial geology established by the government in recognition of his able work in Wisconsin. In 1887 he was elected to the presidency of the University of Wisconsin, a post he held with distinction for four years until he resigned to become head of the department of geology in the new University of Chicago. Happy to be relieved of pressing administrative duties, he turned the whole force of his powerful intellect upon the problems of the origin of the earth. His first nonglacial paper entitled *A Group of Hypotheses Bearing on Climatic Changes* appeared in 1897. Out of this paper came the planetesimal theory.

Science is the one human activity that is truly progressive. The positive and demonstrable knowledge of one generation is transmitted to another. That the planetesimal theory of Chamberlin's is able to tell us more about the origin of our planet is due not only to those who pioneered before Chamberlin but also to the collaboration of his colleague at the University of Chicago, Professor Forest Ray Moulton, the astronomer. In an interview published in 1928 in the *Open Court Magazine* shortly before he died Chamberlin tells the story of his co-operative venture with Moulton. It is remarkably interesting. "One day I happened to meet Moulton on the campus. I had had some acquaintance with him and he had been helpful in some things before. He was then a young instructor or graduate student. So I put it up to him. . . . That was the beginning of our co-operative work, and perhaps I may be pardoned for saying that it was a rather unusual combination in that field. Moulton, you see, was strong on celestial mechanics and on mathematics, whereas I was a naturalist. I worked from the earth; Laplace and Kant and all those men had been working from the heavens—working down. . . . While Moulton and I worked in close co-operation we worked independently; yet we so depended upon each other that it is a joint work, and that is the way the public should understand it."

11

At the outset of this exposition of the planetesimal theory it must be emphasized that the shift from Laplace to Chamberlin has in no way invalidated the idea of solar evolution—nor does it do away with the suggestion that the solar system has originated from a nebula. Rather to the contrary, the new theory has strengthened these views and has put them on a firmer footing than was the case before. Whereas the Laplacian theory holds that the sun broke up through excess of rotation, the planetesimal view maintains that this could not have happened. Actually, the birth of the planets was due to two forces (like father and mother): the gravitational effect of a passing star (father), which acted in conjunction with the eruptive powers of the sun (mother).

Unlike the nebular theory, the new one is based on numerous physical laws which have been discovered in recent years. In place of the concept of a solar system evolved from an evenly diffused gas the Chamberlin theory sees it evolved from irregularly scattered matter of various kinds (planetesimals), some of it solid and some gaseous. This material is derived from a body already in existence, called the ancestral sun, because it once contained the material now distributed among the several planets and satellites.

The planetesimal theory holds that at the initial stage in the development of our solar system the ancestral sun, which had existed for billions of years, was disrupted and partly torn by the gravitational effect of a passing star. Vast quantities of solar material were thrown out of the sun, not only because of the gravitational pull of the passing star, but also because of the expulsive power of the sun itself. The near collision (near in the astronomical sense) raised great tides in the hot gaseous surface of the sun just as the moon now raises tides in the oceans of the earth.

Much of the matter ejected or pulled out of these tides fell back into the sun—especially after the visiting star had gone its way. But some of the particles having sufficient velocity streamed away in opposite directions and continued on in a great variety of orbits.

It is known that the stars in our galaxy are moving in diverse directions so that it would indeed seem strange if no close encounter had ever taken place in past astronomical ages. Despite the vast distances that separate stars, such near approaches are believable. No other way has been discovered whereby the sun or any other star by itself can develop a planetary system. An outside agency is needed. To produce this result the close approach of another star is required, sufficiently close to exercise a gravitational effect such as Chamberlin's theory supposes.*

A French astronomer named Roche made in 1850 a very notable estimate of what would happen if two stars of unequal size approached each other within a distance of about two and a half radii. Roche showed that the power of gravitation would be sufficient to tear the structure of the smaller body to pieces. The two and a half radii (more exactly 2.44) is known to astronomy as Roche's limit.

Let us now suppose that these two stars approach each other at an angle that does not come within the explosive area of Roche's limit but dangerously near enough to exert a mutual tidal strain of tremendous power. What happens then? The effect of such proximity would be to raise gigantic tides, vast eruptions of gaseous substance, on each of the stars. As a result large quantities of this stellar stuff would be shot into space. The sudden increase in brilliancy of some stars is supposed to be due to collision—hence the postulated interference of a star with the ancestral sun is not only possible but reasonable. The star need not actually strike the sun in order to tear it to pieces and scatter the fractured material; in fact, a head-on collision probably would not produce the rotary motion possessed by the solar system.

Studies of the behavior of the sun reveal it as a turbulent body hurling enormous masses of flaming solar matter to great heights beyond its edges. The material which is so constantly shot out is, of course, pulled back into the sun by the gravitational attraction of the sun. In order to overcome this pull some force from the outside would have to co-operate as an agency in creating a situation strong enough to prevent the homeward return of the eruptive solar material. Only the force of a passing star can be imagined as capable of (a) pulling out of the sun larger masses than are now being erupted from its surface, and (b) making them pursue paths of their own around the sun. Our solar system, with respect to its momentum, is a very curious affair. The sun rotates slowly in contrast to the swift speed of the planets as they circle it. Of the total momentum of the solar system, the planets possess 97 percent. Thus the

* In recent years astronomers have suggested that planetary systems might originate when an unstable star bursts and we have a "nova." No theory is as yet able to state in detail how our solar system originated.

rotational momentum of the system as a whole is concentrated in the major planets. But the mass resides in the sun. Actually, the total mass of the planets is less than one percent of the mass of the sun. Such a system cannot be imagined to have arisen from within the sun itself by gradual evolutionary changes. The only answer is that some exterior agency caused this kind of situation—that is, some catastrophic action capable, by its great violence, of conferring upon the newly formed planets a much greater momentum than the sun's.

According to Chamberlin's theory the earth began its career as a comparatively small cold mass. This small original mass constituted the core of the earth to be. From time to time this original mass received additions of scattered fragments, large and small, solid and gaseous. All these additions ranging in size from infinitesimal particles to great masses are called planetesimals. This view rejects Laplace's idea of the earth's having been at one time a fiery or molten ball. (The high interior temperature of the earth is doubtless due to impact and compression.)

"The earth," declares Chamberlin, "grew up slowly, and hence when falling bodies struck the atmosphere they became hot but were cold by the time others fell on them; so the earth grew up from the infall of these planetesimals in a relatively cool way and never was molten, never was all gas. All the time it was growing up very slowly—say a billion years or so in growing up—without being very hot." Chamberlin emphatically states that the molten globe idea with the floating crust is a misinterpretation of the facts, which are: that the earth is solid, has always been solid, has grown up as a mass of little solid particles, and that these have worked upon one another. "There is internal reorganziation going on all the time, and that is the explanation of our earth movements or earthquakes, and all of that. Thus we get a very different concept of the great things in geology."

The planet Mars is about one-tenth the size of earth and possesses a thin atmosphere. Chamberlin conjectures that in all probability our planet was originally like Mars both as to size and atmosphere. As the earth grew by gathering in planetesimals, it acquired more mass and therefore more atmosphere. "Quite in contrast with the older pictures of a primitive earth cooling from a gaseous state,

z

the planetesimal hypothesis postulates a solid earth growing up slowly by accessions and becoming clothed gradually with an atmosphere and a hydrosphere. Each of the fundamental parts, the earth, the air and the water, is made to grow up thus together from smaller to larger volumes, without necessarily attaining at any state a very high temperature."

Like our earth, all the planets grew from swarms of planetesimals, around a more or less solid nucleus, instead of condensing from a very hot and greatly expanded gaseous ring. Due to perpetual meteoric bombardment physical and chemical forces have generated the heat in the earth's interior. (Meteors, supposedly belated fragments of the original tearing of the ancestral sun, are swept into our earth at the rate of something like a hundred million each day!) The Laplacian theory could never quite explain the planetoids. In the Chamberlin view they are simply large planetesimals that did not chance to lie near a larger mass or nucleus. Hence they have thus far remained isolated like those myriads of yet smaller fragments of sun-substance called meteorites.

12

The evident superiority of the planetesimal theory over the nebular hypothesis leads one to think that its acceptance would have been rapid. Not at all. Theories like theological dogmas fade slowly and new concepts take generations to become popular. Chamberlin recognized this. "I feel the greatest confidence that this new view of the earth is going to win, because it is built up from the earth, as it were, but it is going to be slow. I said at the start to Salisbury and some others that it will be twenty-five years before the planetesimal hypothesis will come fairly before the world. The twenty-five years are not quite up,* but perhaps twenty-five years was a little scant. However, I think by the end of twenty-five years there will be a rather decided opinion on the part of those who really do the thinking."

It takes a philosopher to say these things and Chamberlin was not only geologically minded but philosophically geared to the cosmos. He held to a strong belief in the future not only on scien-

---

* This was said in 1928 shortly before he died.

tific grounds, as we shall soon see, but also on moral grounds. "I am an advocate of a great future," he once said and declared that this thought was the gist of his famous Boston address of December 27, 1909, when he retired from the presidency of The American Association for the Advancement of Science. It is unquestionably a powerful document delivered by an intellectual giant in terms so simple that to read it is a delight.

To the followers of Laplace who have visualized a dying earth Chamberlin sketched the view that present geological conditions are likely to last for possibly hundreds of millions of years yet to come. The very title of his Boston paper illustrates this point of view: *A Geologic Forecast of the Future Opportunities of Our Race*. He was convinced that the earth sciences give a new forecast to mankind because "the history of the earth stretches back not merely for thousands but for millions and tens of millions of years; that the on-goings of the earth are actuated by energies too broad and deep and strong to be swerved in their course."

It is now just ten years since Chamberlin died. The past decade which has seen a worldwide depression in economic affairs has, by contrast, been witness to a fruitful period of scientific advance. At Chicago where Chamberlin worked, his son Professor Rollin T. Chamberlin is carrying on. At Harvard, Yale, Columbia—in fact, at every leading university—geologists in conjunction with other men of science are building on the foundations of the planetesimal theory. So completely did Chamberlin predict the success of his theory that it can be safely said that there is not a single authority in either geology or astronomy who now accepts the nebular hypothesis.

In recent years two British scientists, Sir James Jeans and Doctor Harold Jeffreys, have advanced certain views which would seem to carry the subject of the origin of our earth somewhat beyond the work of Chamberlin and Moulton. Their views are called the tidal theories. They deviate in detail and method rather than in principle. In fact, the planetesimal theory could have been much better called the tidal-disruption hypothesis, because its central thesis is that of the close encounter of a star and the sun. This is the pivotal idea of the theory that marks it off so completely from that of Laplace's. While the planetesimal view supposes that the existing planets were formed mainly by the slow agglomeration of small cold bodies, the Jeans-Jeffreys view claims they were all once liquid with about the same mass that they now possess, having picked up much less solar matter in later times. Jeans and Jeffreys rest their case more on tidal forces whereas the Chamberlin theory employs both tidal forces and the internal forces of the sun.

Both theories agree that the planets originated from the sun, that they are products of a solar catastrophe incited by the passing of another body near the sun, and that the planets represent the débris of this disaster that occurred millions of years ago.

14. Boas . . . . . . THEORY OF MAN

OF all the persistent misconceptions that haunt the mind of man none is more debauching than those deeply rooted superstitions on the subject of race. In recent years a worldwide tidal wave of race consciousness, ill-founded and preposterous, has engulfed humanity, with the unfortunate result that its weird and vulgar prejudices have achieved an ascendancy over the minds of whole nations.

The current furore over race is a fixation of ardent nationalism and self-importance. Apparently there is no field of knowledge where ignorance is more complacent, cruelty more rampant and dogmatism more arrogant. It is a region of vast mystification in which the half-civilized majority of mankind lives and has its being.

To refute these crude and misleading notions about race is one of the greatest contemporaneous tasks of science.

2

Through the combined efforts of the theory of evolution and the theory of the cell scientists achieved a new understanding. No longer could man's origin be viewed in terms of the primitive Hebrew account of special creation as set forth in the Book of Genesis. In the seventeenth century it was possible for the Reverend Doctor John Lightfoot, Vice-Chancellor of Cambridge, to declare that "man was created by the Trinity on October 23, 4004 B.C., at nine o'clock in the morning." With the growth of scientific knowledge it became evident that man was not made in a single day by a special fiat of the Deity.

Before the rise of Darwin it was common to think of species as being fixed and immovable. People naïvely pictured God bringing into existence each type of plant and animal separately by a single act of creation. That species were actually derived from other species, through long centuries of slow evolutionary change, was an idea remote from their thoughts. Then in 1859 Darwin's classical book appeared, *Origin of Species.* It proved to be a volcanic shock forcing the old biblical theory to undergo a severe and thorough overhauling. This venerable Scriptural misconception of man, which had been dominant for more than two thousand years, finally yielded to evolution.

Coincident with the work of Darwin, those biologists who were investigating the cell made it utterly impossible for man to be regarded any longer as the Great Exception, a creature unrelated to the animal world. Considering that the fundamental structural unit in man, as in all other organisms, is the cell, there was no escaping his kinship. Animals composed of a single cell are termed *protozoa,* those possessing many cells are called *metazoa.* Man is a metazoan whose body is linked to the animal world by an all-pervading similitude of structure. Consider the great number of points shared by man with the apes and monkeys. Like them he is a mammal because he possesses mammary glands and hair and has the thoracic cavity, containing the heart and the lungs, separated from the abdominal cavity by a complete diaphragm. Like his fellow-primates, man's eyes are directed forward so that he can have stereoscopic vision; his fingers and toes are of five digits and, like them, he possesses flat nails and no claws. Thus, man's kinship with animal life indicates his ascent from lower forms—his inheritance being the outcome of prehuman ages. The doctrine of the strict natal continuity between all forms of life, far from being a degrading thought (as most people believed in the early days of Darwinian controversy), shows that man is a scion of an order of living creatures which moved in the direction of improved brains. Moreover, by the time man appears on the outermost edge of history he had already left the other animals a long way behind.

3

It is no mere accident that anthropology is one of the youngest of the sciences. It had to wait until the knowledge of the cell and the knowledge of evolution could be formulated and applied to man. The aftermath of Schwann and Darwin created anthropology.

As we have seen, the story of all science is the story of intense struggle in the face of bitter opposition, for people have persistently viewed natural phenomena through a veil of mysticism and superstition. Was not Socrates attacked for impiety because he taught that the clouds were mechanical emanations and not divine persons? The physical sciences had to put up a long and continuous warfare against the dogmas of theology. Yet their struggle is not comparable to the battles the social sciences had to wage and are still waging on all fronts.

Chemistry, physics, astronomy are removed from the ordinary emotional affairs of the man in the street. But not the science of man himself. To attempt to investigate man impartially—his origin, his body, his nature, his nurture—is to challenge cherished and jealously guarded beliefs. This was clearly exemplified in Germany where the great majority of the members of various anthropological societies, led by no less a person than Rudolf Virchow (1821-1902), took up an attitude of critical hostility toward Darwin. *The Descent of Man* was regarded as fantastic. Not only was the book rejected, but in certain quarters even the very discussion of it was forbidden.

4

The educated public today commands a picture of man which stands as a correction of a great and long-enduring error. That error was born of a noble religious teaching handed down from the early days of Hebrew-Christian theology.

Both the church and the synagogue were interested in man, but in man whose origin and nature are "revealed" in the Scriptures. As the fundamental notions of these great theologies were crystallized centuries before the rise of modern science, it is understandable that they could not set man in proper perspective. The Hebrew-Christian theory was dominated by four errors: (a) that man was created by a special act of God, (b) that there is no linkage between him and the animal kingdom, (c) that man's presence on earth is the supreme act in the great drama of the universe of which the earth is the fixed center, and (d) that certain peoples are the elect of the Deity and therefore superior to others. The first two errors were destroyed by the theory of evolution and the theory of the cell. The third dogma was made untenable by astronomy. And the fourth by anthropology.

Existing man constitutes a single biological species—*Homo sapiens*. Excavations and discoveries have unearthed skulls and bones of extinct varieties, such as *Pithecanthropus* or Java man, *Palaeanthropus* or Heidelberg man, *Eoanthropus* or Piltdown man. These fossil remains (more than a hundred are now known) give a fairly complete knowledge of those bygone creatures allied to existing man. They all belonged to *Hominidae,* that is, to the human family of which modern man, *Homo sapiens,* is now the only representative.

Homo sapiens makes up a single species. In other words, men of all existing races belong to one and the same grouping. To be sure, there exist in this grouping many striking differences, but despite these differences fertile interbreeding is possible between all members. Take, for example, four widely separated individuals—a German blond, an African pigmy, an American Indian, a Chinese: they are mutually fertile. This admittedly is a fact distasteful to many upholders of the dogmas of superiority and "pure" race concepts.

Because all men are of one kind (species) it is correct to say "mankind." We could not as properly speak of fish-kind or insect-kind or bird-kind. It is probable that during the very early evolution of *Homo* the species became divided, owing to geographical and climatic conditions, into several varieties—white, black, yellow—each more or less isolated from the other and each evolving along those lines that would best suit it or adapt it to its own particular environment. Throughout the entire history of *Homo,* which covers several hundred thousand years, there have been many modifications—in stature, skin, color, head form, eyes, nose—but none so complete or enduring as to break up the species.

Despite the enormous progress made by the science of anthropology, there is no other subject in which people are so wont to set up their private and illogical judgments. With the best intentions it is difficult to look at man and his works with candor and detachment. Unable to assess properly the evolutionary point of view, people have long distrusted this branch of science as a body of knowledge essentially hostile to man's good opinion of himself. They have recoiled at the view of his lowly origin, as if dignity is not actually heightened by his upward biological journey.

The attitude toward man, unintelligent as it was (and still is!), has not been nearly so harmful as the so-called popular attitude towards race. Here the fiction of "superiority," which seems to be universally shared by all peoples, has found such a complete lodgement in men's minds that any tendency to dethrone it immediately fans fierce flames of ancient and modern prejudices. Not even the decline in supernaturalism and divine sanctions has been sufficient to overthrow it.

5

In 1492 Columbus discovered America and soon thereafter the sea routes to Asia were opened. Very quickly a piecemeal knowledge of new lands and new peoples was spread over Europe. Those vast expeditions of discovery and exploitation, which carved out huge colonial empires, made the masses of Europeans conscious of so-called racial differences.

Of course, the knowledge gathered about strange peoples in remotely different places proved tremendously fascinating, but it was far from being a true scientific report. Europeans were out to conquer native tribes; consequently, all that they said about them was colored by the crass interests of exploitation. Moreover, they set themselves up as ruling aristocracies. Since any white man was a member of the ruling group, it followed that the black- or brown- or red-skinned man became a member of the subject group. Both sides became increasingly conscious of their physical differences. Especially did the African slave trade stimulate this feeling.

From the outset, Europeans attempted to rationalize the situation and to assure themselves by devious methods of logic that the subjugation of foreign racial groups was both natural and inevitable. As early as 1517 a member of the royal council in Spain suggested that Indians were too low in the scale of humanity to be capable of embracing the Catholic faith. Indians were declared to be of unsound mind and hence unable to own property or to exercise true sovereignty. The Spaniards insisted on considering the natives brutish animals (*bruta animalia*). Nor was this attitude confined to Spaniards. English, French and Dutch masters adopted a similar attitude. For example, we find Samuel Sewall at the beginning of the eighteenth century, when he was a judge of the Superior Court of Massachusetts Bay Colony, noting down in his diary that he had "essayed to prevent Negroes and Indians being rated as cattle, but could not succeed." The Puritans, on the whole, considered the Indians and Negroes accursed savages who might properly be destroyed or enslaved. "We know not when or how these Indians first became inhabitants of the mighty continent, yet we may guess that probably the Devil decoyed these miserable savages hither in hope that the gospel of the Lord Jesus Christ would never come to destroy or disturb his absolute empire over them." So preached Cotton Mather. Thus the power of the sword was buttressed by the sanctions of religion. Because Europeans were members of the "Christian race," it seemed natural that God should reward his own. With such prejudices a systematic and accurate understanding of native peoples was impossible. The unfortunate results of these early misconceptions are at the base of much contemporary confusion.

When the supernatural sanctions of "racial" dominance began to lose their force, the Whites quickly developed other rationalizations to justify their scramble for colonies among the so-called backward peoples. A number of English writers seized upon the concept of ultimate destiny: they visualized the "Anglo-Saxon race" as destined to inhabit and civilize the whole world. In his *Last Will and Testament* Cecil Rhodes, in a rhapsody of race-thinking, declared for "the furtherance of the British Empire for the bringing of the whole uncivilized world under British rule, for the recovery of the United States, for the making of the Anglo-Saxon race but one empire. What a dream! But yet it is probable. It is possible."

6

Of the many people who have passionately believed in the superiority of the white race none has exerted as profound an influence, or has played as important a role among the *idées-forces* of our modern world, as the French journalist and diplomat, Count Arthur de Gobineau (1816-1882). Perhaps no other book on race has had such a tremendous influence, as did his *Essai sur l'énegalité des races humaines* (Essay on the Inequality of Human Races). What Karl Marx's *Das Kapital* has meant to communists, Gobineau's *Essai* has meant to race-dogmatists. It was published in Paris in two volumes between the years 1853-55.

Gobineau was born in Bordeaux, the last scion of a well-to-do family. From the early days of his career he was in revolt against all things bourgeois. With a few kindred souls he formed a group who called themselves Scelti—the Chosen—to promote aristocratic ideas. Gobineau was unquestionably an able and many-sided man —poet, artist, novelist, diplomat, politician, journalist, sculptor, traveler—but his mind was pervaded with a disgust for democracy and a hatred of humanity which can be traced in the forty volumes he has left us. The *Essai,* however, was inspired by Gobineau's researches begun on his own family tree; and by his own admission it was written in part to prove the superiority of his own race. Simply put, Gobineau argued that the white race—the Aryan—is superior to all other races, and of the Aryans (of which Gobineau passionately believed he was a member) the Germans are the purest modern representatives. He was among the first to call the Latin races decadent. Of the population of his own country, Gobineau declared that the vast masses were racially a Gallo-Roman mob "whose chief instinct is envy and revolution." He deplored the fact that France has only a few Aryan Nordics.

The foundation of Gobineau's system is the classification and characterization of the races. He divides mankind into three races: the *black,* which represents passion, is animal-like and capricious, yet possessed of lyricism and the artistic temperament; the *yellow,* which represents mediocrity, is stubborn and apathetic, but is gifted with a sense of order and a sense of practicality; the *white,* which possesses godlike reason and honor, excels in all things. Particularly does it excel in physical beauty. "The peoples who are not of white blood approach beauty but do not attain it." As regards physical strength Gobineau said, "We shall have to give the palm to those who belong to the white race."

Although Gobineau was a Frenchman, it was in Germany that his theories caught on and spread. In France, Gobineau was not at any time too popular; but across the Rhine it was a different story. After the war of 1870 Gobineau made the friendship of Richard Wagner to whom the ideas of the *Essai* appealed. Finding in the Count a kindred spirit, Wagner fêted him at Wahnfried. To seal the friendship, Wagner inscribed to Gobineau his complete prose works. Largely as a result of the great musician's enthusiastic support

Gobineau societies sprang up all over Germany. It was a happy day in the Count's life when his daughter married Baron von Guidencrone.

Gobineau's racial theory furnished a simple explanatory key whereby one could construct a grand and sweeping philosophy of history. "I have become convinced," declared Gobineau with strong dogmatic emphasis, "that everything in the way of human creation, science, art, civilization, all that is great and noble and fruitful on earth, points to a single source, is sprung from one and the same root, belongs only to one family, the various branches of which have dominated every civilized region of the world." This one family, Gobineau revealed, is none other than the Aryan race. All civilization originally sprang from the virile qualities of Aryans, and wherever civilization declines it is because Aryan blood has been bastardized by intermarriage. With the admixture of bloods Aryans always lose their sense of aristocracy and also their high consciousness of race superiority. This then opens the way for decadence and degeneracy which insist on equality—that is, democracy. Although "the white race originally possessed the monopoly of beauty, intelligence and strength, by its union with other varieties hybrids were created, which were beautiful without strength, strong without intelligence, or, if intelligent, both weak and ugly." Thus Gobineau's explanation is simplicity itself. Why do civilizations rise? Because of Aryan blood. Why do they fall? Because that blood is contaminated by foreign elements. Hitler has taken these chapters to heart.

There is a platitude in logic that a man can prove anything if he selects his evidence and uses it to bolster his theory. Take the case, for example, of the good bishop who stood for the first time on Mount Sinai and solemnly ejaculated: "Now I know that Moses wrote the Pentateuch." Patient investigation and dependable evidence had nothing to do with his ecstatic outburst. In a sweep of ecstasy akin to that of the bishop, Gobineau stood one day on an islet in the North Sea, one of the Skaeren, and felt a "mystic conviction" that his remote ancestors originated on this tiny pine-fringed rock. Although the Count was brown-haired with golden brown eyes, this did not prevent him from actually believing that he was a Nordic-Aryan descended from Ottar Jarl, a Viking hero.

FRANZ BOAS

From the painting by Winifred Rieber

Courtesy of Columbia University

Thus Gobineau could not only quote Scripture for his purposes but he was extraordinarily facile in inventing his own passages. He stretched, warped, distorted and created evidence to his own liking, and then permeated the whole with the mysticism of pseudo science which the Germans hungrily absorbed. That the supreme race is the Aryan and the Teutons are its modern wonder-working representatives was most palatable to the Germans embarking upon an ambitious career of exploitation and conquest. The fact that nothing was known scientifically of an Aryan race, that its supposed existence was a purely hpothetical construction, apparently never troubled these dogmatists.

Among those who are without knowledge of the merits and demerits of opposing theories, the one which is understood with the least effort is the one most likely to gain acceptance. Gobineau's contribution in elaborating these Aryan concepts into the Teutonic myth was a considerable factor in the growth of Germany's race vanity, chiming in beautifully with the aspirations of the leaders of Pan-Germanism. It is amusing to note, however, that Gobineau on numerous occasions denied the identity of the heroic Germans or Teutons (*les Germains*) with the modern Germans (*les Allemands*). He even placed the German people below the French in racial value because he thought them more mixed. To the many contradictions in Gobineau's writings the Germans paid slight heed. The Gobineau societies flourished.

7

By the close of the nineteenth century, Gobinism had become a powerful cult with important adherents. A supreme Germany peopled by blond geniuses was a tempting ideal to which few compatriots resisted homage. Books now began to appear, filled with extravagance and bombast and supported by all manner of special pleading. This literature is notorious for its disregard of fact. But such defects apparently make little difference when the will to believe gains momentum and respectability. Richard Wagner became an ardent disciple of Gobinism and added a few elements of his own Wagnerian mysticism. Friedrich Nietzsche was greatly influenced. Theodor Poesche and Professor Carl Penka lent a desired note. Poesche said that the true Aryans were tall, fair-skinned, blue-eyed and heavily bearded. By nature these people, claimed Poesche, were instinctively Protestant, while the shorter and darker folk were submissive and instinctively Catholic.

Gobinism reached its high point in Houston Stewart Chamberlain (1855-1927), who wrote *The Foundation of the Nineteenth Century,* a volume of offensive muddlement which made its appearance in Germany in 1899. Chamberlain like Gobineau was a poet-musician-philosopher. Although born in England of aristocratic parents, he found Germany much more inviting, and he preferred to live and write in that country—and deify its people. He became an enthusiastic follower of Wagner, whose daughter he married, and was a member of the Gobineau society. Chamberlain's writings were so popular with the ruling class in Germany that he became known as the Kaiser's anthropologist.

His work rests on the assumptions of Gobineau, strengthened with additional Aryan material which had been accumulated by lesser Aryanists. Chamberlain wrote with the fire and fanaticism of a prophet. No "cold" scientific facts ever stood in his way. After all, what is science compared to the poetic prophecy of Germany's racial greatness? Despite the size and cost of his books, their sales ran into the scores of thousands. Kaiser Wilhelm was so pleased with them that he made a special appropriation to encourage their wide distribution.

Also like Gobineau, Chamberlain is not quite certain what the Aryans are. Such a minor fact, however, never limits his lyrical descriptions of their qualities, nor his poetic conviction that the Germans are the purest form of Aryans. Often Chamberlain is sorely troubled, but he always finds a solution in using intuition as a guide. This he calls rational anthropology. Intuition told him that Dante, a brunet, was unmistakably Teuton, as was the round-headed Martin Luther, since both their countenances reflect the "vitality" and the "soul power" of the German spirit. By the same method of reasoning, he found that Jesus was an Aryan—as were Peter and Paul. With such divination at his command Chamberlain produced his own proofs and criteria of race. Still, he never ventured to define race; in a moment of rhapsody, he declared, "Whoever reveals himself German by his acts, whatever be his genealogical tree, is a German." Despite its manifest contradictions

Chamberlain's book endeared itself to the German people and added glow to their myth of superiority. It was useful propaganda for keeping Germans conscious of their own worth.

After Chamberlain, a score of boastful race dogmatists emerged who pulled and mauled Gobinism to fit their divergent doctrines. Never have ideas been subjected to such torturing manipulation in order to make them fit the Procrustean bed. There was, for example, Ludwig Woltmann (1871-1907), a man of romantic and mystical temperament whose ideas were singularly impervious to fact or logic. In his youth he transferred his allegiance from Rousseau to Marx, but he finally succumbed to the ideologies of the Gobineau cult and the doctrine of the superiority of the tall blond German. Before his death by drowning he had written some sixty articles and three books.

Woltmann's contribution was to prove that world-famous personalities, no matter what the world thought or their records proved, were Teutons. His method was simplicity itself, a childishly naïve formula: a single Teutonic trait was sufficient to classify one with the Teuton aristocracy. Following the clue of the blue eye, the blond hair and the long head he "proved" that the Italian Giotto was originally the German Jothe; Tasso was Dasse, Leonardo da Vinci was Wincke, and Bruno was Braun. Similarly, the Spaniard Velasquez was originally Velahise, Murillo was Moerl and Vaz was Watz. The great Frenchmen, Aronet, Diderot and Gounod were to be pronounced Arwid, Tietroth and Gundiwald. Curious juglery! When a man is out to prove his own particular brand of race theory, he will often indulge in gross absurdities. It is like that doctor who diagnosed a patient's disease as alcholic poison. "But I have been a teetotaller all my life," protested the patient. The doctor was puzzled. At length he asked, "Where do you work?" "In a brewery," was the reply. "Ah!" said the doctor, "you take it in through the pores of your skin."

These strutting race concepts, with tendencies to state-worship and mass-enthusiasm, continued straight through the World War, as can be seen in Otto Hauser's *Der Blonde Mensch* (1921), and in Hans Günther's *Rassenkunde des Deutschen Volkes* (1923), giving rise to a host of ludicrous ideas and preposterous statements. Pan-

Germanism became the doctrine of race egotism run riot.* It is revealing to note that these concepts of race vanity had been so deeply forced into the consciousness of the German people that despite the terrific setbacks of 1914-1918 it was possible for the Third Reich to loose upon the German people a brand of Gobineau Aryanism that has become the world's most monumental preachment against democracy.

In the United States, Gobinism was slightly rehashed to make it more palatable to the Americans. The clearest expression of this tendency is the voice of Madison Grant. His two books, *The Passing of the Great Race* (1916) and *The Conquest of a Continent* (1933), take up arms in favor of the Nordics. The warning is sounded by Grant—himself, of course, a member of the great race—that the danger in America lies in the "gradual dying out among our people of those hereditary traits through which the principles of our religious, political or social foundations were laid down, and their insidious replacement by traits of less noble character." In recent years the Nordic concept has been advanced in the United States with almost religious zeal. The latest expression of the phobia is a book entitled *We Northmen* (1936) by Lucien Price.

Unfortunately for Mr. Grant his Nordic myth of a fair, tall, and long-headed race of early Americans was rudely upset by Ales Hrdlicka of the United States National Museum at Washington in a book called *The Old Americans* (1925), which showed by careful examination that the early colonists were mostly round-headed and dark or medium in complexion. Similarly, Havelock Ellis in *A Study of British Genius* (1928) presented facts hostile to this myth. For example, in studying exploration Ellis showed that hardly any of the great British explorers were of the Nordic type. It is extremely interesting to note that some of the greatest men Germany produced were not long-headed but moderately, and in some cases extremely, round-headed. One could name Kant, Goethe, Schiller and Beethoven.

Other groups too have been busy in this process of race exaltation. Giuseppe Sergi (1841-   ), the Italian anthropologist, has shown in a series of publications that the Mediterranean race—of which he

* Günther is the official anthropologist of the Nazi regime. Hitler had him appointed professor at Jena.

is a member—is the rightful carrier of the "true" civilization, that the Germans and the Asiatics only destroyed what the Mediterraneans had created. Sergi contradicts Woltmann by an actual study of Dante's bones and finds that Dante represents the most authentic and glorious type of the Mediterranean stock, truly Italian in blood, short and dark in physical characteristics. (Sergi is the anthropologist who thought that the blonde Nordics are bleached Negroes who came out of Africa!)

Various types of "proofs" have been utilized to uphold this or that doctrine of superiority. "Proofs" have been found in the occurrence of long-heads and broad-heads, blue eyes and dark eyes, degrees of pigmentation, tallness and shortness, brain and blood—not to overlook such things as soul, astronomy, climate, intuition, spirit. On the whole, these proofs have been nothing more than arguments to the crowd for praising or damning without the trouble of going into a detailed analysis. Together they represent not science but a cartoon of science.

Consider for a moment the so-called proof of blood. It is a good illustration of error in thinking about races and peoples. The fiction of blood stems from a mistake of Aristotle. So great was Aristotle's influence that the conclusion of much medieval discussion was simply: "Aristotle hath said it." Because of his prestige it took centuries to batter down the theory of the four elements. The Aristotelian obstruction in chemistry was matched by his errors in biology. Blood is one of them. The world had to wait a long time before the cell theory and the science of embryology conclusively proved that Aristotle's blood doctrine was wrong. Today, we know that there is no continuum of blood between parent and offspring; for no blood passes from the mother to the child in her womb. Inheritance is transmitted only by the genes in the chromosomes.

How then did Aristotle make this biological error? He believed that the menstrual periods of a woman, which do not appear during pregnancy, contributed to the growth of the embryo. Among untutored people the fiction of blood is still quite strong. Obviously, the doctrine is not science. Its only place is in a museum of errors.

So much for this one proof. Taken together these various proofs have been made the theme of the most dismal twaddle that has

AA

deluged the world since the days of medieval scholasticism. Were it not that these proofs waste reckless quantities of ink and blood they could be ignored as the babble of fanatics.

In this maze of tangled thoughts, of theories and counter-theories, the work of a few men has stood out. The leader of this group is a scientist with no theory of superiority to uphold. He is the recognized authority on race. The impartial, objective investigation of this question is new, so new that it is bound up with the life of this one man—Franz Boas. For anthropology, as we know it today, is largely Boas.

8

When Benjamin Franklin flew his kite aloft on the banks of the Schuylkill River in 1752, he brought down a spark of electricity out of the clouds. This one act demolished the age-old thesis of the diabolical agency in storms. Just so, a whole world of foolish superstition fell when Magellan in 1519 made his famous voyage around the world. Unfortunately nothing quite so dramatic is possible in destroying the false theories about man. The type of proof that the science of anthropology must necessarily employ requires a far greater comprehension. While it is true that no normal person has less than twice the cranial capacity of the orangutan or chimpanzee, it is amazing how in studying himself modern man has frequently transformed the science of anthropology into "barbarology."

Franz Boas is a composite theorist—a theorist who has absorbed into his mind the labors and achievements of countless thinkers before him. Because his doctrines do not belch and bombard terror into the public mind, the average man knows little or nothing about Boas. Singularly unambitious for fame, he has made himself conspicuous in the history of the theory of man.

Gobineau died in 1882, just a few months after young Boas had received his doctorate from the Univeristy of Kiel. He was twenty-three years old then and he had already attended Heidelberg and Bonn. During these early academic years his work had not touched the field of anthropology. Geography, geology, and physics were his chief interests. It was in pursuit of greater geographical knowledge that Boas stumbled upon anthropology. What Darwin owed to the voyage of the *Beagle*, and Robert Mayer to that memorable trip on the *Java*, the career of Boas owes to an expedition undertaken in 1883-1884 to the area directly north of Hudson Bay—to Cumberland Sound and Davis Strait. Here the youthful scientist spent almost two full years among the Central Eskimo. Upon his return to Germany he brought back not only new material on the geography of that remote region but—and this is more important— abundant information on the Eskimo and his culture. With this unique Eskimo data in his hands Boas now determined to devote his life to anthropology.

In a field so heavily blanketed with dogma—especially the dogmas of Gobineau—it is remarkable that Boas should have entered upon his career of anthropology with the invaluable habit of questioning everything. Perhaps it was only natural that the man who had studied geography, physics, mathematics and geology should have adopted from the earliest days of his first anthropological investigation the outlook of the natural scientist. Progress means that we become freer of the tyranny of the past. Had not Boas adopted the strict discipline of the natural sciences, he could not have broken with this tyranny, nor could he have made "possibly the greatest single contribution of any scholar of the last three generations" to the understanding of man. The essence of immortality is to make an exception of oneself.

He had been teaching geography at the University of Berlin, and at the same time acting as assistant in the Royal Ethnological Museum, when the opportunity came to undertake a new expedition, this time under the auspices of the British Association for the Advancement of Science, to study the Indians of the British Columbia area. In 1886 we find Boas seven thousand miles from Berlin initiating a new and revolutionary approach to the study of man.

He knew that the great need of anthropology was first and foremost reliable data. That is why the bibliography of his work reveals scores of concrete monographic investigations appearing in numerous learned journals. The output of Boas, covering a period of almost sixty consecutive years, is staggering in its immensity and diversity. He is a seeker after data. Data belong to a stage in the investigation which comes before the attainment of knowledge.

In 1888 Boas secured his first academic connection in the United States at Clark University. Eight years later he began lecturing at Columbia, the university with which he has identified himself from that time. Today Franz Boas is in his eightieth year. Distinguished honors have been conferred upon him, including the presidency of the American Association for the Advancement of Science. But greater than these honors is the fact that almost every American anthropologist has been his student. Out of his capacity for unusual penetration he has built a permanent highway leading to a scientific knowledge of man.

Unlike Gobineau the work of Boas is devoid of subjective phantasy. There are no easily won conclusions, no preconceived ideas, no political theories to uphold, no prejudices to bolster, no animus to defend. Gobineau's books are a phantom stage of anthropology crowded with illusory scenery. Upon this stage the Aryan theory is the chief actor. Gobineau, however, never allowed his favorite actor to run the gauntlet of facts. On the other hand, consider the work of Boas: his repeated trips to study primitive peoples, his measurements of all types and classes of human beings from inhabitants of the crowded city of New York to the Indians of British Columbia, his careful collections of ethnographical specimens, his vast linguistic studies—only then can it be appreciated how he has tunneled through the complex data on man until fact meets fact in significant penetration. With Boas no unproved assumptions are permissible. Upon the sunken piers of obsolete theories his work rears its giant superstructure.

9

The clash between the ideas of Gobineau and Boas possesses contemporary world significance—not because the concept of a superior race was new or original with Gobineau, but because few examples serve better to illustrate its creedal vainglory than his Aryan theory.

Ideas of superiority, delusions of grandeur and megalomania probably emerged with the first consciousness of man that his racial group was different from others. Wherever we meet the superiority theories, in antiquity or modern times, they are all extraordinarily alike. They constitute the faith of the unenlightened, maintained, of course, by the stupidity of the many and the cunning of the few.

Aristotle, in the fifth century B.C., declared that the peoples of northern Europe—that is, the Nordic barbarians—were spirited but lacked intelligence. The Asiatics, he further argued, were intelligent but lacked bravery and spirit. Therefore, he concluded, the Greeks, because they were geographically intermediate, were fitted by nature to rule the world. He pictured the Greeks living on a garlanded island in the waste sea of *barbaroi*. Aristotle carried this same doctrine into the domain of class distinctions, claiming that superiority and inferiority exist there as between man and woman, master and slave, intellectual and laborer. Not only are these broad distinctions rooted in social realities, he said, but they are justified by nature—that is, they are inherent biologically. The Greeks believed they had a natural right to rule over barbarians, as Euripides wrote in *Iphigenia:*

> It is meet
> That Greek should over Barbarians bear sway,
> Not that Barbarians lord it over Greece;
> Nature hath formed them slaves, the Grecians free.

Later, when the Romans became powerful conquerors, they also felt the need of explaining their superiority. Vitruvius, in the second century B.C., merely shifted the Aristotelian argument somewhat to the west, and "proved" that the Romans had the highest degree of intelligence and spirit. Like the ancient Greeks who considered themselves the "best" people and all others *barbaroi,* so the ancient Hebrews declared that they were the "chosen" of Yahweh in contradistinction to the Gentiles. This teaching of the synagogue was matched by the doctrine of the Christian church that humanity is divided into two groups: Christian and heathen. Christians enjoy the approval of God as the special objects of his solicitude, whereas all heathen peoples are under the dominion of Satan and his diabolical devices.

Certain American Indian tribes felt sure that they were superior to all other groups of mankind. A folk tale speaks of the Creator baking three loaves of bread. The first loaf he took from the oven was underdone, pasty and light. This became the white people. Another loaf was burned, also not fit for use, and this black crisp became the Negro people. But the third loaf was baked to perfection, brown and beautifully done, and this, of course, became the Indians.

The tribes of Africa also consider themselves the bravest and best of all peoples. One tribe tells the story that in the beginning all peoples were dark. One day the Creator had a fearful task which he wanted his people to perform, and those who turned white with fright retained that color to become white people.

The Greeks felt superior. So did the Egyptians, the Romans, the Hebrews. All peoples have their own stories to validate this feeling —each people declaring that only they are the salt of the earth. In the sixteenth century, Jean Bodin (1530-1596) of France showed astronomically that the planets exerted themselves in most favorable combination over France, and therefore, indisputably, the French were destined to be the masters of the world. A logical corollary to the sentiment of superiority is that all other groups— or "races"—are naturally inferior.

Besides this, the economic factor has always crept in to complicate matters. Group resentment, reinforced by economics, can be seen in the history of American immigration. Antipathy was first directed against the Irish, and then the German immigrant became the target. Later it was the Jew and the Italian. It is obvious that what is strange and foreign can easily arouse hostility, for the foreigner is always suspect. He wears peculiar clothes, follows absurd customs, speaks in an incomprehensible language, and is regarded as a potential threat to the normal life of decent people. This phenomenon is not peculiar to our own civilization. The Benaue tribe of the Philippines is feared and despised by the neighboring Kiangan people as aliens who mispronounce words, wear G-strings of a different pattern, trim their hair another way, and make baskets of deerskin instead of rattan!

Together with economic necessity, the forces of group solidarity and group loyalty are often as strong as man's attachment to life itself. These basic feelings have been frequently played upon and subtly manipulated to support various theories of racial and national superiority which have had repercussions through the pages of history. Race pride often becomes a sort of "pooled self-esteem," fiercely upholding any pseudoscientific theory which guarantees its own excellence. Apparently it makes no difference that these assumptions and claims are perpetrated in the face of objective facts to the contrary. An appreciation of the absurdities of these views led to the definition of a nation as "a society united by a common error as to its origin and a common aversion to its neighbors." Or, as Daniel Defoe poetically stated it in the eighteenth century:

> Proudly they learn all mankind to contemn;
> And all their race are true-born Englishmen.

10

Gobineau's entire concept of superiority received a withering refutation from Boas in *The Mind of Primitive Man* (1911), a book which is interwoven by chains of reasoning as strong as they are gripping. Throughout it is pervaded with the scientific spirit, carrying both an intellectual and moral response to any disclosure of truth. Within less than three hundred pages Boas accomplishes the gigantic task of putting in order the enormous muddle of provable data, binding them together and interconnecting all parts into a unitary structure. You cannot read him without an innate respect for the scientist who unmistakably displays exceptional penetration, integrity and courage.

The Mind of Primitive Man is made up of ten short chapters, the first being entitled "Racial Prejudices." After a brief introductory paragraph Boas begins at once to pulverize the naïve assumption of the superiority of European nations and their descendants, (a) that the white race represents the highest type of perfection, (b) that a race is lower the more fundamentally it differs from the white. "Differences between the white race and other races must not be interpreted to mean superiority of the former, inferiority of the latter, unless this relation can be proved by anatomical or physiological considerations." To state that the Mongols and Negroes are anatomically closer to the ape-form is to assume an untested and unsupported view. The assumption by itself is an insufficient guarantee of truth. Boas patiently examined what purports to be the evidence and found that there is nothing to warrant the glibly announced biological inferiority of so-called backward peoples.

The attempt to grade races in a progressive series from the animal upwards cannot be done because "the specifically human characteristics are most highly developed, some in one race, some in another." Take for example just two illustrations: the red external lips of the Negro and the hairy body of the white man. Even the highest animals are devoid of the red lips, which shows that in this one characteristic the Negro is more advanced than the White. Moreover, the Negro, the Mongol and the American Indian have very slight hairiness of the body and the face compared with the more animalistic hair feature of the white man. When men are examined feature by feature it cannot be said that the whites are biologically superior.

But what of mental superiority? Gobineau claimed that the white race tops the list. After a careful examination of this claim, Boas rejected it as a pure assumption. The foundations of Gobineau's theory proved sandy when the spade went deep enough. Boas does not claim the mental equality of the races. He merely examined the assumptions of the Gobineau school and declared that, as yet, there is no proof to establish their doctrine. Without belittling the evidence that exists in favor of racial differences, it is nevertheless certain that, at present, there is no evidence whatsoever to warrant one race's claiming inherent mental superiority over another. "Notwithstanding the numerous attempts that have been made to find structural differences between the brains of different races of man that could be directly interpreted in psychological terms, no conclusive results of any kind have been attained." Anatomists cannot with certainty differentiate between the brain of a German and a Negro.

It is true that the white race has developed a highly mechanical civilization. In certain respects the white man's civilization stands immeasurably above all others. Hence the flattering inference that there is only one great civilization. In essence Gobineau's doctrine was this: *Men are many, civilization is one,* meaning that the mental qualities and capacities of the races are not only different but immutable, and that one race alone—the white race—has produced a "true" civilization. Gobineau stressed the thought that the human race is not a unit but a congeries of ethnic groups intellectually unequal. On the other hand, Boas, out of his vast contacts with peoples and cultures, has shown that just the very opposite is true: *Man is one, civilizations are many.*

When civilizations are examined scientifically and dispassionately, no claim can be made that the culture of the white race is point by point superior to all others. With only fragmentary knowledge of cultures and civilizations, Gobineau attempted to present a view which would have universal validity. As a matter of historical record it is only since the fifteenth century that "white superiority" has been at all manifest. Before that, Europe was constantly on the defensive against the hordes of Asia. It is generally agreed that until the seventeenth century Europe produced no state which was as well organized as China and no army which was as well drilled as the followers of the Mongol khans. "We must bear in mind," argued Boas, "that none of these civilizations was the product of the genius of a single people. Ideas and inventions were carried from one to the other; and, although intercommunication was slow, each people which participated in the ancient development contributed its share to the general progress. Proofs without number have been forthcoming which show that ideas have been disseminated as long as people have come into contact with one another, and that neither race nor language nor distance limits their diffusion. As all have worked together in the development of the ancient civilizations, we must bow to the genius of all, whatever group of mankind they may represent—Hamitic, Semitic, Aryan, or Mongol."

11

The main scientific idea that emerges from Boas is the unity of mankind. Races are more similar than dissimilar. The strong line of demarcation that Gobineau made between the white, the yellow, and the black does not exist. Nor is there any such permanence or immutability of racial type as Gobineau believed. Even in the absence of racial intermixture, racial types are by no means permanent. What Galileo said of the earth *e pur se muove,* Boas has said of race. Not immobility but *mobility* is the law. Race is everywhere dynamic. The various types of men differ from each other in degree and not in kind. All men belong to one species and they are connected with each other by innumerable gradations.

Nor is there any such thing as a "pure" race. The concept appealed to Gobineau's fancy, but it is without foundation. Of all people the whites are the most mixed—presenting striking diversity of bodily traits. As a consequence of wars, migrations, raids, trade, colonization and other factors, race minglings have been going on for many thousands of years. Out of these minglings of races new races have arisen. This makes the problem of classifications difficult, for there has been so much mingling that clear-cut definitions are well-nigh impossible. As a matter of fact, no anthropologist knows where Caucasian leaves off and where Mongolian begins. Inasmuch as all races are hopelessly mixed, any theory of race superiority will have to find a more convincing argument than the fiction of "purity."

To Boas, the world is a vast melting pot, more so today than ever before in the history of man. Races are now mingling on a gigantic scale, and in this process older races are doomed to be absorbed in the wider complex now forming. Is this good or bad for mankind as a whole? No simple reply can be given. Boas merely says that there are excellences present among all people no matter how complexly blended. Fusions have taken place in the past and they are taking place today—despite decrees of kings, dictators, parliaments or race-dogmatists. And even if it were possible to isolate or segregate races (and of course it is not), still the task would be futile because all peoples are already inextricably blended; the population of every nation rests upon a mixed racial basis. Intermixtures of diverse stocks, which have been going on for countless centuries, offer no ground whatsoever for the fears of racial degeneracy which haunted Gobineau and his followers. Race mixture has occurred through the ages and the whole future trend of mankind points to an amalgamation of peoples on a scale never before accomplished. In the long course of man's existence on earth race mixtures have proceeded at times vigorously and at times slowly. Race has never been static—never the biological fixture that Gobineau believed. "The history of Europe proves," declares Boas, "that there has been no racial purity anywhere for exceedingly long periods, neither has the continued intermixture of European types shown any degrading effect upon any of the European nationalities."

In the final chapter of *The Mind of Primitive Man* entitled "Race Problems in the United States," Franz Boas brings to bear upon the melting pot of the American Union the full force of scientific anthropology. Because the large Negro population forms about one-eighth of the whole nation, Boas devotes considerable attention to the colored man. Rejecting the doctrine of inferiority, Boas writes: "The traits of the American Negro are adequately explained on the basis of his history and social status. The tearing-away from the African soil and the consequent complete loss of the old standards of life, which were replaced by the dependency of slavery and by all it entailed, followed by a period of disorganization and by a severe economic struggle against heavy odds, are sufficient to explain the inferiority of the status of the race, without falling back upon the theory of hereditary inferiority. In short, there is every reason to believe that the Negro, when given facility and opportunity, is perfectly able to fulfill the duties of citizenship as well as his white neighbor."

Much happens in nature for which science has yet no complete analysis. The study of heredity, environment, diet, and other complex subjects are in their raw infancy. "Too little is known" is a common phrase which runs through the cautious writings of Boas. Much in science is not final, only an interim report. Science, therefore, recognizes the unknown but not the unknowable. When we know we don't know that in itself is helpful, for then men become honest with themselves and the field may be cleared of the rubbish of mysticism and confusion. "Is it not then our plain duty," Boas asks, "to inform ourselves that, so far as that can be done, deliberate consideration of observation may take the place of heated discussion of beliefs in matters that concern not only ourselves, but also the welfare of millions of Negroes?" His plea did not go unheeded. Today the veteran anthropologist of Columbia can boast that his disciples are studying all races and all cultures scientifically, dispassionately, without praise or blame.

Race is one of the great idols of our time—a veritable Moloch to whom men sacrifice themselves and their children. But an idol is useless unless it can prove itself a reality. "Ye rub them with oil and wax and the flies stick to them" (Koran). To purge the world of this idolatry has been the lifelong task of Franz Boas. In the Temple of Science where he works there are no incantations. No potent arcana lie hidden. There are no sacred books and no scrolls are sealed. Its walls have no mystic symbols and no priest represents the deity.

The concluding paragraph of *The Mind of Primitive Man* is a good example of the reasonableness and fairness of the scientific point of view. "I hope the discussions contained in these pages have shown that the data of anthropology teach us a greater tolerance of forms of civilization different from our own, and that we should learn to look upon foreign races with greater sympathy, and with the conviction that, as all races have contributed in the past to cultural progress in one way or another, so they will be capable of advancing the interests of mankind, if we are only willing to give them a fair opportunity."

If science is capable of carrying with its sterner disciplines a spiritual promise to humanity, then that promise may very well be found in a reasonableness of outlook enabling man to transcend his bestiality as life transcends dust. It was a murderer who asked indignantly, "Am I my brother's keeper?" But it was a philosopher who said, "I am a man and nothing that is human is alien to me."

15. Einstein . THEORY OF RELATIVITY

OF the few cities that have been intimately connected with the lives of the great theorists Munich ranks with London and Paris. Count Rumford lived there for more than a decade, and Max Joseph von Pettenkofer after him spent his entire life in the Bavarian capital, where he laid the foundations of modern hygiene. Among the many notable statues that adorn its streets and parks —statues of Goethe the poet, Wagner the musician, Liebig the chemist—there is one of Rumford and one of Pettenkofer. But none of Einstein.

Yet Einstein spent his youth in Munich. He was born in Ulm, Württemberg, on the Danube, on May 14, 1879. From infancy there was an atmosphere of science about him; for his father, though a merchant, possessed a particular inclination for technical matters. In 1880, a few months after Albert's birth, Herr Einstein became part owner of an electro-technical plant in Munich and moved there with his wife Pauline and their infant son.

2

As a youth in Munich Einstein exhibited no particular precocity: he was dreamy, sensitive, shy, even mentally awkward, certainly undistinguished. He displayed no outward sign of the genius that was to follow. Perhaps the type of instruction given to him in the Bavarian elementary school—mechanically dull and at times brutal —did much to stifle his spirit. It left him uninspired, crushed, and lonely. Particularly because he was Jewish it was difficult for him to identify himself with teachers and pupils who were permanently hostile. On one occasion an instructor brought a large nail to class and told his pupils that it was the iron which the Jews had used to nail Jesus to the cross. The incident, to be sure, did not help the cause of religion; nor did it improve young Einstein's status.

Among all the unpleasant experiences that wounded him, one genuinely happy and helpful contact emerges from these Munich days. At the Luitpold Gymnasium there was an instructor who had a remarkable talent for inspiring his pupils. From this man, whose name was Reuss, young Einstein learned the beauties of the classical world. Once having caught the spirit of Shakespeare, Goethe, and Schiller, his inner hunger found nourishment. Poetry and literature now became a permanent element of the creative world he was seeking to build. Vaguely he discerned in himself the tendency to generalize and to realize his world as an aesthetic, ordered, comprehensive unity. His love for music, his religious devotion to the wonders of nature, heightened the emotional effect of his endeavors.

Then there was his passion for mathematics, particularly geometry whose theorems and constructions gave him almost mystical delight. "It brought him," says his biographer Anton Reiser, "the classical experience of perfect harmony, and his preoccupation with mathematics became the most beautiful adventure of his youth." Until Albert was fifteen years old Munich claimed him, first in the elementary school and afterwards in the Luitpold Gymnasium. Perhaps he would have continued on, graduating from the high school and the local university, had his family not moved to Italy. By transferring his business from Munich to Milan, Herr Einstein, never too successful with his electro-technical enterprise, had hoped to give his small family something more than the illusion of a living.

3

Settled in Milan, without any attachment to scholastic studies, Albert felt free to roam for a while, to take long hikes and bask in the warm Italian sun, to indulge his gypsy nature, to study art, to play his violin, to philosophize, to visit interesting places, to read with pleasure, to wander through libraries and galleries, to think of ships and long to sail. This period marks the beginning of his unwearying exploration into the varied domains of knowledge, and the deepening of his love for music and boats. Did not Isaac Newton picture himself standing on the shore of the vast ocean of knowledge holding a mere pebble in his hand, symbolic of man's eternal quest? Not on the shore but on some gallant ship, rigged out with sails of expectation, the youthful Einstein visualized his desire to search for new horizons:

> And though thy soul sail leagues and leagues beyond,—
> Still, leagues beyond those leagues, there is more sea.*

The family fortunes, always thin but now at low ebb, made it necessary for him to decide at once on a career. He chose to undertake a pilgrimage to Switzerland in an effort to enter the Polytechnic Academy at Zürich. At first he was rejected, but in the following year the doors of the institution opened to this determined boy who had already mapped out for himself his own philosophy of life. Like Pasteur he wanted to be a teacher; that was his immediate objective. To devote himself ultimately to the discovery of theoretical truths was his one surpassing ambition. In pursuit of these far-off expectations he crossed the national boundaries of Europe—from Germany—to Switzerland—to Italy—and back again to Switzerland. And then, years later, from Germany to America. Down the vista of the years these crossings have come to have a strange symbolic meaning: on the one hand they are eloquent with the beauty of the international spirit of Einstein, singularly at home wherever men strive to know; and on the other hand they speak of the tragedy of exile. Somehow the biography of this man seems to embody the experiences and vicissitudes shared by all men of science across time and space.

4

He was only seventeen when he entered the Zürich Polytechnic Academy. He was happy, now that he was in the right school, headed in the right direction. Here he met Mileva Maric, a talented Serbian girl, a fellow student who was to become the first Mrs. Einstein. Here too he met, and was influenced by, the great mathematician Hermann Minkowski, then a professor, who ten years later made an extremely important contribution to Einstein's investigations. His chief interest at this time, however, was not mathematics but physics and he was thinking largely in terms of the classical manner of the nineteenth century scientists, while he roamed in asso-

* Dante Gabriel Rossetti: Sonnet 37, *The Choice*.

ciation with all the great physicists of the past. Yet his eyes, turning away from the dimensional concepts of the commonplace, were beginning to see the wonders of another world. Unthought-of things now began to thread themselves together in new and wonderful combinations full of surprising affinities and unexpected relations of opposites. In him the boldness of science—its surprises, its paradoxes—took hold together with an eagerness to push forward the frontiers of knowledge. Here were the age-old problems of physical phenomena. Could they be adequately solved by the accepted doctrines of orthodox science? He entertained certain doubts about that.

By this time his father's business in Italy had declined so greatly that when Einstein had reached his twenty-second year, he was forced to take employment in the International Patent Office at Bern. Being an examiner of patents was for him an admittedly bread and cheese affair, not altogether dull but certainly too much of a routine. Still, it did not deter him from pursuing his graduate studies at the University of Zürich, nor did it prevent him from pioneering a new world of thought and laying those mighty foundations of his career as a scientific colossus who was to bestride the wide universe of natural phenomena.

Early in 1903 he married Mileva Maric. The small salary of the Patent Office enabled him to establish a home, a tiny top-floor apartment where he could receive his guests and discuss the structural aspects of the new theory that was slowly taking shape in his mind. These were days of great imagination, the early creative years of relativity when ideas came to him in startling profusion—thoughts of almost inhuman immensity in sheer vastness of reach and span. He divided his time between the Patent Office and his apartment, working feverishly on those sparks of illuminative insight that had set his mind aglow with the possibility of an epochal discovery. By 1904 his thoughts had clarified; he was now ready to present to the world the first formulation of the special theory of relativity. A treatise appeared entitled *Toward the Electrodynamics of Moving Bodies,* published in 1905. It was soon followed by several shorter papers: *The Law of Brownian Movement; On the Quantum Nature of Rays; Identity of Mass and Energy.* A storm of scientific creativity had been unleashed within him. The genius of Einstein had emerged.

Recognition came fast. From Berlin the great physicist Max Planck, father of the quantum theory, wrote him a letter of heartiest congratulations. Then there was Professor Kleiner of Zürich, under whom Einstein had studied, who now used his influence to secure for his younger colleague a teaching post at the University of Bern. Gone now was the drudgery at the Patent Office. That had not been without its compensations, but he was headed in another direction: his new duties at the university and the acclaim of the world which culminated in an invitation to lecture on relativity and the constitution of light before the Congress of Scientists which was to meet in 1908 in Salzburg. From Bern Einstein was called in 1909 to a professorship at the University of Zürich.

5

What were the steps that led Einstein to relativity? He began his thinking in terms of orthodox science, with the accepted ideas, notions, concepts and theories of the nineteenth century physicists. These stalwart thinkers were like the ancients with their pillars of Hercules, inscribing on their columns of faith *Ne Plus Ultra*— "Nothing More Beyond." The inscription was a good defense mechanism, a safety device of no mean significance to the thinkers of the Victorian Age. For beyond those pillars stretched out a vast sea, terrifying in its unimaginable depth. While Einstein was still a student at the Polytechnic Academy he soon came to doubt the validity of *Ne Plus Ultra*. To extend the range of his thought to include that sea at present inaccessible, became his surpassing ambition. Was there not something intuitive in Columbus' audacious move to venture beyond the gates of Hercules? It is not just simply imagination but *prepared* imagination that is competent to take the creative leap into the unknown. Preparation is light; imagination is *vision*—not of course the vision of immediate things but of the unseen. From boyhood, Einstein had been attracted to the ideas of the whole, the universal—always enthralled by the synthesis of the parts. No mind on earth has ever been so congenial to the vastness of the cosmos ranging from the magnitude of the sidereal universe to the inverse immensity of the atom. The possibility of his mind's seizing formative power, that is, a unifying interconnection, became more and more real.

But the orthodox traditions of science, stemming from Sir Francis Bacon, left little room for hypothesis. Bacon himself regarded them with grave suspicion, for he had an aversion to "phantoms" of any sort. In his opinion hypothesis had no lawful place in scientific procedure, and he went so far as to urge that it be banished as a disturbing element. Hypothesis came to mean the illusory, the fanciful, the hallucinatory which could build an imposing but unreal system of thought. Consequently, Bacon urged a knowledge of general laws extracted from nature through direct observation. Because an hypothesis has often exercised a distorting influence (since the idea involves anticipation of the fact) he washed his hands of them all.

Man, however, is an incorrigible universe builder. From Thales to Einstein—a space of twenty-five hundred years—he has thrown the full weight of his genius into the scales of speculative theorizing. Plato spoke of man as the "microcosm," as if in him the multitudinousness of the world found epitome. The overwhelming figure of Einstein supports this view: in him men sense that humanity has reached a fullness of energy in a gigantic effort to know the world. Such is the wonder of mind—man's mind—unique in the animal kingdom. Six monkeys set to strum on a typewriter for untold millions of years could not produce one sentence of Einstein's books.

"It seems as if the subject to which I am about to invite your attention could be treated only in poetry," Taine exclaims eloquently in introducing his lecture on *The Ideal in Art*. To appreciate Einstein, to know why he and no one else became the author of the theory of relativity, is to understand the role of intuition and inspiration in science. "When the eclipse of 1919 confirmed my intuition, I was not in the least surprised. In fact, I would have been astonished had it turned out otherwise. Imagination is more important than knowledge. For knowledge is limited, whereas imagination embraces the entire world, stimulating progress. It is, strictly speaking, a real factor in scientific research." Einstein's astounding conceptions originated in a series of daring hypotheses whose unifying features at first resembled the flight of poetic imagination. However, deliverances of intuition cannot be taken at their face value. They need to be examined, submitted to the processes of minute analysis and definition. Thus the work of Einstein begins as philosophy and ends as art; it arises in intuitive hypotheses and flows into achievement.

The writings of Henri Poincaré (1854-1912) did much to encourage young Einstein in his novel way of thinking. Poincaré—steeped in mathematics, astronomy and physics—was one of the most critical, daring and philosophical thinkers of the pre-Einstein era. His mind ranged over the great speculative problems of science and the results were given to the world in a series of brilliant essays which have been collected in one volume entitled *The Foundations of Science*. Poincaré's aim was to give careful scrutiny to these foundations, particularly where they are mathematical in character. One glance at those essays illustrates how Poincaré challenged the foundations which orthodox scientists viewed as completely settled, beyond controversy. It was evident to this French savant that as knowledge advances a theoretical orthodoxy grows less possible, less definable, less conceivable.

Consider space. It is possible to have two kinds of geometries that will attack this problem, namely, a Euclidean geometry and a non-Euclidean geometry. The geometry of figures traced on a flat surface will be Euclidean. But suppose the surface, instead of being flat, is spherical like the surface of the ocean viewed on a large scale: the geometry of figures traced on it will exhibit the non-Euclidean properties of a surface of positive curvature. Which then is the true geometry? Poincaré answered this question to Einstein's inquiring satisfaction: "One geometry cannot be more true than another; it can only be more *convenient*."

In several important respects the geometry of a spherical surface differs from that of a plane. On the surface of a sphere the shortest distance between any two points, as every navigator knows, is an arc of a great circle. Geometry therefore, argued Poincaré, is a highly relative discipline. A sphere, for example, is convex in all directions, but there are other surfaces such as a stem of a wineglass, a saddle, or a mountain pass which are convex in one direction and concave in another and for these types of surfaces still other types of geometries are necessary. Now, a plane surface is said to have no curvature. The geometry of Euclid is that of figures on a plane surface; hence Euclidean geometry is *plane* geometry. Euclid assumed space to be subjected to his plane treatment—therefore, he assumed space to be Euclidean. (All non-Euclidean surfaces owe their peculiar properties to the fact that they are curved in special ways.)

That Newton thought in terms of Euclidean geometry is common knowledge. Yet he could not have done otherwise, for the developments of non-Euclidean geometry were not even dreamed of. Still, Euclidean geometry was adequate for his purposes. But for relativity Einstein had to employ the non-Euclidean systems. So completely did Einstein accept Poincaré's point of view (namely, that in many respects classical physics suffers from internal contradictions) that shortly before Poincaré died he issued to the world the following tribute to the struggling young scientist. "Einstein," wrote Poincaré, "is one of the most original minds that I have ever met. In spite of his youth he already occupies a very honorable position among the foremost savants of his time. What we marvel at in him, above all, is the ease with which he adjusts himself to new conceptions and draws all possible deductions from them. He does not cling to classical principles, but sees all conceivable possibilities when he is confronted with a physical problem. In his mind this becomes transformed into an anticipation of new phenomena that may some day be verified in actual experience. The future will give more and more proofs of the merits of Albert Einstein, and the university that succeeds in attracting him may be certain that it will derive honor from its connection with the young master."

Einstein had already come to grips with the interrelated problems of space, time, and matter. At first sight these three aspects of the universe appear distinct and incapable of intermixture. But Einstein soon arrived at the view that they are not forms of separation, independent and isolated from each other as Newton believed; on the contrary, they are interlocked—that is, relative to each other. There is no such thing, for example, as a timeless object or a period of time not marked off by objects in space. Newton however, regarded space and time as real entities, things of an absolute * physical character which exist exterior to our mental perception of them—in other words, free from conditions imposed from without. The Newtonian doctrine may be stated in the following two propositions in Newton's own language: (A) Absolute, true, mathematical time flows on by virtue of its own nature, uniformly, and unrelated to any outward circumstance; (B) Absolute space always remains the same by virtue of its own nature, unrelated to outward circumstances, and immovable.

When Einstein was a beginning student he believed in these Newtonian conceptions. As he progressed skepticism grew apace. He could not read Poincaré without seeing that Newtonian physics was built upon a dogmatic foundation that took too much for granted. This foundation gave rise to prejudices and habits of thought which stood in the way of solving innumerable difficult problems. In other words, the foundation of Newton—the doctrine of absolute space and absolute time—occasioned unnecessary difficulties.

Wherein lay the error? In Newton's separation of time and space.

The separation of time and space is a misleading theory because they profoundly interpenetrate. To isolate them is to mutilate one's thinking about them. For time and space are not separate things; they are relative to each other, constituent elements in a deeper synthesis. Thus time is as much the essence of things as space. Time is not something extra and superadded to things in their behavior; it is basic to their constitution. The world, therefore, does not possess three dimensions but four. Time is the fourth dimension.

Examine for a moment the following illustration. An accident, let us say, occurred at Forty-second Street (this is one dimension). To say that it happened at Forty-second and Broadway is to add a second dimension. When it is further stated that the accident took place in the subway—that gives a third dimension. And to declare that it took place at two o'clock last Tuesday afternoon gives us the fourth dimension. Thus the accident happened in "space-time"

---

* The word absolute comes from the Latin verb *absolvo* and means *detached*. In the course of time it also acquired the connotation of *unconditioned, unfettered, independent*.

on a four-dimensional basis: length, breadth, depth, and time.* By means of the space-time system, any event, anywhere, anytime, may be indexed and filed away.

Besides his debt to Poincaré, much of the cyclopean architecture of Einstein's early thinking was directly due to the formative influence of another unorthodox scientist, Ernst Mach (1838-1916) who had been professor of mathematics and physics at the Universities of Graz, Vienna, and Prague. Like Einstein, his early youth and first teaching experience were spent in comparative poverty, against which he struggled with rare patience and resolution.

Mach was among the early pioneers of relativity. It took great courage to challenge Newton. Next to reforming a religion the most difficult task is to reform a science. "We can see that the physicists are on the surest road to becoming a church, and are already appropriating all the customary means to this end"—so wrote Mach in rebellion against "The communion of the Faithful." Mach strongly differed with Newton's concept of an absolute space and an absolute time, which he characterized as medieval. In an attempt to replace it he wrote a book called *The Science of Mechanics* (1883), in which he anticipated the theory of relativity by considering the mutual relationship of things, not in a small isolated system, but in the vast and interconnected system of the cosmos. Mach denounced all isolated systems, all isolated experiments. "When we say that a body preserves unchanged its direction and velocity *in space,* our assertion is nothing more or less than an abbreviated *reference to the entire universe.*" This one sentence states the most luminous thought of relativity: that every action has a direct connection with the entire universe no matter whether its separate particles be miles or millions of light years from us.

Einstein could not have been so profoundly influenced by Poincaré and Mach had he not had an unusual mathematical background. Graham Wallas in his *Art of Thought* speaks of four stages in the act of discovery: first, there is preparation, then incubation, then illumination, and lastly verification. Einstein's mathematical

* Or, if we prefer—(1) north-south, (2) east-west, (3) up-down, and (4) time. All direction, of course, is relative. Chicago is east of San Francisco but west of New York. That which is "up" to one observer may be "down" to another. For a person at the North Pole there is no north, west or east, only south.

knowledge was decidedly preparatory: it pointed to a new synthesis through which the very terms and strategies of the older physics were to be dissolved and their rigid granite frames replaced by relativistic frames of reference. It is the supreme task of the theorist to compress all knowledge within his domain into an understandable point of view, perpetually remolding his ideas, as his experience widens and his insight becomes more penetrating.

6

It is the mathematical side of relativity that is full of the bewilderment of new-found thought. Much of it is deliriously confusing, for it is intellectual champagne with a terrific fizz and sparkle. A prolonged bout with it leaves one a bit groggy. However, if you drink it slowly, it is not too difficult to absorb and to understand it. Once we see or comprehend the historical development of a theory we are surprised out of our habitual stolidity and blindness.

From the early days of antiquity it was found that mathematical formulae can express certain laws governing the world that we observe. The Greeks were particularly cognizant of this fact. In the history of mathematics the postulates of Euclid represent a synthesis of Greek geometric ideas and relationships. With these postulates as a basis, a comprehensive geometric theory was developed whose chief feature dealt with the curves known as conic sections. Centuries later, Kepler found that the theory of conic sections was precisely what he needed to develop the laws of planetary motion. The next great step in mathematics was the synthesis of algebra and geometry into the analytic work of Descartes. Then, through the efforts of Newton and Leibnitz, the science of mathematics grew again in the discovery of calculus. This resulted in forging the most powerful mathematical investigation which had yet been known and enabled Newton to substantiate his theory of gravitation by deducing Kepler's laws from it. During the two centuries following the death of Newton his successors continued to develop a comprehensive and majestic theory of the motions of heavenly bodies upon the mathematical foundation which he helped to create.

Now the great systemization of Greek geometry which was effected by Euclid (although his reduction of the system to its essential assumptions was not final) was such as to awaken the admiration of great mathematicians in every succeeding century. But there is one point in which the Euclidean reduction is notably imperfect—the so-called parallel axiom. This says essentially that through a given point only one line can be drawn parallel to a given straight line. In 1733 appeared Girolamo Saccheri's book on Euclid. The importance of this book consists in the fact that, although it was written to vindicate Euclid's parallel axiom once for all, it contains the first outline as it were of a non-Euclidean geometry. Slowly, and very gradually, the foundations of a new system of mathematics were being laid. As a result of the work of the Hungarian Johann Bolyai (1802-1860) and the Russian Nikolas Lobatchevsky (1793-1856), logically consistent geometries were produced in which the famous parallel postulate of Euclid was replaced by an essentially different one. This marks the real beginning of the non-Euclidean geometries. It would not have been possible for Einstein to replace Newton had he not been able to employ the ideas evolved in the non-Euclidean geometries. By sheer mathematical skill, making full use of the beautiful theoretical apparatus acquired from his predecessors—including men like Gauss, Riemann, Ricci and Levi-Civita —Einstein was able to point to a new comprehension. He widened the scope of mathematics to embrace phenomena of a vastly different kind than Newton had under consideration. Consequently, it was to be expected that his theory would take a form not very simple in statement and beyond the capacity of the average man to understand.

In summing up the influences that molded Einstein—Poincaré, Mach, the non-Euclidean mathematicians—there stands out, above them all, the figure of Isaac Newton. He is the giant that dwarfs everyone else.

When Einstein promulgated the theory of relativity, much of the popular enthusiasm that accompanied it was associated with the false impression that it constituted a complete overthrow of Newton. Actually, however, relativity is an expansion and refinement of Newton's views. "In one person," declared Einstein in a recent tribute to the Cambridge scientist, "he combined the experimenter, the theorist, the mechanic and, not the least, the artist in exposition. He stands before us strong, certain, and alone; his joy in creation and his minute precision are evident in every word and in every figure."

On another occasion, the two-hundredth anniversary of the death of Newton, Einstein set forth the significance of his great predecessor in relation to the growth of the theory of relativity.* It is a profound appreciation of Newton such as we would naturally look for in so great a student as Albert Einstein. Not only is Newton the leading figure in the invention of certain mathematical tools, such as infinitesimal calculus, but he was among the first to state clearly the needed union between the experimental and mathematical methods. He took vague terms like force and mass and gave them a precise meaning. "Newton's basic principles were so satisfying from a logical standpoint that the impulse to fresh departures could only come from the pressure of the facts of experience. Before I enter into this I must emphasize that Newton himself was better aware of the weak side of his thought-structure than the succeeding generations of students. This fact has always excited my reverent admiration."

The "weak side" of Newton became the strong side of Einstein, as will now be seen. "The immense ocean of truth," once declared Newton, "extends itself unexplored."

7

Just as the story of the atom stretches back centuries before Dalton to the ancient Greek thinkers, so the central idea of Einstein's work long occupied the minds of philosophers. He mastered the best in others to co-ordinate their creations. The merit of Einstein is, therefore, this: for the first time he gave scientific validity to the conception of relativity by establishing its mathematical proofs. In a sense it grew out of the philosophic notion of the relativity of all knowledge. He laid hold of the idea that everything is measured by, or considered *relative* to, something else; that our concepts of absolute time, space, motion are groundless for the very simple reason that man does not possess any immovable or unchangeable standard. By giving these thoughts a coherent mathematical basis he was able to formulate a particular theory which co-ordinates and

* First published in the *Manchester Guardian*, March 19, 1927. Reprinted in the Annual Report of the Smithsonian Institution (1927).

satisfies the observed laws of nature and accounts for discrepancies which long troubled the scientists.

So much in science changes; facts and laws which reign triumphantly today are dethroned tomorrow. The truth of yesterday is so expanded that it ceases to be the truth. Yesterday we believed in the sufficiency of Euclidean geometry, today it is non-Euclidean. What does not change is the method of science. How this method works may be seen in the genesis of the *special* theory of relativity.

By the time Einstein began his serious thinking, progressive physical research had established with great certainty two important facts which appeared to be mutually contradictory: (a) the principle of relativity and (b) the constancy of the velocity of light. To resolve this conflict became the leading problem of science, for if one principle is right the other must be wrong. The problem was worked over by many men, but in spite of this all physical experiments and experience only led back to these two opposing principles. Here was an impasse. It was then that Albert Einstein came to the rescue, when he stated: "We cannot doubt the truth of both principles in question, in as far as we can trust the evidence of our senses at all; nor can any fault be found with the logical thought-process that proves the antagonism between the two principles. But in the considerations connected with that proof there are certain suppositions concerning the absoluteness and independence of our notions of time and space, which appear to us so self-evident, that up to the present nobody has ever doubted their truth. A more careful analysis of these suppositions, however, shows that they only *appear* to be self-evident, and that they are not absolute conceptual necessities. Furthermore, by suitable modification of these concepts, the antagonism between the two aforementioned principles disappears."

This indeed was a rare gleam of insight in the wilderness of thought. As our knowledge of nature can only be altered by the acquisition of new knowledge, this new discovery proved a decisive step, for it enabled Einstein to derive conclusions arising from the simultaneous validity of two conflicting principles. The sum-total of these conclusions is called the *special* theory of relativity.

The main achievement of the *special* theory is the recognition that the description of an event, which is admittedly only perfect if both the space and time co-ordinates are specified, will vary according to the relative motion of the observer. It is called the *special* theory because it affirms the relativity of uniform motions only, and is therefore valid only for this special class of motions (Einstein did not at this time, for example, consider curvilinear motions). It is of course a matter of everyday experience that all mechanical events take place in a system which is moving uniformly and rectilinearly. Seated in a perfectly smooth-running train a man could not tell that it was running if the shades were down, any more than he could tell that the earth rotates if there were no heavenly bodies. Motion is apparent only when compared.

Suppose we are on a ship. We cannot assert that it is in motion unless we look out of the portholes and watch the passing waves. In that way we perceive that there is a relative motion between the ship and the ocean. Or, to vary our example a little, let us say that our ship lies at anchor and another passes it with uniform velocity. (Theoretically you would feel just as comfortable on a uniformly moving train or ship as you do in a room in a house.) One does not notice the uniform motion. As a matter of fact, all phenomena would take place in the interiors of both ships in exactly the same way; and if we were in their interiors we would not be cognizant of motion. However, when we stand on the deck of one ship and look at the other we know that they are moving with respect to each other. Thus, the detection of uniform rectilinear motion is impossible without reference to the surroundings. Consequently, the principle of relativity is valid for mechanical processes. With the single exception of the velocity of light, absolute motions are impossible to measure or even to detect. The observed motions of the universe are all of a relative nature. Any attempt to detect absolute motion would be invariably frustrated by the very nature of the interrelationship of matter and space.

Imagine you are on a ship moving down the Hudson River. At exactly halfway between the bow and the stern you roll two balls down the deck at the same time with the same strength. One ball you roll forward, the other aft. It is obvious that the first ball will arrive at the bow of the ship at about the same time that the second ball arrives at the stern. So far as you are concerned, the balls traveled at the same speed. But to a man on the shore observing your rolling, the speed of the balls would not be the same for him as they were for you. The man on the shore would say that the ball which rolled forward moved faster than the ball which rolled aft. He would say that the speed of the first ball was its original speed plus the speed of the ship and the speed of the other ball was the original speed minus the speed of the ship. Both you and he would be right. The difference depends on the body referred to for measurement. In your case it was the ship, in his, the shore.

From this relativity of motion, or more exactly of uniform motion, there follows the relativity of distances between points in space. Suppose you are on a train and decide to walk forward to the dining car. You start at one moment and a few minutes later you arrive at your table in the diner. What is the distance you have moved? It depends on how you measure it. If you measure it relatively to the train it will be a rather short distance, perhaps three hundred and fifty feet. If you measure the distance traveled with respect to the earth it would be an entirely different quantity, which depends on the speed of the train. Now whether you walked three hundred and fifty feet or, say, a mile depends on your frame of reference. Relatively to the train you walked three hundred and fifty feet; relative to the earth you covered a mile.

This remodeling of Newtonian conceptions led Einstein to other discoveries of fundamental importance. For example, it uncovered the surprising fact that the old conception of the *simultaneity* of events at different points of space (the conception on which all time-measurements are based) has only a relative significance. This means that two events that are simultaneous for one observer will not, in general, be simultaneous for another.

We ordinarily imagine all processes to take place in the world according to a simple time. But time is relative—even so-called "simultaneous" events. There is no general world time, but only times for each observer. Different times can be mathematically related to each other only by taking into account the relative motion of the observers. Each observer has his own time, and therefore two events at different places which are simultaneous for one observer are not so for another.

A simple illustration will lay bare the meaning of the relativity of simultaneity. Einstein illustrates this fact by asking us to imagine

ALBERT EINSTEIN

Photograph by John Hagemeyer

two points, A and B, very far apart on a railway track. An observer
is on a stationary embankment at M, midway between A and B.
Let us imagine that lightning strikes the rails at the two points
A and B. If the observer sees the two flashes at the same instant
we say that the two flashes occur simultaneously. Suppose you are
now on a high-speed train moving along the track and that when
you reach the point M (that is, exactly opposite the observer on the
embankment) you see the same lightning flashes. Would the two
lightning strokes at A and B, which are simultaneous with respect
to the embankment, also be simultaneous with respect to you on
the moving train? No. The reason is that the motion of the train
is carrying you toward one flash and away from another. Therefore, argues Einstein, we are forced to the conclusion that events
which are simultaneous for one rigid body of reference (embankment) are not simultaneous for another body of reference (the
train). Consequently, all statements of time depend on the standpoint of the observer describing them, and are thus different for
two observers who are in motion with respect to each other.

The idea that time flows equally for all bodies regardless of their
motion is Newtonian but inaccurate. Go back to the ship illustration. It will show how and why the notion of absolute simultaneity
is not true. Our belief that *now* is the same now for every atom
in the universe turns out to be wholly erroneous. Thus, if the two
balls strike the two ends of the ship respectively at the same instant,
we have assumed (erroneously, of course) that such an instant is
the same for the man on the ship as well as the man on the shore.
Indeed, we have assumed that such an instant would be the same
for every man *anywhere*. But that cannot be true, for an observer
at rest in regard to the two events may observe them to be simultaneous whereas an observer in motion will observe the one sooner
than the other. There is no reason whatever for assuming that
events, separate in space, can be unified in time. The distance in
time, for example, between two events taking place in Jupiter and
Mars will appear different to an observer on the earth and one on
another planet. In other words, again, what seems simultaneous
in one frame of reference will not be simultaneous in another.

Similar reasoning applies in the case of the distance between two
points on a rigid body. The length of a rod is defined as the dis-

tance between the two points which are occupied *simultaneously* by the two ends. Since simultaneity is definitely relative, therefore the distance between two points (since they depend on a simultaneous reading of two events) is also relative. Consequently, length has meaning only in relation to a body of reference. It has not, as Newton believed, the same volume and shape whatever its motion. Relativity affirms that any change of motion entails a corresponding change of length so that the "actual" length of a body in the absolute Newtonian sense does not exist. The newer theory therefore demonstrates that most of the traditional scientific laws consist of pure conventions as to measurement, strictly analogous to the "great law" that there are three feet to a yard.

8

Contrary to expectations, Einstein had no great love for his professorship at the University of Zürich. The duties of the office encroached upon his time. He was in the midst of elaborating his theory and needed a certain solitude, free from the claims of the lecture room. Nor could he become genuinely interested in faculty life, its conversations, clubs, and social life. He knew what he wanted—a quiet, meditative life removed from time-consuming duties and meaningless social activities. Could he achieve that?

After spending several years at Zürich and one year at the German University of Prague, his dream was fulfilled. Einstein was called to Berlin where Kaiser Wilhelm signed a special dispensation permitting him, though he was now a Swiss national, to become professor at a newly created institute which bore the royal name of the reigning emperor—The Kaiser Wilhelm Institute for Physics. At the same time he was elected a member of the Prussian Academy of Sciences. Practically all his wishes were to be granted; all extraneous duties were to be reduced to a minimum in order to give him the necessary independence for research.

In the spring of 1914 Einstein began his new work in Berlin. He knew now that his field was pure theory rather than experiment. Was relativity a comprehensive world-view? Yes, he believed it was. Otherwise he would not have labored at it with such tenacity since the publication of the restricted theory. And just as the special (or restricted) theory had long been an alluring goal of science which he alone was able to achieve, so now the earlier ambitious attempt at synthesis was expanded into the *general* theory of relativity. With unyielding logic he pursued to their farthest points the implications and prior conditions of facts which he knew with a high degree of precision. He combined the accumulated knowledge with the imaginative visioning of possibilities in such a way as to predict the character of the still unexplored portions of nature.

As the special theory is only valid for uniform rectilinear motions, it became desirable to be able to affirm that *every* motion is relative. Having achieved success with one particular class of motions, he set out to create a general theory of relativity that would embrace the *whole* realm of physics. These efforts were brought to a successful conclusion just one year after he had moved to Berlin. It is this general theory (not the special theory) that led Einstein to a new treatment of gravitational phenomena, thereby taking physics very far beyond Newton.

The general theory brought the domain of physics into good order. Its chief quality is an internal logical coherence which only the language of mathematics can express. Matter, electricity, radiation, energy—all are included. It obliterated the barrier between matter and energy by furnishing a formula for their transformation. The central result is Einstein's law of gravitation which he achieved by an extraordinarily brilliant piece of mathematical analysis. The fusion of the forces of gravity with those of inertia into one single whole is the fundamental idea of his gravitational system. Though entirely different from Newton's in mathematical form, Einstein's law gives results almost identical with those of Newton. Had it not been so the new theory could not have been right, for Newton's law of the inverse square is able to predict the movements of the sun, moon, and planets with great precision, as well as explain in detail the procession of the equinoxes, the tides, the figure of the earth and many other phenomena. For ordinary purposes the two laws come to the same thing. However, it must be borne in mind that Einstein's theory is no more of an *explanation* of gravity than Newton's. But it is a more correct *description*. While it gives results identical with those of Newton's, it does a certain job which the Newtonian apparatus could not do.

The historian of science of the future, standing farther from the events of today than we can do, will see much better the back-yards of science littered with discarded theories, laws, principles, hypotheses. Of all the theories of the cause of gravitation that have been propounded since the time of Newton, Einstein's marks the first positive advance in two centuries. The *Annual Report* of the Smithsonian Institution for 1876 lists more than twenty-five theories which found their way into print after Newton wrote his *Principia* (still rated the most massive addition to scientific thought ever made by one man). Since 1876 one may safely add another dozen. Some of these attempts at theory have been nothing more than meaningless mysticism and others nothing more than a profound investigation of an empty mare's nest. Einstein's alone has emerged, has survived and grown and produced momentous results.

Most people think that the explanation of falling bodies, as due to an attracting force exerted by the earth, was wholly original with Newton. This is not true. Galileo was familiar with the idea; and Aristotle, living more than fifteen hundred years before Newton, knew about it. Even the law of the inverse square had suggested itself to more than one mind before Newton. Wherein then lay Newton's especial contribution? His was the conception and the mathematical demonstration of the universality of gravitation: that the law of the inverse square was a sufficient explanation for (a) the motion of the moon around the earth, (b) the motion of the various planets around the sun, (c) the motions of every member of the stellar universe. The success of relativity does not lessen the grandeur of this accomplishment or minimize the significance of the inscription which appears on Newton's monument: "Let mortals congratulate themselves that so great an ornament of the human race has existed."

9

Over a century elapsed before any serious divergence of observation from Newton's theory became noticeable. In 1845 the French astronomer Leverrier called attention to the fact that the planet Mercury showed a slight irregularity in its motion inconsistent with Newton's law of the inverse square, and too large to be explained as an error of observation. Fast-moving Mercury—in defiance of Newton—moves round the sun in an orbit which is, at a first approximation, an ellipse. Closer study shows that the position of this ellipse undergoes a change in the course of time, so that the point at which Mercury is nearest the sun (its perihelion) is not fixed, as the old law stated, but slowly revolving. The greater part of this revolution is explained by the influence of other planets. This accounts for an advance of 532 seconds of arc per century. But the observed amount is 574. The 42 seconds left over, which had not been satisfactorily accounted for, although numerous hypotheses had been framed, was taken by Einstein's theory in its stride. Einstein's law of gravitation explained the discrepancy in exactly the amount predicted by the general theory.

This was an achievement which greatly enhanced the probability of Einstein's being correct. Calculation showed that there were other phenomena—problems not solved by Newton—which would naturally follow as a consequence of the truth of the newer law.

The first of these relates to the bending of light. Einstein predicted that the mass of the sun would curve the space near it to such an extent that light from the stars passing through this space would be bent. Calculating the deflection of a ray bent by the sun, he concluded that it would be twice what the Newtonian theory indicated. He accomplished his calculations independently and alone. It is true that a forgotten young German astronomer, Soldner of Munich, had studied this problem (1805) and arrived at the result that light passing near the edge of the sun will be bent. Knowing nothing of the labors of Soldner, Einstein was led to the same thought. Soldner's calculations were erroneous, claiming that the light would be bent through one second of arc. Einstein, however, on the basis of his general theory, claimed that the deflection would amount to 1.75 seconds of arc. The total eclipse of May 29, 1919, confirmed the accuracy of Einstein's predictions. These again were checked and the calculations again confirmed at the eclipse of September, 1922. As Einstein's formula gave the exact result without upsetting the calculations in any other case, the principle of relativity received powerful support.

The second test which Einstein proposed for the verification of this theory was his prediction of a slight displacement in position of the lines in the solar spectrum. In many ways this proved to be the most beautiful test of all, for Einstein predicted an effect not only unlooked for by Newton and his theory but wholly unexplainable in any other way except on the grounds of relativity. To verify this was a matter of considerable difficulty. However, the problem was attacked by several astronomers. As Einstein does not work in a vacuum, the problems he ponders are probed by others. They came to the conclusion that the displacement toward the red end of the spectrum predicted by Einstein was, despite disturbing effects due to other causes, in just the amount that Einstein had stated.

Thus Einstein's theory fits more types of facts than does Newton's, and includes all the facts covered by Newton's. It gains in comprehension but loses in simplicity. Newton created a marvelous pattern into which facts could be fitted. Einstein created still another pattern into which these same facts, together with others heretofore neglected, could be fitted. It proved to be uncannily true and those who were initially hostile to it yielded. His theory stands confirmed, a memorial to his exact and painstaking industry.

The confirmation of Einstein's predictions again certified to the world the value of the role of the mathematical theorist in the realm of the physical sciences. It is small wonder that Galileo and others called mathematics *divine*—"What we can measure we can know." Mathematics works. Was it not out of pure mathematical calculation that James Clerk Maxwell predicted wireless waves? Those invisible rays were not discovered by accident; they were deduced in 1867 by this English theorist when he demonstrated that the electromagnetic theory of light implied the possibility of producing waves invisible to the eye. Twenty years later such waves were made and measured by Hertz. Ten years later Marconi used them in telegraphing to a ship ten miles offshore. By 1902 wireless telegrams were transmitted across the Atlantic. Yet more was to follow: the wonders of radio, television, the telephoto: practical results emanating from the highly abstract mathematical equations of a lone theorist.

10

Relativity in no way starts with the destruction of old fundamental principles but rather corrects prejudices and habits of thought which have occasioned unnecessary difficulties. Not destruction but revision—extension—ultimate simplification—has been its effect. Einstein saw the whole of a vast problem as a coherent mathematical unity; his daring structure renders the old Newtonian theory only an approximate one. As Sir Arthur Eddington has said: "When Einstein overthrew Newton's theory, he took Newton's plant which had outgrown its pot, and transplanted it to a more open field."

The end result of Einstein's thinking leaves the average person bewildered. Not because it is so difficult but because it is as yet so unfamiliar. Newton's concepts, so well known to us now, must have seemed completely incomprehensible to the nonscientific when first put forward. Relativity must be grasped slowly, imaginatively, until what is seen only in flashes becomes a connected part of one's normal intellectual equipment. Patience, time, and familiarity will confer understanding. It must be remembered that even so elementary a subject as a high school algebra text contains concepts which first required the genius of a Descartes to formulate. Einstein forged a strong chain of reasoning that pulled Newton's law of universal gravitation from its Olympian pedestal. Without the mathematical machinery of the tensor calculus (which developed from the algebraic work of Cayley and Sylvester) it is improbable that Einstein could have ever budged the Newtonian theory of gravitation.

What of space? Is it curved? Lobatchevsky, Riemann, and other non-Euclidean mathematicians contended for "curvature of space" and Einstein's theory demands it. The conception of space-curvature can be made understandable without the help of the prohibitively complicated intricacies of higher mathematics. Say, for purposes of illustration, that you fill your bathtub and lay upon the surface of the water a large cake of soap so that it will actually float without breaking through the water, so that, in other words, there is no displacement of the water. You have now rendered the previously flat surface of the water about the soap non-Euclidean (for the cake of soap has bent the surface into a cusp or depression). Suppose now you take a tiny piece of cork and throw it into the tub. As long as the cork is not near the soap it occupies a flat or Euclidean region of the surface. But if it floats toward the soap it will slowly enter the cusped or non-Euclidean area depressed by the comparatively large mass of the soap. By moving into the bent area, the piece of cork is forced to yield a portion of its straight path and for a time is subjected to a twist while passing through the cusp. This bathtub illustration helps make clear the contention of Einstein that space near matter must be curved. The larger the mass, the greater must be the curvature.* Because Einstein ascribed curvature of space to the presence of matter in it, he was quite logical in saying that if there were no matter all space would be Euclidean.

Simply put, the theory of relativity arrives at the conclusion that every gravitational field—of the sun, of the earth, of every piece of matter in the universe—causes curvature of space. A cannon ball shot through space describes a curve and falls to the earth. The planets circle around the sun. What does this mean? Simply this: gravity is not a force acting at a distance as Newton believed but an effect due to the modification of space in the immediate neighborhood of the body acted upon.

On the basis of the Newtonian teaching the curvatures of the paths of planets, of tennis balls, of projectiles in general were all attributed to a "force" of gravitation. Relativity has another interpretation. It dismisses this force as a pure figment of the imagination. It is the curvature of space, not a supposed force of gravity, which causes the projectile to fall to the earth in a curved path. In this way the theory of relativity builds a bridge between geometry and physics. From the standpoint of the Newtonian theory geometry precedes physics. With the coming of Einstein geometry is no longer antecedent to physics but indissolubly fused with it into a single discipline.

11

The very idea of the roundness of the earth—the curvature of its surface—is rather recent. It took humanity a long time to recognize it. Why? Because moving on its surface in a given direction one gets the feeling of traveling in a *straight* line. Actually, of course, it is not so; and the proof of it is that if one were to travel on in the same direction on the earth's surface he would finally return to his original point of departure. This demonstrates that the earth is boundless but not infinite.

* That is why Einstein predicted that astronomers would find the light rays of the stars bent near the sun, the bending being greatest near the edge of the great solar body and decreased farther away from it.

A basketball hangs in my room. The ball is boundless and the fly that is now walking round its surface could go on walking freely for many millions of years without ever finding on the surface of my basketball a boundary. The surface of the ball is indeed boundless but not *infinite*. To prove that it is not infinite, the surface can be measured in exact mathematical terms of square inches. As with the basketball so it is with the earth. The earth is a sphere; it is curved, although there are still some people who think it flat. If you are among these living persons who do not believe that the earth is flat (which the phenomena connected with the existence of the *horizon* would quickly disprove), then you are prepared to understand the far more difficult problem of the noninfinity of the Einsteinian universe. For just as the earth's surface, like a curved plane, bends back upon itself and is boundless but not infinite, so too is the entire universe. This is the foundation for the statement of Sir James Jeans that "light and wireless signals travel at the same rate because, of course, they are essentially the same thing; and this thing takes a seventh of a second to travel round the world, and probably something like 100,000 million years to travel round the Universe."

As long as men thought of space as Euclidean and time as Newtonian they were compelled to assume that the universe is infinite. Once, however, they began to think in terms of relativity it was obvious that space, being non-Euclidean, is "curved" and that the universe in consequence is finite in its dimensions. This opens up a new understanding which profoundly affects our views about the physical universe.

In similar vein, Einstein's conception of mass and energy changes the old-established classical views. Just as space and time are brought together into a deeper synthesis by the doctrine of relativity, so mass and energy are connected by the equation $E = Mc^2$ where c is the velocity of light. Lavoisier's conservation of matter and Mayer's conservation of energy are thus united so that mass and energy are to be understood as essentially alike—different expressions of the same thing, complementary aspects of an underlying unity.

Whatever may be said of the mathematical difficulties of relativity (and they are admittedly great) still those who come after Einstein will forever see natural phenomena in a wholly new and different light. As Darwin changed the thinking of men toward all things organic, so Einstein has conferred a new understanding of the nature of the physical world.

12

Always interested in the spectacular, the public fancy has taken more to Einstein's work on relativity than to his less-known but equally important contributions to atomic physics and radiation— the especial domain of Max Planck. Very early in his studies in physics Einstein was attracted to the revolutionary concepts of his senior colleague, who had done for the microcosm (atom, energy, atom) what Einstein was to do for the macrocosm (space, time, matter, gravitation, electromagnetism). In the same year that he announced to the world the special theory of relativity, Einstein presented a solution of the photoelectric effect on the basis of Planck's quantum. Thus Einstein's contributions to the quantum theory have been responsible for much of the marvelous progress in spectroscopy and atomic structure. Curiously enough, when he was awarded the Nobel Prize in 1921 it was not in recognition of his work on relativity but for "the discovery of the law of photo-electric effect." *

Today, Professor Planck is an aged man (eighty years old on April 23, 1938) laden with distinctions, including the Nobel Prize which he received in 1919. At a banquet given in his honor several years ago, Albert Einstein paid the quantum physicist a memorable tribute: "Many kinds of men devote themselves to science, and not all for the sake of science herself. There are some who come into her temple because it offers them the opportunity to display their particular talents. To this class of men science is a kind of sport in the practice of which they exult, just as an athlete exults in the exercise of his muscular prowess. There is another class of men who come into the temple to make an offering of their brain pulp in the hope of securing a profitable return. These men are scientists only by the chance of some circumstance which offered itself when making a choice of career. If the attending circumstance had been different they might have become politicians or captains

* The reason is that the Nobel Prize is given for work in experimental physics.

of business. Should an angel of God descend and drive from the temple of science all those who belong to the categories I have mentioned, I fear the temple would be nearly emptied. But a few worshipers would still remain—some from former times and some from ours. To these latter belongs our Planck. And that is why we love him."

13

Einstein had been at his tasks in Berlin only a short while when he married his widowed cousin Elsa, his marriage to his first wife having been dissolved. Then came the World War—a bath of blood and fire. He refused to have anything to do with it. If the German scientists wanted to issue a manifesto supporting their government, he would not join them. "We stand, therefore, at the parting of the ways. Whether we find the way of peace or continue along the old road of brute force, so unworthy of our civilization, depends on ourselves." Month after month, year after year, he watched the youth of Germany marching through the streets of Berlin on their way to the battlefields. No words explain more his depth of suffering than his denunciation of the military system: "That a man can take pleasure in marching in fours to the strains of a band is enough to make me despise him. He has only been given his big brain by mistake; a backbone was all he needed. This plague-spot of civilization ought to be abolished with all possible speed. Heroism by order, senseless violence and all the pestilent nonsense that goes by the name of patriotism—how I hate them! War seems to me a mean contemptible thing: I would rather be hacked in pieces than take part in such an abominable business."

These are indeed the passionate and powerful words of a great moral leader as well as a seer of science. Since the rise of fascism, and especially since Hitler's accession to power, Einstein has modified his views. Today, he is an American citizen having escaped the inquisitions of a regime that burnt his books, confiscated his property and put a price on his head. Seeing in the totalitarian state a brute attack upon civilization he advocates resistance to evil. After all, the price of liberty is still eternal vigilance.

No one will claim that the World War solved any problems. What with millions of men maimed and slaughtered, governments uprooted, huge property losses sustained, it is no wonder that misery and economic depression stalked a world full of the horrors of dislocation. Out of the cruel and negative results of the great conflict there has emerged one solid achievement, the work of a solitary, lonely scientist trying to be sane in a world gone mad. The war delayed the reception of relativity. In 1915 Einstein had finished his general theory but communication with the scientists in England and France was cut off. Six months after the armistice was signed Arthur Eddington headed a British expedition to study the eclipse of May 29, 1919, in an effort to check Einstein. He did—and Einstein's theory became the possession of the peaceful international world of knowledge, science and philosophy.

Shortly before his fiftieth birthday Einstein, still in Berlin (1929), presented to the Prussian Academy of Sciences a brief communication, less than six pages of print, entitled *Toward a Unified Field Theory*. For ten years he had been at work on its vast complexities in an effort to achieve a new synthesis of his own theories. The original special theory of relativity dealt with phenomena occurring in the electromagnetic field of visual events. The general theory is an extension of the special, concerned chiefly with occurrences in the gravitational field. (The two theories involve the use of radically different systems of mathematical equations.) With the announcement of the unified field theory, the world of aroused public interest realized that Einstein had initiated a bold attempt to combine the conceptions of electromagnetism and gravitation in a logical and inherent unity. Just as heat waves and light waves and radio waves may be regarded as variations of wave phenomena, so his numerous (and as yet unsuccessful) attempts to achieve a unified theory are based upon the belief that electromagnetism and gravitation are manifestations of one and the same thing. If experiment shall ultimately demonstrate its essential accuracy the unified theory promises to be "the greatest merger ever effected in human thought."

14

As a result of the labors of Einstein and Planck, theoretical physics is now divided into the domain of microscopical phenomena, covered largely by the quantum theory, and the realm of the macroscopical which the formulae of relativity unite and explain. The next stupendous advance in science is destined to bring these two theories together. Already there are foreshadowings, as yet unpicturable and unimaginable. Eddington and Dirac are prominent among those seeking this newer world.

And Einstein too.

Like the aged king Ulysses of Tennyson's poem, Albert Einstein sits at Princeton, the white-haired monarch of all theorists—of those who have died and of those who are living. As in the days of his youth he still loves his ships and sailing craft, for they are symbols of far-off adventure in an expanding universe. And he has convinced others too that his doctrine of an expanding universe is a significant consequence of his theory of relativity: de Sitter, Eddington, Jeans, Lemaître, Hubble. . . .

> There lies the port; the vessel puffs her sail:
> There gloom the dark broad seas. My mariners,
> Souls that have toil'd, and wrought, and thought with me—
>   . . . Come, my friends,
> 'Tis not too late to seek a newer world.

BIBLIOGRAPHY

ABOUT THEORIES

The Grammar of Science. Karl Pearson. 3rd Ed. London, 1911.

The Foundations of Science. Henri Poincaré. Trans. from French. New York, 1913.

Science and the Human Mind. W. C. D. Wetham. London, 1912.

The Art of Thought. Graham Wallas. London, 1926.

An Introduction to the History of Science. Walter Libby. London, 1917.

Science and History. A. L. Rowse. London, 1928.

The Domain of Natural Science. E. W. Hobson. Aberdeen, 1922.

Science and Civilization. F. S. Marvin. Oxford, 1923.

The Nature of Physical Theory. P. W. Bridgman. London, 1936.

Introduction to the History of Science. George Sarton. London, 1927.

The Bases of Modern Science. J. W. N. Sullivan. London, 1928.

Discovery. Sir Richard Gregory. London, 1923.

The Scientific Habit of Thought. Frederick Barry. London, 1927.

The Nature of Hypothesis. Myron L. Ashley. Chicago University, 1903.

The Study of the History of Science. George Sarton. London, 1936.

Science and the Human Temperament. Erwin Schrödinger. Trans. from German. London, 1935.

The Story of Human Error. Edited by Joseph Jastrow. New York, 1936.

The Anatomy of Modern Science. Bernhard Bavink. Trans. from German. London, 1932.

Science and Life. Frederick Soddy. London, 1920.

Aspects of Science. J. W. N. Sullivan. London, 1927.

The New Background of Science. Sir J. H. Jeans. Cambridge, 1933.

The Place of Science in Modern Civilization. Thorstein Veblen. New York, 1919.

The Scientific Method. F. W. Westaway. London, 1937.

THEORY OF THE SOLAR SYSTEM

ON COPERNICUS:

"The Copernican Revolution," ch. 2 in *A History of Science, Technology and Philosophy*. A. Wolf. London, 1935.

History of the Inductive Sciences. Vol. I. William Whewell. 3rd Ed. New York, 1875.

Nicolaus Copernicus. Leopold Prowe. Berlin, 1883.

Pioneers of Science. Sir Oliver Lodge. London, 1926.

Great Men of Science. Philipp Lenard. Trans. from German. London, 1933.

ON GALILEO, BRUNO, ETC.:

Galileo. J. J. Fahie. London, 1903.

The Martyrs of Science. David Brewster. New York, 1841.

Galileo. W. W. Bryant. London, 1918.

The Struggle Between Science and Superstition. A. M. Lewis. Chicago, 1916.

Giordano Bruno. William Boulting. London, 1914.

Johann Kepler: A Tercentenary Commemoration. Auspices of the History of Science Society. Baltimore, 1931.

GENERAL:

History of the Planetary Systems from Thales to Kepler. J. L. E. Dreyer. Cambridge, 1906.

The Gradual Acceptance of the Copernican Theory. Dorothy Stimson. New York, 1917.

The History of the Warfare of Science with Theology. Andrew D. White. New York, 1897.

A Short History of Astronomy. Arthur Berry. New York, 1910.

A Source Book in Astronomy. Shapley and Howarth. New York, 1929.

Theoretical Astrophysics. S. Rosseland. Oxford, 1936.

Kosmos. W. de Sitter. London, 1932.

The Place of Observation in Astronomy. (Lecture) H. H. Plaskett. Oxford, 1933.

THEORY OF THE EARTH

ON HUTTON :

Biographical Account of James Hutton. John Playfair. Edinburgh, 1797.

"James Hutton" (article) in *Dictionary of National Biography*. Oxford University Press, 1921.

The Scottish School of Geology (an address). A. Geikie. Edinburgh, 1871.

"La Synthèse Géologique de 1775 à 1918" (article). George Sarton in *Isis*. Vol. 2 (1919).

Passages in the History of Geology (lecture). Andrew C. Ramsay. London, 1848.

ON WERNER:

History of Geology. K. A. von Zittel. Trans. from German. London, 1901.
This Puzzling Planet. E. T. Brewster. New York, 1928.
Founders of Geology. Sir Archibald Geikie. London, 1897.
Geschichte und Literatur der Geognosie. C. Keferstein. Halle, 1840.

GENERAL:

Illustrations of the Huttonian Theory. John Playfair. Edinburgh, 1802.
History of Geology. H. B. Woodward. London, 1911.
The Earth and Its History. J. H. Bradley. New York, 1928.
A Comparative View of the Huttonian and Neptunian Systems of Geology. Edinburgh, 1802.
Geology from Original Sources. Agar, Flint and Longwell. New York, 1929.
Errors of Geology. John Kelly. London, 1864.
Mineralogy and Geology. Parker Cleaveland. Boston, 1816.
"On Theories of the Earth," ch. 46 in *A System of Geology.* John MacCulloch. London, 1831.
Series of Experiments Shewing the Effects of Compression in Modifying the Action of Heat. James Hall. Edinburgh, 1805.
The Story of Geology. A. L. Benson. New York, 1927.

THEORY OF THE STRUCTURE OF MATTER

ON DALTON:

Life of Dalton. W. C. Henry. London, 1884.
John Dalton. L. J. Neville-Polley. London, 1920.
The Makers of Chemistry. E. J. Holmyard. Oxford, 1931.
A New View of the Origin of Dalton's Atomic Theory. Roscoe and Harden. London, 1896.
Famous Chemists. E. Roberts. London, 1911.
History of Chemistry. F. J. Moore. New York, 1931.

ON BOYLE:

Makers of Science. Ivor B. Hart. London, 1924.
Essays in Historical Chemistry. E. Thorpe. London, 1931.

GENERAL:

"The Corpuscular Theories of Matter," ch. 7 in *The Domain of Science*. E. W. Hobson. Aberdeen, 1922.

The Corpuscular Theory of Matter. Sir J. J. Thomson. London, 1907.

Atom and Cosmos. Hans Reichanbach. London, 1933.

A Short History of Atomism. J. C. Gregory. London, 1931.

Recent Developments in Atomic Theory. C. G. Darwin. Oxford, 1927.

The A. B. C. of Atoms. B. Russell. London, 1923.

The Atomic Theory. J. J. Thomson. Oxford, 1914.

Modern Theories in Chemistry. L. Meyer. London, 1888.

Architecture of the Universe. W. F. G. Swann. London, 1934.

The Electron in Chemistry. Sir J. J. Thomson. London, 1923.

The Drama of Chemistry. S. J. French. New York, 1937.

THEORY OF FIRE

ON LAVOISIER:

"Lavoisier," ch. 21 in *Master Minds in Medicine*. J. C. Hemmeter. New York, 1927.

Life of Lavoisier. Mary Foster. Smith College Monographs No. 1 (1926).

Lavoisier. J. A. Cochrane. London, 1931.

Crusaders of Chemistry. J. N. Leonard. New York, 1930.

Antoine Lavoisier. Douglas McKie. London, 1935.

ON STAHL:

The Study of Chemical Composition. Ida Freund. Cambridge, 1904.

Das Buch Der Grossen Chemiker. Vol. I. Gunther Bugge. Berlin, 1929.

The Chemistry of Combustion. J. N. Friend. London, 1922.

The History of Biology. Erik Nordenskiöld. Trans. from Swedish. London, 1928.

ON PRIESTLEY:

Joseph Priestley. E. T. Thorpe. London, 1906.

Three Philosophers. W. R. Aykroyd. London, 1935.

Crucibles: The Lives and Achievements of the Great Chemists. Bernard Jaffee. New York, 1930.

The History of the Phlogiston Theory. J. H. White. London, 1932.

GENERAL:

"The Phlogiston Theory in Chemistry," ch. 1 of Book IV in *A History of Science*. Henry Smith Williams. New York, 1904.

Alchemy: Child of Greek Philosophy. Arthur J. Hopkins. London, 1934.
The Story of Early Chemistry. J. M. Stillman. New York, 1924.
Famous Chemists. W. A. Tilden. London, 1921.
Prelude to Chemistry. John Read. London, 1937.
The History of Chemistry from the Earliest Times. J. C. Brown. 2nd Ed. Philadelphia, 1920.
Essays in Historical Chemistry. E. Thorpe. London, 1931.
History of Chemical Theories and Laws. M. M. P. Muir. New York, 1907.
A History of Chemical Theory. A. Wurtz. Trans. from French. London, 1869.

THEORY OF HEAT

ON RUMFORD:

Memoir of Sir Benjamin Thompson. G. E. Ellis. Boston, 1871.
General Gage's Informers. Allen French. Ann Arbor, 1932.
Count Rumford of Massachusetts. J. A. Thompson. New York, 1935.
"Count Rumford," in *New Fragments.* John Tyndall. London, 1898.
The Royal Institution: Its Founder and its First Professors. Bence Jones. London, 1871.

ON MAYER:

"The Copley Medalist of 1871," in Vol. I. *Fragments of Science.* John Tyndall. 6th Ed. London, 1899.
"Robert Mayer," in *Trail Blazers of Science.* Martin Gumpert. Trans. from German. New York, 1936.
J. Robert Mayer. Bernhard Hell. Stuttgart, 1925.

GENERAL:

Theory of Heat. Thomas Preston. 4th Ed. London, 1929.
Heat. P. G. Tait. London, 1904.
Mechanical Theory of Heat. R. S. McCulloch. New York, 1876.
Heat as a Mode of Motion. John Tyndall. London, 1863.
An Outline of the Theory of Thermodynamics. Edgar Buckingham. New York, 1900.
The General Theory of Thermodynamics. J. E. Trevor. New York, 1927.
Heat and Thermodynamics. J. K. Roberts. London, 1933.
The Correlation and Conservation of Forces. Grove, Helmholtz, Mayer, *et al.* New York, 1872.
Theories of Energy. Horace Perry. New York, 1918.
Theory of Heat. Max Planck. Trans. from German. London, 1932.

THEORY OF LIGHT

ON HUYGENS:

A History of Science in the Sixteenth and Seventeenth Centuries. A. Wolf. London, 1935.

"Christiaan Huygens." Florian Cajori in *Scientific Monthly* (March, 1929).

Oeuvres Complètes. Published by the Society of Science of Holland. The Hague, 1888.

Great Men of Science. Philipp Lenard. Trans. from German. London, 1933.

Le Séjour de Christiaan Huygens à Paris. H. L. Brugmans. Paris, 1935.

ON NEWTON:

Memoirs of Sir Isaac Newton. David Brewster. Edinburgh, 1885.

Sir Isaac Newton. Selig Brodetsky. London, 1927.

Essays on the Life and Work of Newton. Augustus de Morgan. Chicago, 1914.

Matter and Gravity in Newton's Physical Philosophy. A. J. Snow. New York, 1926.

ON YOUNG AND FRESNEL:

"Thomas Young's Place in the History of the Wave Theory of Light." Henry Crew in *The Journal of the Optical Society of America.* Vol. 20 (Jan. 1930).

"Epoch of Young and Fresnel," in Vol. II, *History of the Inductive Sciences.* William Whewell. 3rd Ed. New York, 1875.

Life of Dr. Young. G. Peacock. London, 1855.

Oeuvres Complètes d'Augustin Fresnel. Paris, 1866–70.

ON FARADAY:

Faraday as a Discoverer. John Tyndall. London, 1870.

Michael Faraday. W. L. Randell. London, 1924.

Life and Letters of Faraday. H. B. Jones. London, 1870.

ON MAXWELL:

James Clerk Maxwell and Modern Physics. R. T. Glazebrook. London, 1901.

La Théorie de Maxwell. H. Poincaré. Paris, 1899.

The Life of James Clerk Maxwell. Campbell and Garnett. London, 1882.

James Clerk Maxwell. A Commemorative Volume. Cambridge, 1931.

ON HERTZ:

The Work of Hertz. Sir Oliver Lodge. London, 1898.
Great Men of Science. Philipp Lenard. Trans. from German. London, 1933.
Pioneers of Wireless. Ellison Hawkes. London, 1927.
Pioneers of Electrical Communication. Rollo Appleyard. London, 1930.

ON PLANCK:

"Max Planck: A Biographical Sketch." James Murphy in *Where is Science Going?* Max Planck. London, 1932.
Max Planck als Forscher. Albert Einstein. Berlin, 1913.

GENERAL:

Theory of Light. R. C. Maclaurin. Cambridge, 1908.
The Wave Theory of Light. Humphrey Lloyd. London, 1837.
Optical Theories. D. N. Mallik. Cambridge, 1921.
Six Lectures on Light. John Tyndall. London, 1873.
"The Ether Theories of Electrification." Fernando Sanford. *Scientific Monthly.* Vol. 24 (1922).
The Electromagnetic Theory of Light. C. E. Curry. London, 1905.
Optics. Isaac Newton. (Reprinted from the 4th Ed. with a foreword by Albert Einstein.) London, 1931.
Treatise on Light. Christiaan Huygens. (Rendered into English by Silvanus P. Thompson.) London, 1912.
The Revolution in Physics. Ernst Zimmer. Trans. from German. London, 1936.
"Particles and Waves." H. B. Lemon in *The World and Man.* F. R. Moulton (Editor). New York, 1937.
"What is Light?" Arthur H. Compton in *Scientific Monthly.* (April, 1929.)
The Quantum and Its Interpretation. H. S. Allen. London, 1928.
The Quantum Theory. Fritz Reiche. Trans. from German. London, 1935.
Waves and Ripples in Water, Air, and Aether. J. A. Fleming. London, 1902.
A History of the Theories of Aether. E. T. Whittaker. London, 1910.

THEORY OF POPULATION

ON MALTHUS:

Malthus and His Work. James Bonar. London, 1885.
Essays in Biography. John M. Keynes. London, 1933.

412   BIBLIOGRAPHY

"Malthus: A Revaluation." Ezra Bowen. Article in *Scientific Monthly*. Vol. 30 (Jan.-June 1930).

Population Problems of the Age of Malthus. G. Talbot Griffith. Cambridge, 1926.

ON GODWIN:

"William Godwin" (an essay). William Hazlitt in *Spirit of the Age*. London, 1825.

The Life of William Godwin. F. K. Brown. London, 1926.

Shelley, Godwin, and Their Circle. H. N. Brailsford. London, 1913.

William Godwin: His Friends and Contemporaries. C. K. Paul, Boston, 1876.

ON PLACE:

Life of Francis Place. Graham Wallas. London, 1898.

Place on Population. Norman E. Himes. London, 1930.

The Early Propagandist Movement in English Population Theory. James A. Field. Bul. Amer. Economic Assoc. 4th Series, 1911.

Medical History of Contraception. Norman E. Himes. London, 1936.

Pioneers of Birth Control. Victor Robinson. New York, 1919.

ON GALTON:

Life, Letters and Labours of Francis Galton. Karl Pearson. Vol. I, Cambridge, 1914; Vol. II, Cambridge, 1924.

Great Biologists. Sir J. Arthur Thomson. London, 1932.

"Francis Galton," in *Introduction to Biology and Other Papers*. A. B. Darbishire. New York, 1917.

GENERAL:

World Population. A. M. Carr-Saunders. Oxford, 1936.

Population Problems. W. S. Thompson. New York, 1935.

Heredity and Environment in the Development of Man. E. G. Conklin. London, 1920.

Nature and Nurture. L. T. Hogben. London, 1933.

Mankind at the Crossroads. E. M. East. New York, 1923.

The Early American Reaction to the Theory of Malthus. George J. Cady. Chicago, 1931.

Pre-Malthusian Doctrines of Population. C. E. Strangeland. New York, 1904.

THEORY OF THE CELL

ON SCHWANN:

Manifestation en L'Honneur de M. Le Professeur Th. Schwann. Dusseldorf, 1879.

The Great Biologists. Sir J. Arthur Thomson. London, 1932.

Biology and its Makers. W. A. Locy. 3rd Ed. London, 1915.

Makers of Modern Medicine. J. J. Walsh. New York, 1907.

"Schleiden and Schwann," ch. 18 in *Pathfinders in Medicine.* Victor Robinson. New York, 1929.

ON WOLFF:

"Caspar Friedrich Wolff and the Theoria Generationis." W. M. Wheeler in *Biological Lectures of Wood's Holl.* Boston, 1899.

"Kaspar Friedrich Wolff," in *Trail Blazers of Science.* Martin Gumpert. Trans. from German. New York, 1936.

ON HALLER, BONNET:

Early Theories of Sexual Generation. F. J. Cole. Oxford, 193c

Growth of Biology. W. A. Locy. New York, 1925.

ON HOOKE, GREW, ETC.:

History of Botany. Julius von Sachs. Trans. from German. Oxford, 1890.

"The Biological Sciences," ch. 18 in *A History of Science.* A. Wolf. London, 1935.

The Early Naturalists. L. C. Miall. London, 1912.

ON MENDEL:

"Mendel the Man." Paul Popenoe. *Journal of Heredity.* Vol. 16 (1925).

The Physical Basis of Heredity. T. H. Morgan. Philadelphia, 1919.

Life of Mendel. Hugo Iltis. Trans. from German. New York, 1932.

GENERAL:

Cell in Development and Inheritance. E. B. Wilson. 3rd Ed. London, 1925.

Histoire des Origines de la Théorie Cellulaire. Marc Klein. Paris, 1936.

The Cell Doctrine. James Tyson. Philadelphia, 1878.

Science and Human Affairs. W. C. Curtis. New York, 1922.

"The Rise of Genetics." T. H. Morgan. *Science.* Vol. 76, p. 261 (1932).

"Human Genetics and Human Ideals." J. B. S. Haldane in *Scientific Progress.* New York, 1936.

"Heredity and Human Affairs." L. Hogben in *Science Today.* Sir J. Arthur Thomson (Editor). London, 1934.

Theory of the Gene. T. H. Morgan. London, 1926.
Human Genetics and its Social Import. S. J. Holmes. New York, 1936.

THEORY OF EVOLUTION

ON DARWIN:

The Evolution of Charles Darwin. G. A. Dorsey. London, 1927.
Darwin. Gamaliel Bradford. Boston, 1926.
Charles Darwin and the Theory of Natural Selection. E. B. Poulton. London, 1896.
Charles Darwin. C. F. Holden. New York, 1891.
Darwin and the Humanities. J. M. Baldwin. London, 1910.

ON DARWIN'S PREDECESSORS:

Pioneers of Evolution. E. Clodd. London, 1897.
From the Greeks to Darwin. H. F. Osborn. New York, 1894.

ON WALLACE:

Alfred Russel Wallace. L. T. Hogben. London, 1918.
Impressions of Great Naturalists. H. F. Osborn. New York, 1925.
My Life. Alfred Russel Wallace. London, 1905.

GENERAL:

Creation: A History of Non-Evolutionary Theories. E. T. Brewster. Indianapolis, 1927.
The History of Biological Theories. Emanuel Radl. Trans. from German. Oxford, 1930.
Darwin and Modern Science. A. C. Seward. Cambridge, 1909.
A Critique of the Theory of Evolution. T. H. Morgan. Princeton, 1916.
Darwinism. Alfred Russel Wallace. London, 1891.
Darwinism To-day. Vernon L. Kellog. New York, 1908.
The First Principles of Evolution. S. Herbert. London, 1919.
Modern Theories of Development. L. von Bertalanffy. Trans. from German. Oxford, 1933.
The Theory of Evolution. W. B. Scott. London, 1918.
Darwin's Theory Applied to Mankind. Alfred Machin. London, 1937.
Evolution and its Modern Critics. A. M. Davies. London, 1937.

THEORY OF THE ECONOMIC INTERPRETATION OF HISTORY

ON MARX:

From Hegel to Marx. Sidney Hook. London, 1936.

Karl Marx. Franz Mehring. London, 1935.

Marx und Hegel. G. Fischer. Jena, 1922.

Karl Marx and Engels. D. Riazanov. New York, 1927.

Karl Marx: His Life and Work. Otto Rühle. Trans. from German. London, 1929.

Karl Marx. Harold J. Laski. London, 1922.

Karl Marx. Raymond Postgate. London, 1933.

Proudhon et Karl Marx. E. Drumont. Paris, 1901.

GENERAL:

Karl Marx's Interpretation of History. M. M. Bober. Harvard University Press, 1927.

The Theoretical System of Karl Marx. L. B. Boudin. Chicago, 1910.

What Marx Really Meant. G. D. H. Cole. London, 1934.

Towards the Understanding of Karl Marx. Sidney Hook. London, 1933.

Le Déterminisme Économique. Paul Lafargue. Paris, 1907.

Essays in the History of Materialism. G. V. Plekhanov. Trans. from Russian. London, 1934.

The Economic Interpretation of History. Henri Sée. Trans. from French. New York, 1929.

Aspects of Dialectical Materialism. H. Levy and J. Macmurray. London, 1935.

"The Economic Determination of History." Harry Elmer Barnes in *Essays in Intellectual History.* New York, 1929.

Karl Marx als Geschichtsphilosoph. Alfred Braunthal. Berlin, 1920.

The Economic Interpretation of History. J. E. T. Rogers. New York, 1888.

THEORY OF DISEASE

ON PASTEUR:

The Genius of Louis Pasteur. Piers Compton. New York, 1932.

Life of Pasteur. R. Vallery-Radot. Trans. from French. New York, 1923.

"Pasteur," ch. 22 in *Master Minds in Medicine.* J. C. Hemmeter. New York, 1927.

"Louis Pasteur," in *New Fragments.* John Tyndall. London, 1898.

Pasteur and His Work. L. Descour. Trans. from French. London, 1922.

ON FRACASTORIUS, KIRCHER, ETC.:

Stalkers of Pestilence. Wade W. Oliver. New York, 1930.
Great Biologists. Sir J. Arthur Thomson. London, 1932.
Catholic Churchmen in Science. J. J. Walsh. Philadelphia, 1906.

GENERAL:

"The Origin of Syphilis," ch. 22 in *Essays in the History of Medicine.* Karl
   Sudhoff. Trans. from German. New York, 1926.
The History and Epidemiology of Syphilis. William A. Pusey. London, 1933.
"The Germ Theory," ch. 5 in *A Hundred Years of Medicine.* W. E. B. Lloyd.
   London, 1936.
Pasteur and Rabies. T. M. Dolan. London, 1890.
Lord Lister. R. Godlee. London, 1917.
"Micro-organisms and Their Roles in Nature." William H. Taliaferro in
   The World and Man. F. R. Moulton (Editor). New York, 1937.
Man vs. Microbes. N. Kopeloff. New York, 1930.
On Fermentation. Paul Schützenberger, 1893.

THEORY OF THE MIND

ON FREUD:

An Autobiographical Study. Sigmund Freud. Trans. from German. London,
   1935.
Past Masters and Other Papers. Thomas Mann. Trans. from German. London,
   1933.
Freud, Goethe, Wagner. Thomas Mann. New York, 1937.
Freud and Marx. Reuben Osborn. London, 1937.
Collected Papers. Sigmund Freud. London, 1924.
"Sigmund Freud in His Historical Setting" (article). C. G. Jung. *Character
   and Personality.* Vol. I. Durham, 1932.
Freud and His Time. Fritz Wittels. Trans. from German. New York, 1931.

GENERAL:

New Introductory Lectures on Psychoanalysis. S. Freud. Trans. from German.
   London, 1933.
Psycho-analysis: Its Theories and Practical Application. A. A. Brill. Philadelphia,
   1923.
The House That Freud Built. J. Jastrow. London, 1932.
"Freud's Theory of Wit." A. A. Brill in *Journal of Abnormal Psychology.*
   Boston, 1911.

Facts and Theories of Psychoanalysis. Ives Hendrik. London, 1934.

Address on Psycho-analysis. J. J. Putnam. London, 1921.

Civilization and its Discontents. Sigmund Freud. London, 1930.

The Interpretation of Dreams. Sigmund Freud. Trans. by A. A. Brill. London, 1927.

Introduction to Psycho-analysis for Teachers. Anna Freud. Trans. from German. London, 1931.

Wish-hunting in the Unconscious. M. Harrington. New York, 1934.

Papers on Psycho-analysis. Ernest Jones. London, 1923.

THEORY OF THE ORIGIN OF OUR PLANET

ON CHAMBERLIN:

"A Distinguished Son of Wisconsin" (article). George Coolie in *Wisconsin Magazine.* Vol. 15 (1932).

"Professor Chamberlin" (article). J. V. Nash in *Open Court Magazine.* Vol. 42 (1928).

"The Sunset of a Great Life" (article). J. V. Nash in *Open Court Magazine.* Vol. 43 (1929).

Thomas C. Chamberlin. B. Willis in Annual Report of the Smithsonian Institution. Washington, 1929.

Chamberlin and Salisbury: Life Partners. Collie and Densmore. Madison, 1932.

Biographical Memoir of Thomas C. Chamberlin. R. T. Chamberlin. Washington, 1934.

"Chamberlin's Work in Wisconsin." C. K. Leith in *Journal of Geology.* Vol. 37 (May–June 1929).

ON KANT AND LAPLACE:

Immanuel Kant. Papers read at Northwestern University on the bicentenary of Kant's birth. Chicago, 1925.

Kant's Cosmogony. W. Hastie. Glasgow, 1900.

A Source Book in Astronomy. Shapley and Howarth. New York, 1929.

Modern Cosmogonies. A. M. Clerke. London, 1905.

The Great Astronomers. H. S. Williams. New York, 1930.

A Popular History of Astronomy During the Nineteenth Century. A. M. Clerke. Edinburgh, 1885.

GENERAL:

The Growth of the Earth. T. C. Chamberlin. New York, 1927.

Two Solar Families. T. C. Chamberlin. Chicago, 1928.

"The Origin and History of the Earth." T. C. Chamberlin in *The World and Man*. F. A. Moulton (Editor). New York, 1937.

Outlines of Historical Geology. Charles Schuchert. London, 1931.

Astronomy and Cosmogony. Sir J. H. Jeans. Cambridge, 1929.

The Origin of the Earth. T. C. Chamberlin. University Chicago Press, 1916.

The Life of the Universe: As Conceived by Man from the Earliest Ages to the Present Time. 2 Vols. Svante Arrhenius. Trans. from Swedish. London, 1909.

The Nebular Hypothesis and Modern Cosmogony (The Halley Lecture). Sir J. H. Jeans. Oxford, 1923.

Astronomy for the Millions. G. Van Den Bergh. Trans. from the Dutch. New York, 1937.

Flights from Chaos. Harlow Shapley. New York, 1930.

Star and Planets: Exploring the Universe. D. H. Menzel. New York, 1931.

THEORY OF MAN

ON BOAS:

"Franz Boas." Richard Andree in *Globus*. Vol. 82, p. 306 (1902).

"Franz Boas and the American School of Historical Ethnology." A. Goldenweiser in *The History and Prospects of the Social Sciences*. H. E. Barnes (Editor). New York, 1925.

"Professor Franz Boas." Ruth Benedict in *The Scientific Monthly*. Vol. 32, pp. 278–280 (March, 1931).

"Franz Boas," in *American Men of Science*. New York, 1933.

ON GOBINEAU:

"Arthur, Count of Gobineau, Race Mystic." J. M. Hone in *Contemporary Review*. Vol. 104, pp. 94–103 (1913).

"Gobinism," ch. 3 in *Racial Basis of Civilization*. F. H. Hankins. London, 1926.

"Gobineau," ch. 4 in *Race: A Study in Modern Superstition*. Jacques Barzun. New York, 1937.

GENERAL:

History of Anthropology. A. C. Haddon. London, 1910.

Race and Culture Contacts. E. B. Reuter (Editor). New York, 1934.

We Europeans. J. S. Huxley and A. C. Haddon. London, 1936.

A Hundred Years of Anthropology. T. K. Penniman. London, 1935.

What is Man? Sir J. Arthur Thomson. London, 1924.

The Study of Man. Ralph Linton. New York, 1936.

Apes, Men and Morons. E. A. Hooton. New York, 1937.

The Racial History of Man. R. B. Dixon. New York, 1923.

The Mind of Primitive Man. Franz Boas. London.

Aryan and Non-Aryan (a lecture). Franz Boas. New York, 1934.

Race Differences. Otto Kleinberg. New York, 1935.

Anthropology and Modern Life. Franz Boas. London, 1932.

"Pope Pius III and the American Indians." Lewis Hanke in *Harvard Theological Review.* Vol. 30. No. 2 (April, 1937).

Race: A Study in Modern Superstition. Jacques Barzun. New York, 1937.

THEORY OF RELATIVITY

ON EINSTEIN:

Einstein the Searcher. A. Moskowski. London, 1921.

Albert Einstein. Anton Reiser. London, 1930.

Contemporary Immortals. A. Henderson. New York, 1930.

Albert Einstein. D. Reichinstein. Prague, 1934.

Einstein Visits New York. Scrapbook mounted and bound by the New York Public Library, 1933.

Master Minds of Modern Science. Bridges and Tiltman. London, 1935.

Living Philosophies. Albert Einstein, *et. al.* New York, 1931.

ON NEWTON:

"The Newtonian Synthesis," ch. 7 in *A History of Science.* A. Wolf. London, 1935.

"Newton." Albert Einstein in *Annual Report Smithsonian Institution.* 1927.

The Metaphysical Foundations of Modern Physical Science. E. H. Burtt. London, 1927.

ON POINCARÉ, MACH, ETC.:

A Source Book in Mathematics. D. E. Smith. New York, 1929.

Henri Poincaré. Robert d'Adhémar. Paris, 1914.

Major Prophets of To-day. Edwin E. Slosson. Boston, 1914.

Men of Mathematics. E. T. Bell. New York, 1937.

"Prof. Mach and His Work." Paul Carus in *The Monist,* Vol. 21 (1911).

GENERAL:

Easy Lessons in Einstein. E. E. Slosson. New York, 1921.

Einstein and the Universe. Chas. Nordmann. New York, 1922.

The Theory of Relativity. H. L. Brose. Oxford, 1920.

Philosophy and Modern Science. H. T. Davis. London, 1931.

The Nature of the Physical World. A. S. Eddington. London, 1929.

The World As I See It. Albert Einstein. London, 1934.

The New Physics. Arthur Haas. Trans. from German. London, 1934.

The Fundamental Concepts of Physics. P. R. Heyl. London, 1926.

The Expanding Universe. A. S. Eddington. London, 1933.

The Philosophy of Relativity. A. P. Ushenko. London, 1937.

The Philosophy of Physics. M. Planck. Trans. from German. London, 1936.

INDEX